D1548220

World University Library

The World University Library is an international series
of books, each of which has been specially commissioned.
The authors are leading scientists and scholars from all over
the world who, in an age of increasing specialization, see the
need for a broad, up-to-date presentation of their subject.
The aim is to provide authoritative introductory books for
students which will be of interest also to the general reader.
Publication of the series takes place in Britain, France,
Germany, Holland, Italy, Spain, Sweden and
the United States.

Roger Buvat

Plant Cells

An introduction to plant protoplasm

Translated from the French
by Harold Oldroyd

WITHDRAWN

World University Library

McGraw-Hill Book Company
New York Toronto

© Roger Buvat 1969
English translation © George Weidenfeld and Nicolson Limited
Library of Congress Catalog Card Number: 70-77017
All Rights reserved. No part of this publication may be reproduced,
stored in a retrieval system, or transmitted, in any form or by any
means, electronic, mechanical, photocopying, recording or
otherwise, without the prior permission of the copyright owner

Phototypeset by BAS Printers Limited, Wallop, Hampshire, England
Printed by Officine Grafiche Arnoldo Mondadori, Verona

Contents

Improved optical methods for studying the living cell
The phase-contrast microscope/The ultramicroscope/
Other methods
Vital staining
Vital staining for the vacuoles/Vital staining for the
protoplasm/Tolerance of cells to vital stains
Fixatives
Chemical fixatives/Freezing
Microtomy
The electron microscope
The principle/Construction/The electron microscope in
cytological research
Cytochemical techniques
Isolation of cellular organelles/Autoradiography/
Enzymological techniques

The living cytoplasm
Cytoplasmic movements
Different types of movement/Mechanism of cytoplasmic
movements
Cytoplasmic changes
Cytoplasm under the electron microscope
The endoplasmic reticulum
Morphology/Relationship with the nuclear membrane/
Biochemistry/Function
Ribosomes 'free' in the hyaloplasm
Distribution in the plant cell/Biochemistry/Fine structure/
Function
The hyaloplasm
Microtubules
The Golgi body
The Golgi body in classical cytology/Ultrastructure of
the dictyosomes/Biochemistry of the dictyosomes/
Function of the Golgi body/Origin of the dictyosomes
The cell membrane and the relationship between
different cells
Evidence of its existence/Fine structure/Ultrastructure
of the plasmodesmata/Deformations of the cell mem-
brane resulting from cellular activity/Functions of the
cell membrane

The vacuoles
General aspect of vacuoles in mature cells/Discovery of the tonoplast/The vacuolar contents/Vital staining of vacuoles/Modification during cellular differentiation/ Post-differentiation changes in the vacuole/Special kinds of vacuole/Origin of the vacuole/Function of the vacuole

6 Mitochondria

Some aspects of the living cytoplasm and its changeability
Vital staining
Fixation
Ultrastructure
Biochemistry
Location of various chemical constituents
Physiology
Breakdown of glucose/Tricarboxylic acid cycle/ Electron transport/Phosphorylative activity/Other oxidative activities/Synthetic activities
Evolution during cell differentiation
Origin
Equivalents of mitochondria in Protocaryotes

7 Plastids
Chloroplasts
Shape
Structure
Results before the electron microscope/Ultrastructure under the electron microscope
Biochemistry
Analysis of isolated chloroplasts/Location of chemical constituents
Leucoplasts
Location
Leucoplasts in living tissues
Ultrastructure
Chromoplasts
Location
Appearance in living cells
Ultrastructure
Chromoplasts with dissolved pigments
Chromoplasts with pigment on lipoprotein fibrillae

Growth of the cell/Experiments with cell fragments/
Exchange between nucleus and cytoplasm in Aceta-
bularia/Biochemistry of the resting nucleus/Conclusions
about the functions of the resting nucleus
Nucleus during somatic cell division
Mitosis and amitosis
Karyokinesis in higher plants
Prophase/Metakinesis or prometaphase/Metaphase/
Anaphase/Telophase
Formation of nucleoli
The phragmoplast and cytodiaeresis
Exchange between nucleus and cytoplasm during mitosis
Substances which inhibit mitosis

1 Introduction and historical sketch

Early man was aware of the infinitely great because he could see the Heavens with the naked eye, but he had no means of seeing the infinitely small. We today are so familiar with tiny things that it is strange to realise that they meant nothing to our ancestors until less than four hundred years ago, for the simple reason that their existence could not be detected until we had instruments capable of magnifying them.

Cells, which are the anatomical units of both plants and animals, fall into this category, and cytology, the science of cells, was not possible until physics had provided us with suitable instruments. Our knowledge of the world invisible to the naked eye has kept pace with the development of magnifying instruments, from the simplest magnifying glass down to the modern electron microscope.

The first microscopes and discovery of the cell It is thought that the ancients knew something about lenses and the refraction of light, but they do not appear to have made use of this knowledge to explore an unknown world. The discovery of the invisible world, and the study of what was revealed there, seem to have started towards the close of the sixteenth century, when men of leisure, seeking for a distraction, suddenly developed a craze for looking at a variety of objects through glass lenses. Then it was discovered that if two lenses were combined they would give even greater magnification, and by the end of the century several 'physickers' such as Hans, Zacharias Jansen and Kirchner had already built microscopes essentially similar to the ones we have today, that is comprising a condenser, an objective and an eyepiece.

Nevertheless such instruments were very difficult to construct, and gave only moderate magnification with a great deal of distortion. Meanwhile other 'amateurs' struggled to make lenses of very short focus which would give the same order of magnification in one step. One of these, who was celebrated as much for his skill in lens-making as for the historical importance of his discoveries, was Leeuwenhoek, a cloth merchant and local worthy in Delft. His simple lenses, mounted in elaborately worked stands, and provided with a needle on which to mount the specimen (figure 1·1) made it possible to magnify up to 200 diameters. To him we owe the famous letter of 9 October 1676, addressed to the Royal Society in London, in which bacteria are described for the first time under the name of 'animalcules'.

Some years earlier, in 1665, there appeared a celebrated work with the title: *Micrographia or some physiological descriptions of minute bodies made by magnifying glasses with observations and inquiries thereupon* by the English physician Robert Hooke, who presented a series of drawings of tiny objects that he had seen through a microscope of his own construction (figure 1·2). Here, among other things, were the head of a fly, a flea on a hair, and – what is of most interest to us – two fragments of cork in which was visible, for the first time ever, the cellular structure of plant tissue (figure 1·3).

In his description of this, Hooke used the terms cell and cell wall for the first time, though as far as his knowledge went the cork tissue consisted of empty cavities, and he was using the term 'cell' in its basic, everyday sense. Robert Hooke never suspected what a new world he was opening up, and he never pursued it any further. However, only a few years later Malpighi (1671–87) and Grew (1671–82) published two fundamental treatises almost simultaneously.

Malpighi's *Opera omnia* was without question the first work on the general anatomy of animals and plants, and was notable for its description of cells under the term 'saccules', and of vessels, which he called 'tubes'. Grew's *Anatomy of Plants,* read before the Royal Society of London, already had an almost modern appearance. More than eighty plates, which were among the first to be engraved on copper, showed a host of tissues and organs of plants, with innumerable representations of cells (figure 1·4). Here the parenchymatous tissues are shown as made up of 'cells' and 'vesicles' (transparent bladders), and the term 'vessels' is used not only for organs of transport, but also for such structures as the latex vessels.

Grew, like Hooke, still looked upon the cell wall itself as the plant tissue, rather than its contents. For example, in 1671 Grew described how a parenchyma could form from a liquid during the growth of a seed in these terms: 'And in the Interim of the Coagulation, a gentle Fermentation being also made, the said Parenchyma or Coagulum becometh such, not of any Texture indifferently, but is raised (as we see Bread in Baking) into a Congeries of Bladders: For such is the parenchyma of the whole seed.'

This theory of the formation of cells by the consolidation of

11

1·1 Leeuwenhoek's microscope. A hole in a silver plate was occupied by a simple lens of very short focus. The object was held by a needle, which could be adjusted.

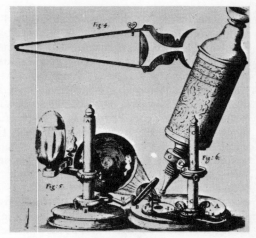

1·2 Hooke's microscope of 1665. The preparation was illuminated by the light of a flame focussed through a 'condenser', in the form of a glass bowl filled with liquid.

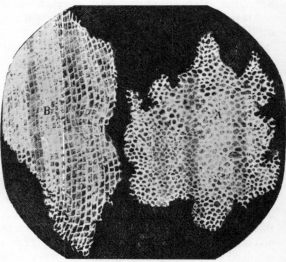

1·3 The first drawing of a vegetable tissue (cork) to show its cellular structure, made by Robert Hooke.

bubbles in some primordial liquid reappears more than two centuries later in the works of the pioneers of cell theory, such as Schleiden (1838).

No advance was made upon the ideas of Malpighi and Grew throughout the eighteenth century, even though many observers published descriptions and drawings of plant tissues and cells. Grew's ideas can be seen repeated almost exactly in the *Theoria generationis* of C. F. Wolff in 1759, though the term 'cell' itself is forgotten.

The tissue theory In the works of Malpighi and Grew, who founded the science of microscopic anatomy, the cell itself did not receive as much attention as did the various tissues which it composed, because the cell contents were still undiscovered. These pioneers were responsible for the concept of a tissue, but their concept was not fully developed for another century, when Brisseau-Mirbel wrote his *Traité d'Anatomie et de Physiologie végétales* ('*An X*' of the Revolutionary Calendar, that is, 1801) and Sprengel his *Anleitung zur Kenntnis der Gewächse* in 1802. These two authors, moreover, disagreed and quarrelled violently about ideas that are now long-forgotten, but both of them believed that cell tissue was formed from some pre-existing liquid.

'Plants', wrote Mirbel, 'are made up of a membranous tissue which, though continuous throughout, composes two different sorts of organs: cellular tissues and tubular tissues.' Thus to him the basic substance is both membranous and homogeneous, and cells are nothing more than cavities formed in this substance. 'These are not little vesicles as most authors think; what happens is that a membrane folds itself in such a way that it encloses little holes adjacent to each other'. Mirbel explained the formation of 'membranous tissue' by adopting Grew's idea of a fermenting liquid in which bubbles coagulated into membranes. This concept implied that every 'membrane' was common to two adjacent cells; a consequence that was the first thing to be disproved, and which quickly wrecked the tissue theory.

The cell theory As early as 1812 in fact several authors showed that plant cells could be isolated from tissues by maceration in water (Moldenhauer), by boiling (Link, using bean pods) or by using nitric acid (Dutrochet 1824), and the ensuing discussions brought Dutrochet and Mirbel into opposition, and spurred them on to even

13

more fruitful studies. At the end of his career Mirbel, in a very elegant memoir on the liverwort *Marchantia polymorpha* (1835) finally concurred in the theories of Dutrochet, and thus set the cellular theory on an established footing.

In 1824 Dutrochet expressed himself in these terms: 'I may repeat here what I have revealed previously about the organic texture of plants. We have seen that these organisms were entirely composed of cells, or of organs obviously derived from cells. We have seen that these hollow organs were simply contiguous, and held to each other by a cohesive force, but that such an assembly of cells did not really form one continuous tissue. Thus it seemed to us that an organic creature consists of an infinite number of microscopic components, which have no relationship to each other beyond that of being adjacent.'

To Raspail, on the other hand, the extraordinary diversity of activities of the cells, which was also shown by Dutrochet, must imply some kind of organisation of the cell contents. Before Schleiden later did so, Raspail stressed the organised activity of the cell contents, tried to analyse it chemically, and thus founded the science of histochemistry (1833). One of the essential elements in this organisation was actually revealed in the same year by R. Brown, who, after making microscopic examinations of orchids, announced that every cell contained a corpuscle to which he gave the name *nucleus*.

Now Schleiden (1838), in his turn, wrote that every plant that is not unicellular is an aggregation of cells. Schleiden considered that every cell is an individual, a kind of being, and living a double life: its own life, tracing out its own development; and a second life as a participant in the life of the whole organism.

Thus for the first forty years of the nineteenth century it was the botanists whose efforts built up step by step the cell theory of organisms. Although the theory was quickly extended to animals (Schwann 1839), the organisation of the cell contents, how they originated and how they multiplied, remained practically unknown.

Discovery of the cell components

1 *Nucleus*. We have seen that the nucleus, which had been sporadically noticed by several microscopists such as Fontana (1781) was systematically studied and interpreted as a regular feature of the cell by Brown (1831–3). Its function remained totally unknown, however, for a long time to come.

14

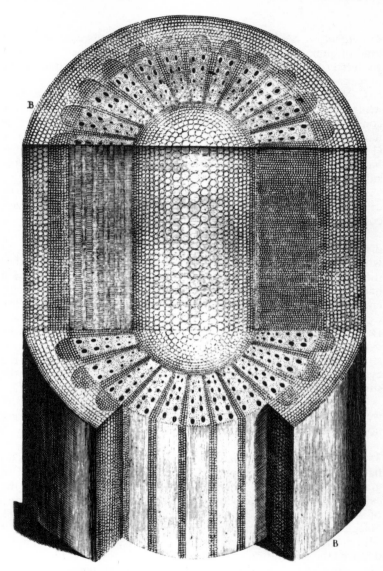

1·4 One of the 83 plates engraved on copper in Grew's
The Anatomy of Plants. The plate shows the cellular structure
of a vine root in transverse and median sections.

2 *Cytoplasm.* Schleiden (1838) described a 'nutritive substance' a kind of gum, to which he gave the name 'cytoblastème', and which gathered round the nucleus in cells which were assumed to be 'in the process of formation'.

C. Naegeli (1844–6) showed that this substance was nitrogenous, while H. Mohl (1846) regarded it as the substance from which all the constituents of the cell originated, nucleus included; he gave it the name of *protoplasm,* a word which had been invented by Purkinje (1840) with quite another meaning. M. Schultze (1861), on the other hand, considered the protoplasm to be the totality of the living substance except for the nucleus.

Nowadays we use protoplasm for all the living substance of the cell, including the nucleus, and speak of *cytoplasm* for Schultze's concept.

The significance of Naegeli's and Mohl's ideas was that they distinguished the 'protoplasm' from the cellular membrane with which earlier authors had confused it. Thuret (1850) showed that these were two different things when he described plant cells which had no cell walls (the zoospores of algae), and such 'naked cells' enabled Unger (1855) to homologise plant protoplasm with the living substance described twenty years earlier in Protozoa by Dujardin, who called it 'sarcode'. In his brilliant description of the cytoplasm of 'lower animals' Dujardin had noted, as a 'most strange property' the spontaneous production within the body of the cytoplasm of vacuoles, or tiny spherical cavities, filled with the surrounding liquid.

These vacuoles, which are a characteristic structure of cytoplasm, were thus discovered in Protozoa by Dujardin in 1835, but they were not described in plant cells until Naegeli found them in 1844–6.

3 *Plastids and chondriosomes.* Mohl and his pupils (Michler 1837) had recognised that the photosynthetic pigments were located in grains of chlorophyll, which they thought were built up by the cytoplasm, but the real discovery of plastids came with the memoirs of A. Schimper (1880–3) and A. Meyer (1881–3). As early as 1858 Naegeli had studied starch for a long time, without associating it with plastids: he was one of the first to make use of polarised light, deduced the orientation of the starch grains, how they grew, and laid the foundation of the theory of growth in living systems.

It was while they were looking for the location of the starch grains in the cytoplasm that Schimper and Meyer discovered the plastids.

The other 'classic' constituents of the cell were discovered only after technical progress had advanced sufficiently far, not only in the construction of microscopes but also in methods of preparing and studying cells.

As far as microscopes are concerned, the efforts of Abbe towards the end of the nineteenth century led to so much improvement that their resolving powers became nearly as good as they are today. This produced a resurgence of interest in cytology from 1870 onwards, marked by the discoveries of Strasburger, Schimper, Meyer, Flemming, Altmann, Benda and many other microscopists. Alongside the improvement of microscopes came the introduction of fixatives, stains and the cutting of thin sections.

One result was the discovery of chondriosomes, which were first described by Altmann (1890), who stained them by a new method that he invented (Altmann's fuchsin) and gave them the name 'bioblasts'. They were rediscovered and described under the name of *mitochondria* by Benda (1897), who was the first person to regard them as normal constituents of the cell, and not as intracellular bacteria, as Altmann had thought. The works of Benda, Meves, Fauré-Fremiet, Regaud and Guilliermond showed them to be generally present in all cells, whether of vegetable or animal origin.

Technical progress, combined with personal skill, was also responsible for the remarkable researches of H. de Vries (1885) on the osmotic properties of the vacuoles, and the bringing to light of the ectoplasmic and endoplasmic envelopes of the cell, the first of which had been discovered by Pfeffer in 1877. By the beginning of the nineteenth century cytological techniques were sufficiently well-advanced for the study of the development of the constituents of the cell during the process of cell differentiation, and for their reciprocal relationships to be studied (A. Guilliermond and P. A. Dangeard).

The origin and multiplication of cells The problem of the origin of cells and of their constituents had to remain unsolved until the science of genetics arose, when the knowledge of the one evolved alongside that of the other. Nowadays, when the idea of the genetic continuity of cells is as commonplace as the atomic theory, it requires an effort of imagination to put ourselves in the place of the cytologists of the nineteenth century, when they were still trying to find out how cells arose, by what mechanism they multiplied, and how their development was regulated.

1 *Cell continuity*. The discovery of the nucleus by Brown greatly impressed Schleiden, who re-christened it 'cytoblast', but gave a mistaken account of it. He thought that he had seen it arise spontaneously from a homogeneous substance, the 'cytoblastème', and then surround itself with a mucilaginous substance, which later became hollowed out laterally into a cavity full of liquid. The result was a vesicle containing a lateral 'cytoblast'. Thus, according to Schleiden, the cell consisted of a liquid surrounded by an envelope of which the nucleus formed part: he did not recognise the cytoplasm.

About 1835 Mohl carried out observations on algal cells in the process of division, and later saw cambial cells obviously dividing into two, but it was not until 1846 that he decided to dispute Schleiden's theory. Unger, in his turn, had recognised that the arrangement and shape of cells in a growing point suggested that they had arisen by the division of other, pre-existing cells. Furthermore he had clearly seen that the nuclei of the daughter cells made their appearance before the dividing wall appeared. From this he derived the idea that the cell contents played a decisive role in cell division (1841–4).

Naegeli's ideas also gradually diverged from the theories of Schleiden. At first he supposed that when root cells were dividing one cell disappeared and in its place two nuclei arose spontaneously, with a new cell developing around each of them. Later on he admitted that every vegetative cell arose by division from a mother-cell, although he still thought that reproductive cells arose spontaneously, *de novo*. He was thus led into disagreeing with one point after another of Schleiden's theory, and was eventually to deal it a mortal blow.

As a result of this evolution of ideas the cellular theory was perfected by the principle of the continuity of cells. It was the elucidation of this principle that led to the ontogenetic researches into which Naegeli (from 1845) and Hofmeister (several years later) plunged without delay. The same principle was subsequently extended to animals, and this led to the enunciation by Virchow (1855) of his famous dictum: every cell arises from another cell (*omnis cellula e cellula*).

It might be said that the discovery of this continuity of cells, which was genetics in advance of its time, is a landmark in the evolution of biology. The botanist Sachs wrote in 1875 that the progress made between 1840 and 1850 was greater than anything achieved during the following twenty years.

2 *Mitosis and meiosis.* The establishment of the principle of the continuity of cells naturally encouraged study of the development of organisms, and these researches in their turn led to the two fundamental discoveries that remain to be dealt with in this brief introductory history: mitosis and meiosis.

As early as 1848 Hofmeister had published drawings of the structure of pollen grains, in which he evidently saw cell division, without realising either its importance, or the fact that it was a sequence in time. It was not until twenty-five years later that Schneider, in a treatise on flatworms, described the division of the nucleus in some detail. Two more years were needed before the botanist Strasburger (1875) gave a description of the various phases of cell division that was correct in its essentials, but from that moment there was a rush of studies of cell division, and Strasburger himself returned to it several times. Almost simultaneously Flemming (1879) published a description of mitosis in animal cells.

These old descriptions were perfected gradually, the errors that they contained being only tardily eliminated. Even today our knowledge of the phenomena at prophase and telophase is inadequate.

Study of the origin of sex cells in animals led van Beneden to the discovery of meiosis (1883); this time plants did not come first, and it was left to Guignard (1891) to extend these studies to the vegetable kingdom. Thus mitosis and meiosis were brought to light shortly before the rediscovery of the laws of Mendel, which had been forgotten since 1865, and which were revived in 1900 by Correns, de Vries and Tschermak, simultaneously. These laws made it possible to understand the cytological phenomena of fertilisation – seen for the first time by Thuret in 1854 – and progress towards an understanding of the mechanism of cell division moved on a parallel course to the nascent science of genetics. Indeed by 1900 cytology had provided genetics with the facts and ideas about hereditary processes which formed a basis for genetic studies in the present century.

Classical plant cytology Shortly after 1900 a relatively stable picture of the plant cell had been established, based upon a century of observation and thought. From then until 1940 only modifications of detail were made, chiefly as a result of the progress made in biochemistry and genetics. These involved, for example, the chemical composition of mitochondria, and the structure and composition of chromosomes, but they did not conflict with the accepted ideas about the contents of the cell, and their relations with each other. So we could take this classical scheme as a starting-point for our study of the structure of the cell.

Modern plant cytology What we have just called a 'starting-point' might equally well be looked on as a 'point of arrival', a destination reached after the work of the past. In reality it proved to be no more than an intermediate stage, because the application of the electron microscope since 1945 has launched cytology to new heights of achievement.

The difference between the resolving powers of the light (optical) microscope – about 0·2 microns under the best conditions – and electron microscopes – often down to less than 10Å, or 0·001 microns – has changed the whole scale of observation within the cell, and has brought to light a whole range of new ultrastructures.

Like biology and genetics, cytology hopes ultimately to reach down to the level of macromolecules, so as to be able to recognise individual molecules while they are actually participating in the life of the cell. It follows from this that when we do get down to such limits the frontiers of cytology and biochemistry will merge, and the two disciplines will help each other. We shall see, in fact, how progress in biochemistry and biophysics can be most advantageously linked to the possibilities of cytology.

This quick run through the history of plant cytology, though it has given only a sketchy idea of the difficulties of penetrating into the world of the infinitely small, does illustrate the tireless perseverance that scientists need if they are to probe the secrets of nature. Every now and then some invention of more powerful apparatus, or of more subtle techniques, produces a rapid burst of progress, after which the speed of development settles back to its usual slow pace. This is the time which the investigator should employ to go over the field again and fill in all the details.

Structure of the plant cell visible under the light microscope

In order to give our studies a sound basis it might be as well to recapitulate what we know of the contents of the cell, as far as these can be seen with an ordinary light microscope. We may take as an example a cell containing chlorophyll, from the parenchyma of a leaf of *Elodea canadensis*, an aquatic plant that has often been used

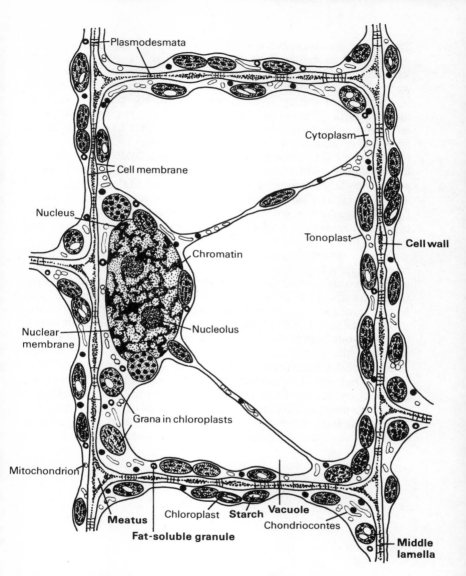

1·5 A leaf cell of *Elodea canadensis* to show the structures visible under the light microscope. Labelling in bold refers to paraplasmic (ergastic) substances; other labels refer to protoplasmic constituents.

for cytological studies because it is easy to observe (figure 1·5).

The 'cell' as a living organism is effectively confined within a 'cell' in the etymological sense, by means of a pectocellulose cell wall. The totality of living matter constitutes the protoplasm, and is made up of the cytoplasm, the nucleus, the plastids and the mitochondria. These constituents, in their turn, enclose other sub-structures, which are non-living ingredients that have either been absorbed or manufactured by the living system.

The most bulky organelles are the vacuoles, hydrophilic ('water-loving') spaces, which in typical adult plant cells run together into a single, very large vacuole. The cytoplasm also contains particles with a high refractive index, and are generally of a fatty nature; these fat-soluble granules gather together all the hydrophobic ('water-repellent') by-products of the cell (neutral fats, essential oils, and so on . . .).

Other products may be built up within the cell, generally as food reserves. Thus sometimes there are protein stores in the cytoplasm, in the plastids or even inside the nucleus, as well as starch grains, which are always built up inside plastids. The paraplasm is a collective term for these inert food stores together with the cell wall.

The present account of the plant cell will follow the pattern just outlined, but before starting on this we must recall, as simply as possible, the chemical composition and physical state of the fundamental constituents of the cell. A knowledge of these will explain, not only how certain cell structures come into being, but also why certain methods of study are appropriate to cytology. So let us examine in succession the principal structures of the cell, their physiological function, and the results of their activity. Then finally we shall take a look at the mechanism of cell division.

2 Chemical properties

Chemical analysis of a typical plant cell It is theoretically possible to characterise every species of living creature, and possibly each type of cell within the same species, according to the chemical composition of its protoplasm. Hence the differences of detail between the cells of creatures throughout the world together with the variations that occur according to age and physiological state must be virtually infinite. Nevertheless all cells, animal and vegetable, have a significant quantity of substances in common.

Before the invention of certain recent techniques that we shall describe shortly, the difficulty of analysing plant protoplasm arose from the great abundance of inclusion bodies and membranes, which occur in most plant tissues. For this reason the first authors who tried to distinguish between the active cell substances and the products of their activity studied exceptional plants in which the cell wall was absent: the plasmodia of Myxomycetes (slime-moulds). Table 1 is taken from Lepeschkine (1923).

This table – which was compiled before our knowledge of nucleoproteins took its recent astonishing leap forward – demonstrates the quantitative importance of these various substances in a simple plasmodium. We shall see later that the proportion of nucleoproteins varies with the age and activity of the cells, and that it can be even greater in cells that are both young and actively dividing. When cells have become differentiated into tissues the proportion of nucleoproteins falls, not merely in line with the fall in absolute quantity of nucleic acids present, but also as a result of the accumulation of cytoplasmic by-products. The latter are already abundant in the plasmodium studied above, in spite of the fact that there are no membranes to be included. Part of the proteins, the lipids (glycerides, for instance), as well as the soluble glucosides and the greater part of the mineral ash, are all paraplasmic products.

Proteins The proteins are fundamental constituents of protoplasm. Their importance can be appreciated if we remember that they include all the enzymes, which participate in the building up of all the cellular organelles. Two categories are distinguished: holo-

Table 1 Chemical composition of a plasmodium of the Myxomycete *Fuligio varians*

Percentage of living weight

Water	82·6
Dry material	17·4

Percentage of dry weight

Proteins and nitrogenous matter

Amino acids, organic bases, amides, soluble proteins	24·3	
Albumins	2·0	
Globulins	0·5	61·8
'Free' nucleic acids	2·5	
Nucleoproteins	32·5	

Lipids or fat-soluble substances

Glycerides (neutral fats)	6·8	
Steroids (phytosterols)	3·2	11·3
Phospholipids (complex fats)	1·3	
Lipoproteins	4·8	
Monosaccharides	14·2	
Other organic matter	3·5	
Minerals (ash)	4·4	

proteins, or simple proteins, which on hydrolysis produce only amino acids, and heteroproteins, or complex proteins, which combine a simple protein with other, non-protein molecules, which constitute an additive group.

1 *Holoproteins.* Holoproteins consist entirely of amino acids, which are the same for both plant and animal cells. The most complex proteins contain up to about twenty-five different amino acids, but it is a remarkable fact that the overwhelming majority of proteins contain no more than twenty – the same twenty – and differ only in the proportions of each one and their sequence.

The twenty universal amino acids are: glycine, alanine, valine, leucine, isoleucine, proline, phenylalanine, tyrosine, serine, threonine, asparagine, glutamine, aspartic acid, glutamic acid, arginine, lysine, histidine, tryptophane, cysteine, methionine.

The formula of the naturally occurring amino acids is:

$$R-CH\underset{COOH}{\overset{NH_2}{<}}$$

Moreover, with the exception of glycine in which the residual group, or 'residue' **R** is replaced by a second hydrogen atom, the carbon atom is asymmetrical, since its four valencies are filled by four different radicals. In theory, therefore, each amino acid should exist in two optical isomers, but in practice all naturally occurring amino acids are only the laevo-isomer (L-alanine, L-valine, etc).

The majority of the amino acids listed in table 2 could be regarded as derivatives of alanine:

$$CH_3-CH\underset{COOH}{\overset{NH_2}{<}}$$

in which one hydrogen atom of the methyl (**CH₃**) radical has been replaced by a more or less complex group. For example, phenylalanine is produced by replacing one of the hydrogens with the phenyl radical, or benzene ring:

$$HO-C\underset{CH-CH}{\overset{CH=CH}{<}}\!\!\!>C-CH_2-CH\underset{COOH}{\overset{NH_2}{<}}$$

In the case of the amino acid tryptophane the residue (**R**) consists of the nucleus of *indole*:

$$HC\underset{HC}{\overset{CH}{<}}\!\!\!\!\underset{CH\quad NH}{\overset{C----C}{<}}\!\!\!>CH-CH_2----CH\underset{COOH}{\overset{NH_2}{<}}$$

Proline has a peculiar structure, in the sense that the amino group is itself the nucleus of pyrrole:

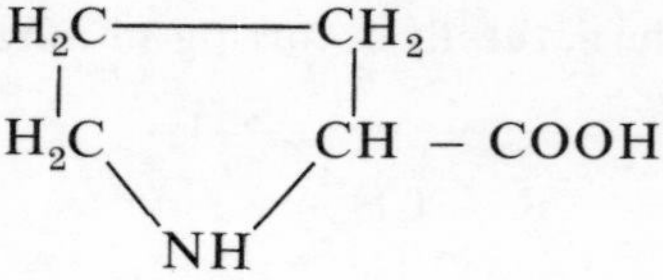

$$H_2C \text{———} CH_2$$
$$H_2C \qquad CH - COOH$$
$$NH$$

All amino acids have a dual function, as acids (through the $-COOH$ group) and as amines (through the $-NH$ group); in solution some behave as acids (for example, glutamic and aspartic acids). Others, in contrast, have their amino function to excess, and in solution their reaction is alkaline (for example lysine and arginine).

Finally, cysteine and methionine have sulphur incorporated into their structure. For example, cysteine:

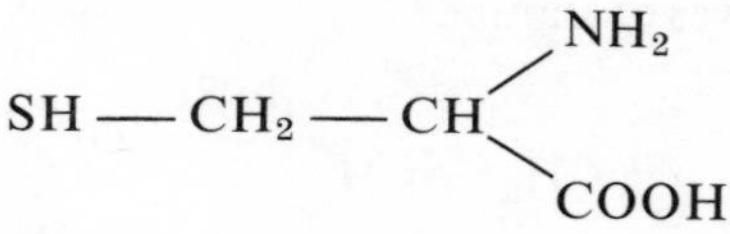

$$SH - CH_2 - CH \Big\langle {{NH_2} \atop {COOH}}$$

generally exists in the form of cystine, which is two molecules of cysteine joined together, with the loss of two atoms of hydrogen.

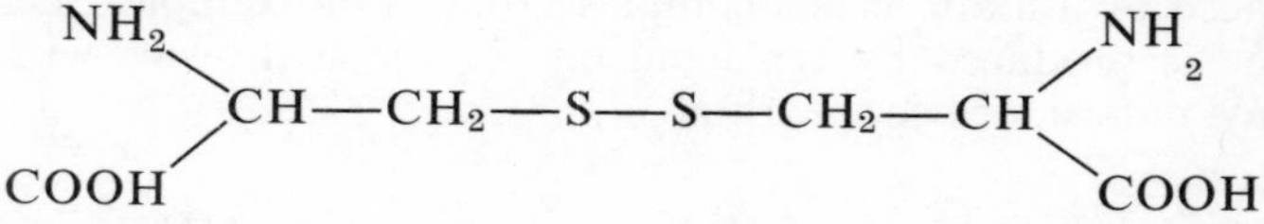

$${{NH_2} \atop {COOH}}\Big\rangle CH - CH_2 - S - S - CH_2 - CH \Big\langle {{NH_2} \atop {COOH}}$$

The 'bridges' between two sulphur atoms ($-S - S -$) are of major importance in the architecture of protein molecules, as we shall see later, after we have first seen how the amino acids are combined in simple proteins.

Amino acids combine together by linking the acid group of the one with the amino group of the other, and thereby assemble themselves into linear molecules called di-, or tri- or poly-peptides.

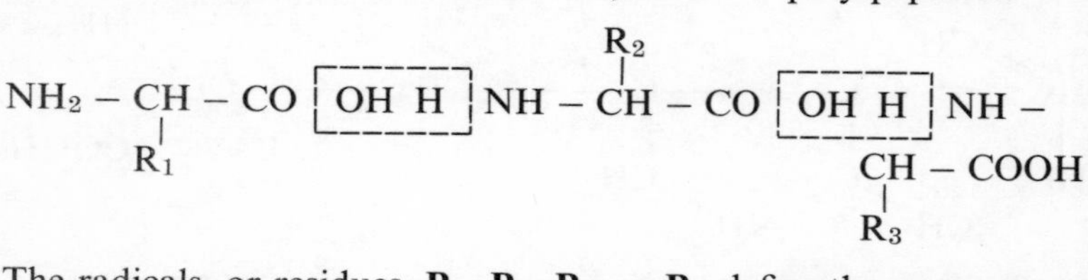

$$NH_2 - CH - CO \; \boxed{OH \; H} \; NH - \overset{R_2}{CH} - CO \; \boxed{OH \; H} \; NH -$$
$$\quad\quad\;\; R_1 \qquad\qquad\qquad\qquad\qquad\qquad CH - COOH$$
$$\qquad\qquad\qquad\qquad\qquad\qquad\qquad\qquad\qquad R_3$$

The radicals, or residues, R_1, R_2, R_3 ... R_n define the sequence or the amino acids in the polypeptide chain that is thus formed:

26

$$NH_2 - \underset{\underset{R_1}{|}}{CH} - CO - NH - \overset{\overset{R_2}{|}}{CH} - CO\ldots NH - \underset{\underset{R_n}{|}}{CH} - COOH$$

It will be noticed that this chain has an acid end, where the terminal radical is –**COOH** and an amino, or base end, with the terminal group –NH_2, and a protein with this structure is a primary protein. The constituent atoms, with their respective valencies and distances apart, form a three dimensional structure and if we neglect the space occupied by the residues R_1 etc. and reckon only the main structure, it occupies a cross-section of about 3·5Å. Each residue takes up a length of chain ranging from 2·1 to 2·6Å, thus:

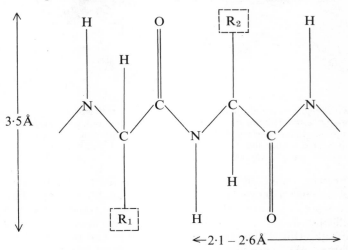

Modern electron microscopes may have a resolving power down to less than 5Å, and so theoretically even a primary protein molecule such as these should become visible with their aid.

Moreover, protein molecules rarely maintain their primary structure for very long. The forces generated by the principal valencies of the atoms and radicals, combining with other forces that we shall discuss later, usually deform the primary linear chain. This results in more or less irregular helicoid or spiral formations (secondary structure of the molecule) which are further folded in ways that are strictly determined by the sequence of amino acids

27

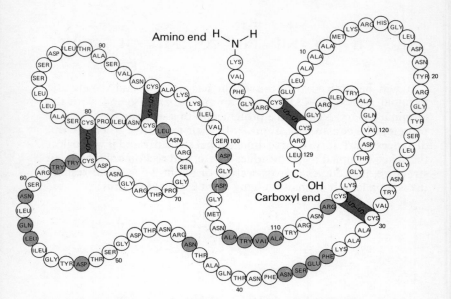

2·1 A two-dimensional model to show the tertiary structure of a protein molecule — lysozyme. This enzyme breaks down polysaccharides, especially those of the cell walls of bacteria. The folds in the polypeptide chain (composed of 129 amino acids) are brought about mainly by the four 'di-sulphur' bonds between the 8 cysteine (cys) residues.

in the primary chain. By this means some of the most important proteins acquire a more or less spherical or globular shape, like balls of wool, and are called globulins. The proteins that are metabolically active in protoplasm generally have a tertiary structure like this. Often the tertiary structure can be altered by temperature, pH, poisons, and so on, and if these agents are able to deform the protein it loses its specific properties more or less completely, and is said to be denatured. Figure 2·1 shows a protein of which the tertiary structure is completely known.

Under other circumstances two, or several, polypeptide chains may become associated in some specific and precise way, thus forming a functional protein molecule with a quaternary structure, for example, haemoglobin. Protein molecules with a tertiary or quaternary structure are clearly well above the powers of resolution of electron microscopes. Many globulin enzymes have diameters in excess of 30–50Å, and some are bigger still.

2 *Heteroproteins.* When heteroproteins are hydrolysed they produce amino acids and a diversity of other products, and heteroproteins are characterised according to the nature of the latter. The most important categories are the nucleoproteins, but protoplasm also contains phosphoproteins, glucoproteins and chromoproteins.

Nucleoproteins These are compounds that can be precipitated from an aqueous solution of fresh tissue by treating with dilute acids. Their hydrolysis can be carried out in two stages:

(1) nucleoprotein + dilute HCl⟶holoprotein + heteroprotein
(2) heteroprotein + trypsin + dilute NaOH⟶holoprotein + nucleic acid.

The holoprotein produced by the first reaction generally has a high molecular weight, and in solution does not give a very alkaline reaction (that is, it is a higher protein). That produced by the second reaction on the other hand is strongly alkaline in solution, and has a comparatively low molecular weight (histone or protamine). The nucleic acid plays the part of the additive group in the nucleo-protein.

The nucleoprotein can be progressively hydrolysed either by using dilute sulphuric acid, or by means of an enzyme, leading to even simpler molecules, the nucleotides. These, again, can liberate phosphoric acid and leave a residue called a nucleoside, composed of a sugar with five carbon atoms (a pentose) plus an organic base. The pentose can only be either ribose ($C_5H_{10}O_5$) or deoxyribose ($C_5H_{10}O_4$), and all the various natural nucleic acids produce between them only five fundamental bases: three pyrimidines (cytosine, thymine, uracil) and two purines (adenine and guanine). Moreover, each nucleic acid contains only four of these five bases, thymine and uracil being mutually exclusive. Thus every nucleic acid contains the bases cytosine, adenine and guanine, but some have thymine for their fourth base, and the others have uracil.

Furthermore, thymine occurs only in those nucleic acids in which the pentose is deoxyribose, and these two constituents characterise deoxyribonucleic acids, or DNA. Uracil, on the other hand, occurs only in nucleic acids with ribose as their pentose, and these are ribonucleic acids, or RNA.

Thus in both vegetable and animal cells there are two categories of nucleic acids. All the nucleic acids of the living world are built up from eight universal ingredients: five bases, two pentoses and phosphoric acid. From these eight, each molecule of a nucleic acid has a choice of six: four bases, one pentose and phosphoric acid. The link between the bases and the pentoses takes place on the first carbon atom of the pentose:

Adenine   +   Ribose   or   Deoxyribose
                (X = OH)   (X = H)

Ribo- or Deoxyribo-adenosine

Guanine and cytosine can form a nucleoside with either pentose (ribonucleosides and deoxyribonucleosides), but uracil can combine only with ribose (to form uridine) and thymine with deoxyribose (to form thymidine) – at least in living cells.

These binary constituents combine with phosphoric acid to form *nucleotides*. The reaction is an esterification between the phosphoric acid and the pentose through its primary alcohol group – CH_2OH. Similar processes will yield uridine phosphoric acid, where the sugar must always be ribose, thymidine phosphoric acid, where the sugar must be deoxyribose, and guanosine and cytidine phosphoric acids which can make use of either of the two pentoses.

These nucleotides are essential materials for the construction of the nucleic acids, which are *chains of nucleotides* produced by esterification between one of two remaining acid bonds of the phosphoric acid and alcohol bond borne by the third carbon atom of the pentose.

The molecular chain thus formed can be represented schematically as in figure 2·2, where **P** is the residue of the phosphoric acid molecule, **R** is the pentose, ribose or deoxyribose, and **B** are the purine and pyrimidine bases.

The number of nucleotides to be linked together in a chain in this way may be as many as 1,000 to 2,000, or even more, and then the nucleic acid becomes an elongate macromolecule, with a molecular weight that sometimes exceeds 10^8. When RNA is concerned, however, the number of nucleotides rarely exceeds a few hundred, and it is only when DNA is involved that the greater numbers are reached. On the other hand, the molecular weight per unit length of the chain, based upon the known dimensions of the atoms and of the interatomic bonds, can be explained only if the chain is double, and the researches of Watson and Crick (1953) led those authors to the conclusion that DNA exists normally as a double chain. The two filaments are linked together by electrostatic bonds of a kind similar to the hydrogen bonds that form between bases, so that thymine is associated with adenine and cytosine with guanine, according to the scheme set out in figure 2·2.

It is self-evident that Watson and Crick's concept requires the associated bases to be equal in number, so that

$$\frac{A}{T} = 1 \; ; \; \frac{C}{G} = 1 \; ; \quad \text{or} \; \frac{A + C}{T + G} = 1$$

where **A** = adenine, **C** = cytosine, **G** = guanine and **T** = thymine. Analyses of purified DNA have substantially confirmed this fact.

Then again, the spatial orientations of the valencies (bonds) in the macromolecule lead to the presumption that it takes a helical shape, and the diameter of the spiral can be calculated as being about 20Å (figure 2·2). Starting from aqueous solutions of DNA, which were then dried on a coated specimen grid of the electron microscope, it has been possible to see the molecules of DNA actually taking the shape of an irregular spiral with a diameter of approximately 20Å.

The nucleic acids are now known to be the ultimate repositories of the specificity of living creatures, that is, the location of the characteristic differences between one kind and another. Since the skeletal structure of these acids is perfectly uniform, consisting of a succession of phosphoric acid residues, alternating with molecules of the pentose, the acids can only differ from each other in two ways: in the number of nucleotides they contain, and in the order of succession of the (four) bases. The latter enables us to symbolise a nucleic acid by a series of letters, the initials of the bases, in the same order as they occur in the molecule, for example, TACGAATGC ATCTAG... If the above sequence of bases is present in one filament of the double helix of DNA, since we know that A must always be linked with T and C with G, we can deduce the sequence of bases in the other filament to be ATGCTTACGTAGATC. This symbolism is the basis of the genetic code, which is outside the scope of the present work.

In the nucleoproteins nucleic acids are in association with holo-proteins, of which, as we have seen, two categories exist. One group, with relatively low molecular weight, and an alkaline reaction (histones, protamines) are linked to their nucleic acids by means of the acid bonds arising from the phosphoric acid residues along their nucleotide chain. This combination results in nucleohistones, which have been obtained by extraction, and which appear under the electron microscope as convoluted filaments with diameters of 30 to 40Å. These nucleohistones, in their turn, are usually associated with proteins of high molecular weight (higher proteins), but we still have very little information about the nature of this association.

The structures just discussed are essentially peculiar to DNA, which is to be found inside the nucleus of the cell, in the chromosomes. The associations between RNA and the proteins is even less clearly understood, although RNA is to be found associated with proteins in various structures of the cell, such as ribosomes and the nucleolus. We shall return to the various types of DNA and RNA, and their distribution within the cell, when we come to study the cell constituents, or organelles.

Other heteroproteins The protoplasm of the plant cell contains a variety of the other heteroproteins, many of which are also to be found in animal cells. For instance, certain proteins can attach to phosphoric acid other than in the form of a nucleic acid: such a protein is zymocasein from yeast, in which the bond is made by esterification on to an amino acid of the protein, the serine. (In the

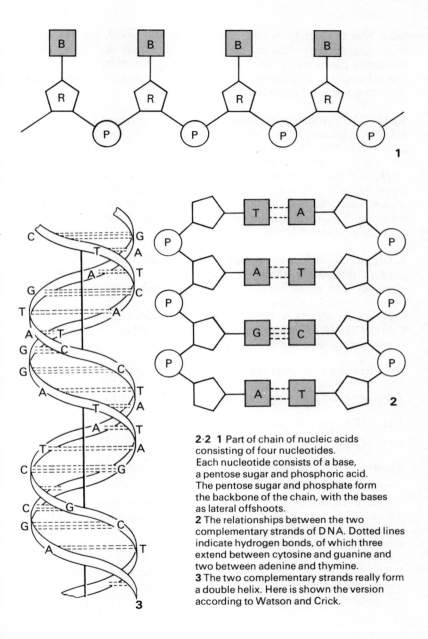

2·2 1 Part of chain of nucleic acids
consisting of four nucleotides.
Each nucleotide consists of a base,
a pentose sugar and phosphoric acid.
The pentose sugar and phosphate form
the backbone of the chain, with the bases
as lateral offshoots.
2 The relationships between the two
complementary strands of DNA. Dotted lines
indicate hydrogen bonds, of which three
extend between cytosine and guanine and
two between adenine and thymine.
3 The two complementary strands really form
a double helix. Here is shown the version
according to Watson and Crick.

same way the sericin of silk, the fibrin of the blood, the casein of milk, are derived, and so on ...). Many algae contain 'supernumerary pigments', chromoproteins, which complete the action of the chlorophyll: phycocyanin and phycoerythrin are heteroproteins with an additional chromophore.

Lipids The cytoplasm of plant cells contains a great variety of fat-soluble substances, but many of these are by-products of the activities of the cell, and do not form part of its living matter. Such are the glycerides, or neutral fats, the waxes and sometimes the steroids if these accumulate in great quantity. On the other hand some of the steroids in plant cells may have an important physiological function, even though this is as yet little understood. The phospholipids are concerned in the building-up of some of the most fundamental structures of the cytoplasm.

1 *Glycerides.* It will be enough to note briefly that these are paraplasmic substances which are esters of fatty acids combined with glycerol. The acids concerned are either saturated acids of the general formula $C_nH_{2n+1}COOH$ (example: stearic acid $C_{17}H_{35}COOH$), or else they have an ethylene bond such as oleic acid $C_{17}H_{33}COOH$. Their general formula is $C_nH_{2n-1}COOH$. Other acids contain several double bonds.

Tristearine may be taken as typical of this group of compounds.

$$
\begin{array}{l}
CH_2 \;[OH \quad\;\; H]O\;\; OC—C_{17}H_{35} \qquad CH_2—O—CO—C_{17}H_{35} \\
\;| \qquad\qquad\qquad\qquad\qquad\qquad\qquad\quad | \\
CH \;\;[OH + H]O\;\; OC—C_{17}H_{35} \rightleftharpoons CH\;\;—O—CO—C_{17}H_{35} \\
\;| \qquad\qquad\qquad\qquad\qquad\qquad\qquad\quad | \\
CH_2 \;[OH \quad\;\; H]O\;\; OC—C_{17}H_{35} \qquad CH_2—O—CO—C_{17}H_{35}
\end{array}
$$

glycerol   3 molecules of   tristearine $+ 3H_2O$
                stearic acid

This reversible reaction is obviously encouraged to proceed towards the right if the water that it produces is removed. This explains why glycerides tend to accumulate in organs that are subject to desiccation, such as certain seeds.

2 *Steroids.* These, too, are esters, but the glycerol is replaced by sterols, alcohols of high molecular weight which have a characteristic polycyclic structure (figure 2·3). There are many different sterols,

2·3 A heterocyclic nucleus characteristic of sterols. The arrangement of its double bonds show it to be one of the sitosterols. Apart from the number of ethylene bonds, sterols also differ from each other in the nature of the radical R . The sitosterols of wheat exist as three isomers, in which the radical is

$$-CH \overset{\overset{\displaystyle CH_3}{|}}{-\!\!\!-} CH_2 \overline{} CH_2 \overline{} C_6H_{13}$$

varying according to the nature of the attached groups; some of them are saturated, but others have one, two or three double bonds which can provide extra attachments.

Vegetable sterols are different from those found in animal cells, of which the best known is cholesterol. The function of the sterols in plant cells is still unknown, though some have a therapeutic value. Thus ergosterol, when irradiated with ultraviolet light, produces calciferol, or vitamin D_2, an agent active against rickets. (This is not the same as vitamin D, which is formed when dehydrogenated cholesterol is irradiated).

3 *Waxes.* These again are esters of fatty acids, but those in which the glycerol is replaced by a higher alcohol, with a high molecular weight, for example:

fatty acid:	cerotic acid	$C_{26}H_{52}O_2$
alcohol:	cerylic alcohol	$C_{26}H_{54}O$

These substances, known as waxes, accumulate on the surface of plants, outside the cuticle, where they act as a protective layer.

4 *Phospholipids.* The phospholipids play a major part in the construction of the organelles of the cell, and their properties are partly responsible for the different ways in which these structures behave, both in the living cell and after fixation.

Actually, although phospholipids are highly soluble in fat-solvents (with the exception of acetone), they are also substances which easily emulsify in water, simply by agitation, and they are readily adsorbed on to other molecules. They are oxidised in air, in light, and in the presence of oxidising agents. They hydrolyse readily in the presence of dilute acids or alkalis. Obviously the phospholipids are very unstable substances, and the structures of which they form part are among those that are most easily changed, if the cells are placed under unnatural conditions.

A great variety of phospholipids exists. As an example, let us consider a lecithin, of a type that is widely distributed among both plants and animals. This substance is composed of three parts: a polyvalent alcohol, the phosphoric acid, and an amino-alcohol (a base). In this case the polyvalent alcohol is glycerol, two valencies of which have formed esters with fatty acids, and the third with the phosphoric acid. Finally, the amino-alcohol is choline:

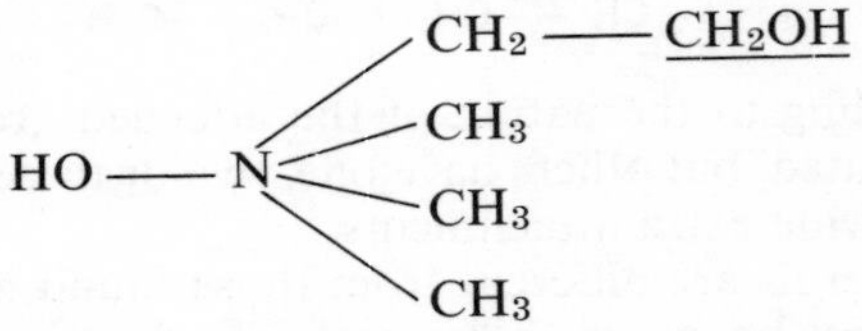

$$HO - N \begin{cases} CH_2 - \underline{CH_2OH} \\ CH_3 \\ CH_3 \\ CH_3 \end{cases}$$

which takes up a second valency of the phosphoric acid by esterifying through the primary alcohol group (shown underlined above). Then a lecithin arises with the structure shown below:

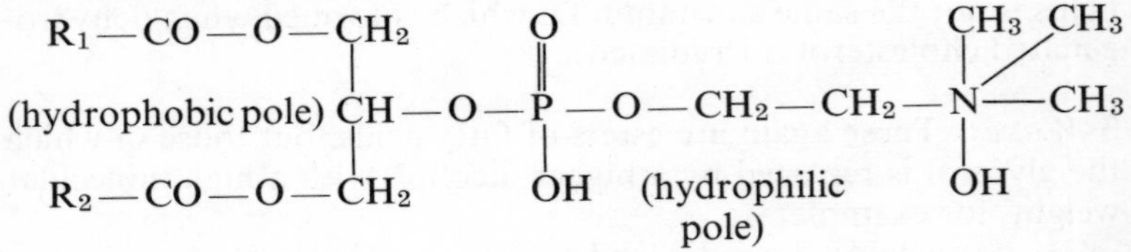

$$\begin{array}{l} R_1 - CO - O - CH_2 \\ \text{(hydrophobic pole)} \ CH - O - \overset{\overset{\displaystyle O}{\parallel}}{P} - O - CH_2 - CH_2 - N \overset{\displaystyle CH_3 \ CH_3}{\underset{OH}{\diagdown}} CH_3 \\ R_2 - CO - O - CH_2 \qquad\ OH \quad \text{(hydrophilic} \\ \qquad\qquad\qquad\qquad\qquad\qquad\qquad\qquad\ \text{pole)} \end{array}$$

where R_1 and R_2 are of the form:

$$CH_3 - CH_2 - CH_2 - - - - - - - - CH_2-$$

That is to say, they constitute a long hydrocarbon chain, and the two chains determine a hydrophobic pole of the long molecule. At the opposite end there are two hydroxyl groups: an acid –OH

36

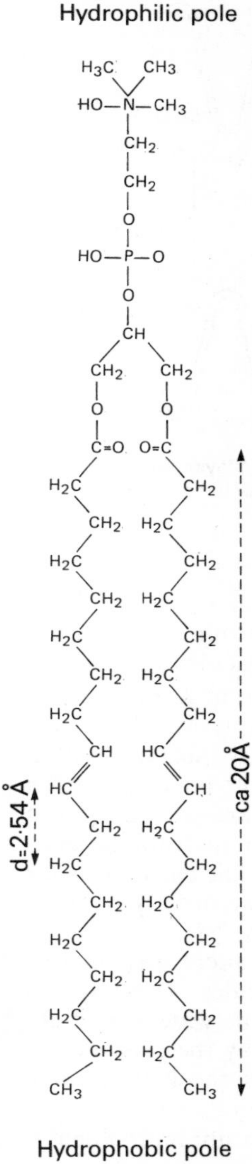

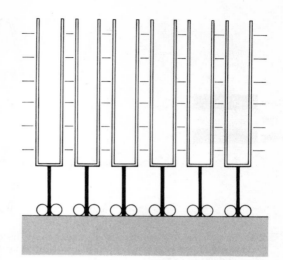

Hydrophilic pole

H₃C   CH₃
HO—N—CH₃
      |
      CH₂
      |
      CH₂
      |
      O
      |
HO—P—O
      |
      O
      |
      CH
     / \
   CH₂   CH₂
    | |
    O   O
    | |
   C=O   O=C
   /   \
 H₂C   CH₂
  | |
  CH₂   H₂C
  | |
 H₂C   CH₂
  | |
  CH₂   H₂C
  | |
 H₂C   CH₂
  | |
  CH₂   H₂C
  | |
 H₂C   CH₂
  | |
  CH   HC
  ‖   ‖
  HC   CH
  | |
  CH₂   H₂C
  | |
 H₂C   CH₂
  | |
  CH₂   H₂C
  | |
 H₂C   CH₂
  | |
  CH₂   H₂C
  | |
 H₂C   CH₂
  | |
  CH₃   CH₃

d=2·54 Å

ca 20 Å

Hydrophobic pole

2·4 A molecule of lecithin, to the right of which is a molecular film lying on a water surface. The hydrophilic poles are aligned on the water, and the hydrophobic poles are as far as possible from the water. The strokes denote hydrophobic bonds between the hydrocarbon chains.

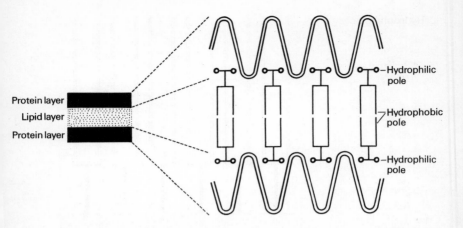

Protein layer
Lipid layer
Protein layer

–Hydrophilic pole

Hydrophobic pole

–Hydrophilic pole

2·5 The structure of the lipoprotein cell membrane. The lipid layer consists of two rows of phospholipid molecules, joined together by their hydrophobic poles and linked to the protein by their hydrophilic poles.

from the phosphoric acid, and a basic –OH from the choline. These groups readily attach the –OH and –H groups from water, and so constitute a hydrophilic pole to the molecule (figure 2·4).

Phospholipids are present in all cells, and are to a great extent linked to proteins in the form of lipoprotein complexes, which have a big part to play in the operation of various active surfaces within the cell. As a result of the hydrophobic/hydrophilic polarity that we have just described, molecules of lecithin that are spread upon a water surface orientate themselves so that their hydrophilic ends are in contact with the water, and their hydrophobic ends are as far removed as possible. Thus the molecules take up an orderly arrangement and constitute a monomolecular film (figure 2·4).

Films of this kind are present in cytoplasm, where their hydrophilic face is linked to a layer of protein molecules. Their hydrophobic surface, however, is incompatible with the watery medium of the cytoplasm, and this difficulty is avoided by the existence of two monomolecular films, 'back to back', with the hydrophobic ends of the molecules together, and the hydrophilic ends directed to the outside. This then constitutes a cell membrane, which is hydrophilic on both surfaces (figure 2·5).

The importance of these cell membranes will be evident later.

Glucides The glucides, sugars other than d-ribose and deoxyribose, are paraplasmic products, and sometimes present in great quantity. Some of them are soluble, and tend to accumulate in the vacuoles (saccharose, maltose, inulin), while others, which are polymers of the first group, are insoluble, and appear as inclusions either in the cytoplasm itself (the glycogen of fungi) or within specialised structures such as plastids (starch) or the cell wall (cellulose).

Inorganic compounds It is possible to obtain an estimate, though not a very accurate one, of the mineral content of a tissue by the technique of micro-incineration, which assesses the residue that survives after a temperature of about 300°C. The greater part of this residue consists of substances that have accumulated within the paraplasmic structures of the cells, and which do not form part of the living matter (chlorides, phosphates, carbonates, alkalis, or alkaline earths, silica, calcium oxalate). A very small proportion of the mineral residue, however, has been incorporated into complex organic molecules, and has played an important part in the living protoplasm. Such, for example, is iron, which enters into the composition of the cytochromes, compounds which play an indispensable role in the respiration of the cell. Similarly, chlorophyll, upon which photosynthesis depends, contains magnesium. Many enzymes operate with the assistance of coenzymes (zinc, for example, in carbonic anhydrase, molybdenum in nitrate-reductase, and so on).

These mineral elements, which are effective in very small doses, are indispensable to the life of the cell, a fact that can be demonstrated by tissue culture in an entirely synthetic medium. If the medium is deprived of even a trace of one of these 'trace elements', deficiency diseases appear after a few generations (R. Heller).

Many metals and metalloids have been listed as possible trace elements, among them Fe, Mn, Zn, Li, Cu, Al, Si . . . B, F, Br, I, etc. It is generally enough if their concentration in the cell is of the order of 10^{-5} to 10^{-9} of the dry weight. Other elements, called macronutrients, are needed in greater quantity, amounting to 1 per cent of the dry weight. These include K, Ca, Mg, present as ions in the liquid contents of the cell.

This summary of the chemical composition of protoplasm is enough for the purpose of this book, which is a cytological and not a biochemical survey. For further details the reader is referred to textbooks of biochemistry and physiology.

3 Physical properties

The chemical study of protoplasm has shown it to be an aqueous medium (often more than 80 per cent water), in which are distributed a variety of substances, most of which have a high molecular weight. Although these substances are all constructed from a very small number of fundamental chemical units (for example, the twenty amino acids and five bases), the resulting macromolecules possess almost infinite possibilities of variation in detail.

Today, perhaps more than ever before, biologists are convinced that it will never be possible to construct a living cell, even though the progress of biochemistry makes it possible to envisage the time when all the different chemical constituents of the cell can be supplied. To make a living cell it would be necessary to arrange all these substances into a precise organisation, on the scale of the macromolecules, from which arise physical relationships that are often complex. In the following pages we are not attempting anything more than a very much simplified picture of these characters and their subtle interrelations.

The colloidal state An aqueous medium with macromolecules dispersed in it, such as is to be found in the cell, exists in a colloidal state. Nevertheless the physical properties of protoplasm are different from the nearest types of non-living colloids. These colloids are of the type called hydrophilic, in which the dispersed particles have an affinity for water that is greater than their affinity for each other. As a result the action of water is to separate the particles from each other, and to disperse them, ending up with more or less isolated macromolecules. For this reason hydrophilic colloids are molecular colloids, in contrast to those colloids with hydrophobic particles which are micellary colloids, micelles being molecular aggregates that are not penetrated by the medium in which they are suspended.

Molecular colloids may be more or less viscous, and the viscosity may arise either from friction between the macromolecules – especially if these are of fibrous construction – or from attachments that have formed between them. The latter must be considered a little more fully.

In a system that has the consistency of a solid, the cohesion between the molecules arises from the forces of attraction that they exert upon each other. In physics there are certain forces called Van der Waals' forces, which are postulated to account for the difference between the behaviour of the 'perfect gas' and that of real gases, especially under high pressure. These molecular forces are in some degree analagous to Van der Waals' forces.

When the macromolecules are fibrous, like the protein gelatin, these forces tend to dispose these molecules parallel to one another. In the presence of water the attachments between one macromolecule and another are broken, and replaced by bonds between the macromolecules and molecules of water. The macromolecules are pulled apart, then separated, and finally dispersed, so that the system becomes progressively less 'solid', and tends towards a liquid state. The intermediate stages, while some degree of viscosity still persists in the system, are those when attachments still persist between some of the macromolecules. The more numerous these persistent bonds, the more viscous the system remains.

It is thus convenient to divide hydrophilic colloids into hydrosols which have more of a liquid consistency, and hydrogels, which have rather the consistency of a solid or of a jelly (figure 3·1). For example, if a fragment of gelatin is plunged into tepid water, it at first takes on the appearance of a gel (molecular fibres still held together by quite strong cohesive forces), and then becomes a viscous fluid (molecules held together only here and there by occasional cohesive bonds). This is the phenomenon of solvatation.

If a hydrogel of gelatin is heated it changes into a hydrosol as a result of thermal agitation, which ruptures most of the inter-molecular attachments. This phenomenon can be reversed by cooling again; as the thermal agitation diminishes, the forces of cohesion gradually re-establish themselves between compatible atoms in the different macromolecules.

Such colloids which contain fibrous macromolecules form a kind of three-dimensional framework within which the molecules of the dispersive medium (generally water) are more or less imprisoned. These imprisoned molecules are not attached to the macromolecules, and so they constitute 'free water'. This 'immobilisation of the solvent' adds still further to the viscosity of the whole system.

These properties of hydrophilic colloids give no more than an approximate picture of what goes on in living protoplasm. If an inert hydrophilic colloid, such as gelatin, is maintained under

41

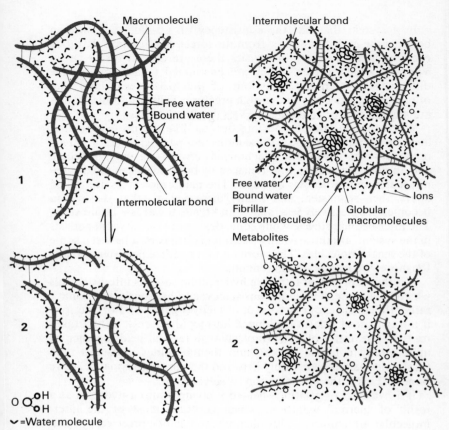

3·1 Molecular diagram of a hydrophilic colloid in its two thixotropic forms – a hydrogel (**1**) and a hydrosol (**2**). The hydrophilic macromolecules are enveloped in a layer of water molecules ('bound water'), except at certain points where there are intermolecular bonds, represented here by short lines. In the hydrosol, these bonds have almost disappeared, which is why the hydrosol is more fluid than the hydrogel. The length of the lines indicating bonds is proportional to the strength of the bond.

3·2 Molecular diagram of protoplasm in its two thixotropic forms – a plasmagel (**1**) and a plasmasol (**2**). The plasmasol retains a significant number of intermolecular bonds, showing that it has a definite structure; the fact that these bonds can fluctuate provides the plasmasol with its fluidity. The dispersion medium contains, in addition to free water, soluble molecules of metabolites and ions, notably Ca^{++}, Mg^{++}, and K^+.

constant external conditions, it does not depart from its state of equilibrium. The forces of cohesion existing between its molecules remain constant as long as temperature, pressure and similar factors do not change.

In contrast to this, it is impossible to maintain living protoplasm in a stationary state, except by keeping it at a temperature below the threshold of vital activity; being alive and being inert are mutually exclusive states. The fact that living organisms are in constant evolution implies that the relationships between macromolecules never reach stability, but go on changing indefinitely with time. Constant changes in the forces of molecular cohesion mean that the molecules are able to move about relative to each other more than they can in an inert colloid of the same molecular concentration, and that a living system is thus less viscous than an inert colloid.

Since it is necessary to stabilise such a system before it can be studied, the cytologist is obliged to fix it, in a most literal sense. This operation, which we shall examine later, transforms a living system into a dead one.

From what has gone before it seems that protoplasm is composed of hydrophilic macromolecules, bathed in a dispersive medium that is mainly water molecules. In addition this medium also contains soluble substances with small molecules (glucose, free amino acids, nucleotides, etc), as well as various ions (K^+, Mg^{++}, Ca^{++}, etc...).

The macromolecules are of many different kinds, and though most of them are simple proteins, others are nucleic acids or heteroproteins. They probably exist partly in globular forms (globulins, and many enzymes) and partly in a fibrous state, judging by the viscous properties of the protoplasm. As a result of their hydrophilic properties, these molecules are covered, over most of their surface, with a monomolecular layer of water molecules, held in position by the cohesive forces between the water and the hydrophilic bonds of the macromolecules. This is the bound water of the colloid (figure 3·2).

On the other hand, the macromolecules are held to each other here and there by intermolecular cohesive forces, forming a network which holds trapped within it the molecules of free water already mentioned, as well as various small molecules and ions (figure 3·2). It is these forces between one molecule and the next which fluctuate with the passage of time, and thus allow the living system to evolve. The changes in strength of these bonds make the protoplasm more fluid or more viscous, and by analogy with inert colloids we can speak of a plasmasol and a plasmagel. We shall see later that this analogy is not entirely accurate.

Some properties resulting from the colloidal state This section gives a brief account of certain properties of colloids which are a direct result of the colloidal state. We shall see that living colloids are more subtle in their reactions than colloids of inert systems, and the conditions of study and the techniques with which we approach living systems must take account of this fact.

1 *Filtration and dialysis.* Hydrophobic colloids, such as colloidal silver, are able to pass through a membrane if the pores of the framework are greater than the smallest dimensions of the colloidal micelles. In particular, they will pass through filter paper, but are stopped by the membranes of parchment or collodion that are used for dialysis.

Hydrophilic colloids, in the form of hydrogels, do not pass through a filter paper, even though their macromolecules have at least one dimension that is much less than that of the pores of the filter. This is because the cohesive forces between one molecule and another prevent them from moving apart, but these forces can be overcome by applying a sufficiently high pressure to the colloid. After filtration under pressure the intermolecular forces are reestablished, and the system returns to its initial state.

A hydrogel in living protoplasm does not behave in the same way as a simple hydrogel. Thus if a plasmodium of a myxomycete is filtered under pressure, what is reconstituted on the other side is an inert colloid. It seems that the state of being alive is dependent upon certain precise (though ever-changing) relationships between the macromolecules, their distances apart, and the forces acting between them. If these relationships are broken down, the process is irreversible, and death supervenes. An impressive confirmation of this fact can be obtained by allowing the plasmodium to grow on the filter paper, when it will penetrate to the other side spontaneously. Under these conditions the part that has been 'filtered' remains alive and normal.

2 *Brownian movement.* The micelles of a hydrophobic colloid are in continuous, irregular motion, as a result of the impact of the molecules of the surrounding medium, which themselves are in thermal agitation. In a hydrogel actual Brownian movement is

44

prevented by the intermolecular forces, and comes into evidence only when the hydrogel is transformed into a hydrosol. Here again, so-called hydrosols that occur in living protoplasm differ from non-living hydrosols in not showing Brownian movement. They also retain a residual viscosity, and these facts taken together indicate that protoplasmic hydrosols, in spite of their fluidity, have some kind of organisation that is more than a random association.

If protoplasm is kept under observation for a long period, under unfavourable conditions, Brownian agitation will eventually make its appearance. This indicates that the cell is undergoing changes, often irreversible changes, which are a prelude to approaching death. The presence or absence of Brownian movement in living cells may be a valuable indication of their state of health.

3 *Diffraction*. The micelles of a hydrophobic colloid generally diffract rays of light, often vigorously (the Tyndall effect), producing an effect that is analogous to what we see when a shaft of sunlight penetrates into a shady place and lights up the dust-particles. The intensity of the effect increases with the difference in refractive index between the particles and the medium in which they are dispersed, and with the size of each particle.

In a hydrophilic colloid the monomolecular layer of water which enshrouds each molecule considerably reduces the difference in refractive index, and consequently the diffractive effect is extremely weak. This can be seen if a tube containing either agar or white of egg is looked at from the side; these colloids show no more than a weak, diffused blue colour. The same is true of protoplasm, so long as we consider only the ground substance, and not the various inclusions that it contains, with their greater or smaller refractive properties. Such a substance is said to be 'optically empty', since nothing shows under the ultramicroscope, which operates by showing up refractive bodies against a dark background.

On the other hand, if the protoplasm is altered an effect takes place that is analogous to the coagulation of egg-white, and the protoplasm becomes diffractive. This change is caused by the stripping-off of the water layer which covers the molecules, so that a significant difference in refractive index is re-established.

4 *Electrical properties*. The reason why colloidal systems remain stable in their dispersed state is very largely the existence on the particles of electrostatic charges of the same sign.

We shall confine ourselves here to discussing those colloidal proteins that are most important to the cytologist, and which have special properties. In practice we find that hydrosol proteins carry a negative charge when they are in a weakly alkaline medium, and a positive when the medium is weakly acid. Consequently, if an alkaline hydrosol protein is gradually acidified, the negative charges of the particles are progressively neutralised; at a certain pH the charges become neutral, and after this progressively more positive. The pH value at which the electrical charges are just neutralised is called the iso-electric point.

At the iso-electric point, the electrical forces of repulsion no longer operate, and the stability of the hydrosol is at the mercy of any molecular impacts which the particles may receive; the iso-electric point is thus the pH at which stability is at a minimum. If the molecules are denser than the surrounding medium they have a tendency to precipitation; if they are less dense than the medium they have a tendency to float.

Similar forces operate in other dispersed systems, and in particular in cultures of bacteria in a liquid medium. Every species of bacteria has its iso-electric point, which may be diagnostic of the species.

5 *Coagulation.* Coagulation takes place when the dispersed particles separate themselves more or less completely from the dispersal medium. This effect can be produced in hydrophobic colloids by neutralising the electric charges of the particles, by supplying cations such as Ca^{++} or Ba^{++} if the particles are negatively charged, or anions such as SO_4^- if the charges are positive, or again, by mixing with a colloid of opposite charge.

In the case of hydrophilic colloids, we have already seen that the dispersal of the macromolecules is caused by their affinity for water, which shrouds them in a more or less continuous layer. Coagulation can be provoked if this layer of bound water can be removed, so as to allow the intermolecular forces to cause the molecules to cohere (figure 3·3). This result can be obtained by using any substance that has a strong affinity for water, that is, a dehydrant such as alcohol or strong acid. These agents are powerful enough to overcome the cohesive forces between the macromolecules and the water, and themselves absorb some, at least, of the water that is set free.

Another way of bringing about coagulation is to heat the system, when the increasing thermal agitation may be enough to break the bonds between the dispersed particles and their bound water. We

46

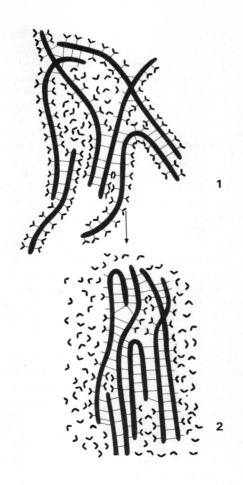

3·3 Molecular diagram of the coagulation of a hydrophilic colloid. **1** is the dispersed state, analogous to figure 3·1 ; **2** is the coagulated state. Loss of bound water allows macromolecules to aggregate under the attraction of intermolecular cohesive forces. Nearly all the bound water is now 'free'.

know, for example, that white of egg can be coagulated by alcohol or heat, and protoplasm can be coagulated by the same means.

An obvious consequence of such coagulation is the release of the bound water, unless it is quickly taken up by the coagulant itself. The destruction of the aqueous envelope of the macromolecules restores their diffractive properties, and so coagulation is commonly accompanied by an increase in opacity of the system.

Coagulation can be reversible under certain conditions, for example, if the liberated water is neither absorbed by the coagulant, nor physically removed from the scene of action. Thus either gentle chemical action, such as the use of dilute acids, or mechanical means such as a sudden shock or increase of pressure may cause temporary, reversible flocculation of protoplasm. This reversibility implies that the free water can return rapidly to its former bound condition as soon as the disturbing factor is removed.

Using an ultramicroscope it is possible to see a transitory cloudiness, lasting perhaps less than one second, appear in a transparent cytoplasm if the cover glass is given a blow, or a light pressure.

From what we have said earlier about the vital importance of spatial arrangement and mutual relationships of molecules in a living system, it follows that any irreversible coagulation will kill the protoplasm at the site where the coagulation occurs.

6 *Osmotic swelling of hydrophilic colloids.* In protoplasm the dispersal medium is not pure water, but a solution of ions and small molecules. Hence the network of macromolecules encloses a fluid that has a definite osmotic pressure. If such a system is immersed in a weaker solution, it will be subject to an influx of water which may cause the system to swell. Conversely it is possible to extract water from such a system by immersing it in a hypertonic solution.

It should be noted that this is an osmotic phenomenon peculiar to hydrophilic colloids, and is different from the usual situation where two media are separated by a membrane. A living cell normally performs both types of osmosis.

7 *Establishment of chemical bonds between molecular colloids.* Another way by which water may be extracted from a hydrophilic colloidal system, is to replace some of the hydrophilic groups by groups that are hydrophobic. Usually this operation increases the bonds which tie the macromolecules to one another, and so makes the system more coherent. This is what happens during the tanning of hides by using hydrophobic phenolic compounds from oak bark. The process is comprehensible when one remembers that the consistency of a colloidal gel is mainly due to the cohesive forces between the macromolecules, of which Van der Waals' effect is typical. Elimination of part of the bound water increases the strength of the intermolecular forces, rather as happens during coagulation.

The mechanical resistance of these colloids may be still further increased if these rather weak cohesive forces are augmented by bonds between the principal valencies of the molecules. The tanning of hides provides an example of this, too. When chromium compounds are used as tanning agents, the atoms of chromium form bridges between the principal valencies of the protein molecules of the skin, giving a very strong attachment:

```
 /\  /\  /\  /\  /\  /\       protein 1
     |           |
     |           |
  — Cr        — Cr            chrome bridges
     |           |
 \  /\  /\  /\  /\  /\        protein 2
```

Moreover, the ability to form bonds of this type is not restricted to hydrophilic colloids. It is the basis for the vulcanisation of rubber, by forming sulphur bonds ($-S-S-$) between the polyterpene macromolecules derived from the rubber latex.

These properties of hardening of hydrophilic colloids are the basis for the techniques of fixation of cell contents described later.

8 *Thixotropy*. An inert gel of a suitable concentration can be converted into a sol by simple agitation. If the system reverts to a gel when the agitation stops, then this reversible gel/sol relationship is called thixotropy.

Thixotropy is explained as a mechanical rupture of the intermolecular bonds which were responsible for the rigidity of the gel. When the liquid phase is allowed to stand, the cohesive forces restore the spatial relationships of the molecules to their former state, and thus the system reverts to being a gel.

Similar processes of gelation and solation take place spontan-

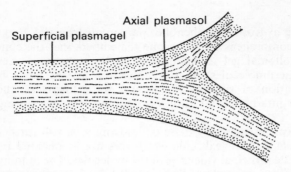

3·4 Diagram of a plasmodial strand of a myxomycete.

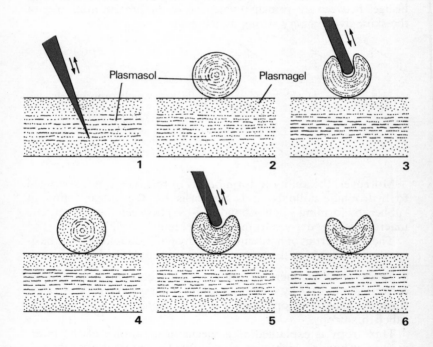

3·5 An experiment showing superficial gelation of cytoplasm. A droplet of plasmasol oozes from the puncture. If this droplet is deformed as soon as it appears, it quickly becomes spherical, but later on any deformation is permanent, for the peripheral cytoplasm of the droplet has become more viscous.

eously in living protoplasm, but this spontaneity is not the only difference from inert systems. Even inside the same cell some regions of the protoplasm are in a gel state, while others exist as a sol (plasmagels and plasmasols). This situation can be easily seen in a plasmodial strand of a myxomycete, where only the internal zone of the protoplasm is fluid and mobile (figure 3·4). The fact that the inner, fluid zone and the outer, gel zone are not two different substances is evident from the way in which local transformations from sol to gel and vice versa go on all the time.

The complete cytoplasm of a cell may be transformed into a gel, or into a sol, by using anaesthetics. Similarly, plasmagel can be reversibly changed into plasmasol by the use of high hydrostatic pressures. Clearly, therefore, in the living cell we are dealing with a single colloidal phase in which the gel and sol forms exist simultaneously in dynamic equilibrium. A non-living gel such as gelatin, in contrast, is in equilibrium only when it exists either entirely as a gel or entirely as a sol.

This thixotropic heterogeneity of the cytoplasm can be shown by the process of superficial gelation, which seems to be a property of all cytoplasms. If a plasmodium of a myxomycete is pricked on the surface (figure 3·5), a tiny droplet of liquid plasmasol appears, and will alter in shape if the surface is squeezed. If the pressure is applied as soon as the drop appears, the deformation disappears as soon as the pressure is released. On the other hand, if the pressure is not applied until some time later, the deformation persists after the pressure is released, showing that the droplet is stiffer than it was. This effect is produced by a second, superficial gelation, on the surface only of the droplet; if this is again pierced, a further, smaller droplet appears.

These thixotropic processes are evidence that the bonds between the macromolecules of living protoplasm change spontaneously with time, but the loosening of these bonds does not lead to the formation of a genuine sol. A molecular organisation still persists, more than could arise by mere chance, and which, in particular, prevents Brownian movement. Figure 3·2 gives a schematic picture of thixotropic transformations within living matter.

During this quick survey of the physical properties of colloids in general, and of protoplasm in particular, we have pointed out that in almost every respect the living protoplasm of cells is distinct from even the most similar non-living colloids. The basis of these differences must be sought in a well-defined organisation which goes right down to molecular level. Anything which artificially alters this organisation runs the risk of changing the protoplasm into an inert colloid, and in an irreversible fashion.

This brings up once again the problem of what distinguishes a living system from a non-living one, a question to which biologists have still no answer, despite their recent spectacular progress. Since the cell structures that we are about to study are essentially machines for converting energy from one form to another, the answer may well have to come from biophysical studies, and particularly from studies of intracellular energetics.

4 Methods of studying the cell

The historical survey given in the first chapter of this book showed how much the progress of cytology owes to the perfecting of methods of observing cellular structures, involving not only optical instruments, but also techniques for preparing cells for observation. Obviously the ideal would be to be able to study the cells while alive and intact. This ideal is seldom feasible, but in order to get as near to the ideal as possible, cytologists have brought into use a variety of methods of vital observation, which are often ingenious in their use of all the resources of physics and chemistry.

All the same, the limitations of the working conditions of the microscope on the one hand, and the fragility and lack of contrast of the specimen on the other, combine to make vital observation difficult and frustrating. Hence cytologists have been compelled to prepare the cell structures in such a way as to make the best use of the microscope, while at the same time trying to avoid changing the appearance of the living structures. This is the purpose of fixation, which – in theory at least – keeps the cell structures as they were, and of differential staining, which accentuates the differences between them.

Let us take a short look at these various techniques before launching into a study of the constituents of the cell.

Observation of the living cell Until very recently living cells could be examined only with light microscopes, using either visible light, or radiations of a kind that were not immediately damaging to the cell (for example, ultraviolet light and x-rays). Possibly we shall soon be able to study living cells with the aid of electron microscopes which make use of very high voltages, and discharges of very low intensity.

Observation of living cells with light microscopes suffers from the two sets of limitations outlined below.

1 *Limitations of the microscope.* Most observations with the light microscope are made by transmitted light, that is to say, the image is formed by light that has passed through the preparation. Hence the

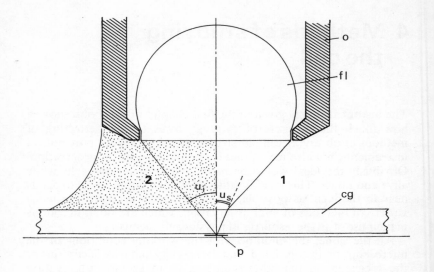

4·1 Aperture of the microscope objective lens.
1 When used in air, the refraction between the
cover glass (cg) and the air limits the usable
cone of light to the angle u_s.
2 When the objective is immersed in a fluid
of the same refractive index ($n \simeq 1·51$)
as the cover glass and is interposed between
the cover object and the front lens (fl) of
the objective (0) rays emerging from
the preparation (p) are no longer refracted and the
usable cone of light now has an angle u_i.
Since u_i is greater than u_s, n sin u is also greater,
and the resolving power of the objective is increased.

object must be made sufficiently transparent for this purpose.
Furthermore the clarity of the image falls off rapidly as the thickness
of the preparation is increased, and so the living tissue must be cut
into very thin sections, a process which leads to damage to the
tissue, and alteration in the appearance of the cells. As a consequence
the study of living structures is restricted to certain kinds of materials:
isolated cells, very thin leaves, pieces of epidermis, and the epidermal
structures known as trichomes, and so on ... and this restricted
choice is not enough.

Another obvious limitation is in the resolving power of light
microscopes, which is given by Abbe's formula:

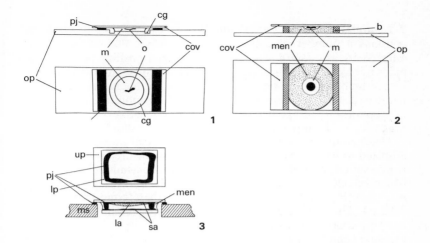

4·2 Apparatus for studying living cells.
1 Ranvier's humid chamber. cg = circular groove cut in object plate (op) acting as an air reservoir; cov = cover glass; m = mounting medium; o = object; pj = petroleum jelly.
2 Comandon and de Fonbrune's oil chamber. b = blocks supporting cover glass; men = meniscus of paraffin oil surrounding mounting medium.
3 Bajer's apparatus for cinematography. sa = thin layer of sugar agar spread over the surface of the plate; la = droplet of liquid albumen spread over upper plate (up); lp = lower plate held by a band of petroleum jelly (pj); ms = microscope stage hollowed out to take upper plate, which is larger than lower plate. The albumen is thus retained in a humid space, and is provided with a sugary nutritive medium. Under these conditions mitosis can continue for more than 48 hours.

$$\varepsilon = \frac{0·6\,\lambda}{n\,\sin u}$$

where λ is the wavelength of the light used, and $n \sin u$ is the numerical aperture of the objective lens (n is the refractive index of the medium which lies between the object and the front lens of the microscope, and u is the demi-angle at the tip of the cone of rays which emerges from the centre of the object and just fills the objective lens) (figure 4·1). The numerical aperture is raised to a maximum of 1·40 by using an oil-immersion objective, and choosing immersion oil of refractive index $n = 1·52$, equal to that of the cover glass of the preparation. Under these conditions the resolving power is in the neighbourhood of $0·2\mu$ for a wavelength of $0·5\mu$.

2 *Limitations of the protoplasm.* We have seen that protoplasm contains a number of colloidal systems which are unstable, and affected by any factor which alters the relationships between the macromolecules and the water. The preparations that are necessary before living cells can be examined under the microscope are very liable to do just this, and to reduce the risk to a minimum, methods of preparation must be devised as far as possible to avoid changes of pressure, or of temperature, osmotic shocks, or shortage of oxygen.

The medium in which cells are to be mounted must therefore be adjusted to be isotonic with the cells, and to ensure an ionic equilibrium similar to that which exists in the protoplasmic colloids of the observed cells (particularly with respect to the ions K^+, Ca^{++}, Mg^{++}, etc, ...). Figure 4·2 shows how some of these conditions can be fulfilled. The objects are studied in a humidity chamber, either in hanging drops, or in watch glasses, avoiding any great changes of pressure, and with access to a reserve of air sufficient to permit prolonged examination. The oil bath devised by Comandon and de Fonbrune for microcinematography is possible only because the liquid paraffin used is permeable to oxygen.

We have no space in this book to go into details of these and similar techniques, and we must end by describing the set-up used by Bajer for observing and filming the phenomenon of cell division or karyokinesis. The material is liquid endosperm from various ova in the process of maturation, which is poured on to a slide coated with a film of sugar agar. The liquid spreads over this until it is restrained by a ring of petroleum jelly. The pool that is formed is covered with a cover slip protected against misting by a film of agar, and the preparation is placed on the stage of the microscope. This arrangement has made possible some remarkable studies of cell division (see chapter 8).

These methods still suffer from the disadvantage that the materials may have a very low contrast, which must be increased as much as possible. Two kinds of methods have been used for this, which will be very briefly described.

Improved optical methods for studying the living cell

1 *The phase-contrast microscope.* The most important of these methods is the phase-contrast microscope. In the operation of the ordinary microscope, the contrast of the image arises in two ways. One is the extent to which the diffracted light is scattered, and this effect is the greater the higher the refractive index of the material.

56

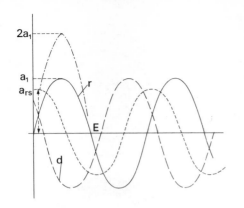

4·3 Interference between two waves, one of which (d) is retarded by $\frac{\lambda}{2} + E$ relative to the other (r).
The resulting amplitude (a_{rs}) is much smaller than the sum of the two waves ($2a_1$), which would have been the amplitude if the two waves had been in phase.

The light that is scattered is lost to the image, consequently the greater the diffraction the darker that part of the image appears.

Secondly, any diffracted rays that do find their way back into the image suffer a retardation of phase relative to the rays that are refracted normally. If the two kinds of rays both take part in forming the image, they will interfere with each other, and this will reduce the brightness of the image at that point, in contrast to the brightness that it would have had if the rays had been all in phase with each other.

The principle of 'phase contrast' consists simply of increasing the proportion of the light that is diffracted, while at the same time increasing the difference of phase by half a wavelength. Figure 4·3 shows that if two rays are combined that are out of phase by $\lambda/2 + \varepsilon$ there is a considerable reduction in the resultant amplitude. In the phase-contrast microscope, in addition to the small retardation of phase produced by diffraction (ε), a further phase change of half a wavelength is artificially imposed on the diffracted rays alone. In addition these rays are again diffracted, in such a way that part of them is lost. These two effects greatly increase the normal small diffraction effect, and so greatly improve the contrast. One of the ways of doing this is to make the diffracted rays pass through a phase-ring which is placed inside the objective lens, and which contains a colloidal layer that diffracts the light and retards its phase at the same time. Part of the diffracted rays that have been picked up by the objective are thus eliminated, and the rest are retarded by half a wavelength (figure 4·4).

2 *The ultramicroscope.* The ultramicroscope is a normal light microscope, but fitted with a special condenser, designed so that

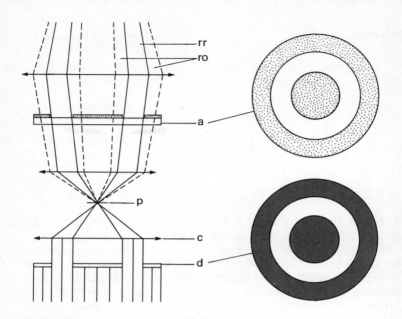

4·4 In the phase contrast microscope, an annular diaphragm (d) inside the condenser (c) is arranged in such a way that the preparation (p) comes just at the tip of a 'hollow cone' of rays. The refracted rays (rr) also form a hollow cone (solid lines), which reaches the objective lens. Other rays (ro) are scattered in all directions by the preparation, and only some of the rays reach the objective. The latter contains a phase ring (a), which provides a clear annulus for the refracted cone of rays, but is covered both inside and outside this ring by a colloidal layer which adds to the scatter as well as imposing a phase difference of $\frac{\lambda}{2}$ between the refracted and the diffracted rays. They interfere with each other, and the net result is an apparent increase in contrast.

the rays that are simply refracted do not reach the objective (figure 4·5). If the preparation does not contain anything diffractive, that is, anything that scatters the light, no light reaches the objective lens, and the field of view remains entirely dark (as with a colloidal gel). If, however, the preparation contains particles that scatter light, some part of this light will reach the objective lens and will form an image of these structures, which will be seen as a bright image on a dark background.

One big advantage of this system is that the scattered light can be

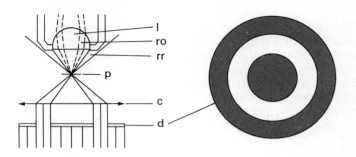

4·5 Diagram of how the condenser is adjusted for dark ground illumination in the ultramicroscope. The diaphragm (d) isolates a cylinder of light rays, which the condenser (c) focusses on to the preparation (p). The optical values are such that the regularly refracted rays (rr) do not enter the first lens of the objective and hence the background remains dark. On the other hand, any diffractive particles in the preparation scatter light in all directions, and some of this (ro) will reach the objective. Hence any diffractive particles show up as more or less brilliant spots of light against the dark ground.

seen even when the particle itself is much smaller than the resolving power of the microscope. Figure 4·5 shows one of a number of designs of condenser that have been used. We have no space to go into the refinements of the ultramicroscope that have been perfected, but it has made possible observations of living systems of a type that were previously out of reach. For example, it has made visible the swimming movements of typhoid bacilli, which are quite different from anything that might be inferred from what can be seen in dead and stained bacilli; the latter effects are clearly artifacts. The ultramicroscope has also enabled studies to be made of living protoplasm during its 'optically empty' phase, and the modifications of this state that occur when the cells change, and die.

3 *Other methods.* Other optical methods have been very useful in the study of living material, such as, for example the use of polarised light, which has made it possible to detect those structures in the cell that are anisotropic, that is, have a different refractive index in different directions (for example, starch, the cellulose cell wall, and the cell spindle).

To increase the resolving power of the light microscope we may make use of ultraviolet light. As will be seen from Abbe's formula (p. 55), a reduction in λ will produce a reduction in ε.

The opacity of ordinary glass makes it necessary to make quartz lenses or to use mirrors in microscopes; these microscopes have been used to study the fine structure in cell organelles.

Again, by using ultraviolet light in ordinary microscopes it has been possible to excite the natural fluorescence of certain constituents of the cell, which can then be detected even in a living cell. The fluorescence microscope can be used to study differentiation in chloroplasts, by making use of the fluorescence of the chlorophyll.

Vital staining Some studies of living cells have made use of the natural colours of the structures examined: for example the vacuoles present in certain tissues contain pigments, either violet (anthocyanin) or yellow (oxyflavones). The greater part of the cell contents, however, is naturally colourless, or inconspicuous (mitochondria, for example).

Most stains, even if they have a selective affinity for particular constituents of the cell, either do not penetrate readily, or penetrate only after having killed the cell. These stains are useless for the study of living cells, but others have proved valuable because they can penetrate into the living cell without killing it, and even without altering it visibly, at least for some time. These vital stains are usually aniline derivatives, and are used in the form of salts (chlorohydrates), in which the colour group is the cation. They are therefore *basic* stains, which are electropositive, with few exceptions. They can be divided into two groups, those which accumulate in the vacuoles, and those which attach themselves to protoplasmic structures while these are still alive.

1 *Vital staining for the vacuoles*. These stains pass through the cytoplasm without being taken up by it, and they accumulate inside the vacuoles. They thus have the unusual ability of being able to penetrate the cell membrane, as well as the vacuolar membrane (or tonoplast), without staining the protoplasm. This seems to be a result of their lack of affinity for protoplasmic substances, which implies that they do not appreciably change the molecular order in living substances. Nevertheless most cells cannot tolerate these stains indefinitely without suffering some damage.

The chief vital vacuolar stains are neutral red, neutral violet and cresyl blue.

2 *Vital staining for the protoplasm*. These are stains that attach

60

themselves to the living constituents of the cells and so they alter the structure of the molecules, and hence they are always more toxic to the cell than are the vacuolar stains. For this reason they are more difficult and more critical to use. They must be allowed to operate in very great dilution, and stopped as soon as they begin to stain the protoplasm, because if they are allowed to continue they do irreparable damage. In fact one can say that these stains are 'sublethal' rather than vital. Examples are Janus Green B and Methyl Violet, which selectively stain the mitochondria; Dahlia Violet and Crystal Violet, which attach themselves particularly to the nucleus; and rhodamine, a vital stain for the chloroplasts.

Vital stains have been useful not only for morphological studies, but sometimes also in cell physiology. Some, such as neutral red, are indicators of pH; others are indicators of rH (redox potential), such as Janus Green, which attaches itself to the mitochondria because these are sites where oxidation and reduction take place.

Guilliermond and Gautheret have studied a great many other live stains, many of which are either more general, or more specific, than the examples quoted above.

3 *Tolerance of cells to vital stains.* Vital staining is liable to certain hazards, depending on the physiological state of the cells, on their degree of specialisation, on their pH, their content of parasplasmic material, and on what phase of cell division they happen to be in. Thus cells that are in process of mitosis are usually not capable of being stained with live protoplasmic stains. The same is true of plant extremities that are in full growth, such as those of the hyphae of fungi (Siphomycetes).

The tolerance of cells for vacuolar stains also varies with both the stain and the plant species. For instance Guilliermond has been able to induce both growth and sporulation in *Saprolegnia* (a Siphomycete) on a medium to which neutral red had been added, and the vacuoles of the fungus remained vitally stained throughout their development. Alternatively other fungi (Septomycetes, and especially yeasts) after staining with neutral red, expel the stain into the surrounding medium before they proliferate by budding (Guilliermond and Gautheret).

Fixatives Observation of the living cell has only limited possibilities, in spite of all the technical improvements that have taken place. Moreover the movements of living structures make prolonged examination difficult, because protoplasm is both fragile and unstable. Cytologists have therefore looked for some way of fixing the structures in the most literal sense, so that they can be examined at leisure. The method of fixation must preserve at least the most important features of the living appearance, as well as making the cell tough enough to stand up to being sliced into very thin sections, for more detailed study.

Fixation, therefore, should ideally stop all movement, and all deterioration, without introducing any changes on its own account. This presupposes an instant death, and it must be admitted that this is an ideal, which can only be approached as closely as possible, since if it were fully attained no chemical action at all would take place! What we have seen already of the physical structure of the cell makes it clear that unless the molecular structure is altered in some way the cell will not die, and therefore cannot be fixed.

Indeed alteration is a *sine qua non* of fixation, but we must try to keep alteration to a minimum, or at any rate restrict it to effects which will not jeopardise the studies we wish to make. Two main types of fixatives can be recognised: a variety of chemical fixatives on the one hand, and one purely physical method: freezing.

1 *Chemical fixatives.* These are generally toxic substances, whose function is to consolidate the cell structures in a state as nearly as possible that in which they existed at the moment of fixation.

The first fixatives made use of alcohol and acids. Nowadays we are aware that these agents consolidate the protoplasm of the cell violently, increasing the forces of cohesion between the molecules, and causing them to coagulate. Fixatives of this type therefore produce coarse artifacts, but they have the advantage that they produce preparations that can afterwards be easily stained. Hence their main use is for histological and cytological work (counting chromosomes), or for cytochemical studies in which all the nucleic acids, proteins, etc must be retained within the cell.

These fixatives either destroy or greatly alter any structures that are rich in fat, such as mitochondria, and so other fixatives have been devised which are less strongly acid, and which render the fat-soluble substances as insoluble as possible. This research led to such 'mitochondrial fixatives' as formol, potassium dichromate and osmium tetroxide, which are much kinder to the cytoplasmic structures. More recently the incomparably greater demands made by the electron microscope have stimulated a search for fixatives that would give a result as faithful to the living original as possible. In time, no doubt, progress in our knowledge of the physical properties of protoplasm, as summarised in the preceding chapter, will enable us to approach this problem in a less empirical manner.

It was necessary to find fixatives that would consolidate living matter, while disturbing the spatial arrangement as little as possible. Hence it was necessary to discover non-coagulating fixatives, which would confine their activities to merely joining the macromolecules together with bonds that were strong enough to keep these molecules indefinitely in the exact relationships that they held at the moment of fixation. This requirement calls for just those bonds of the principal valencies between the molecules that we have already mentioned when we were discussing the physical conditions within the cell.

Provided that they are used correctly, some of the fixatives used for the light microscope have also proved effective for the purposes of the electron microscope (notably formaldehyde, potassium dichromate and osmium tetroxide), while others have only recently been brought into use (potassium permanganate, glutaraldehyde). It is believed that they all work in much the same way as we have already discussed, though the exact details of how they act on the various constituents of the cell have not yet been worked out.

By way of example we might consider fixation with osmium tetroxide, OsO_4. In aqueous solution this substance is known to transform protein sols into gels, so it is claimed, without coagulating them. This action is explained by saying that osmium tetroxide has a special affinity for ethylene bonds, opening them out and forming four bonds of principal valencies disposed in the form of a cross:

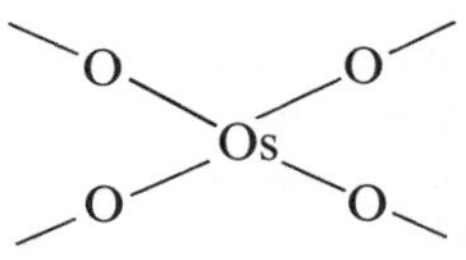

This disposition explains the consolidative action of the fixative. The fixative can link with two ethylene groups of two protein molecules:

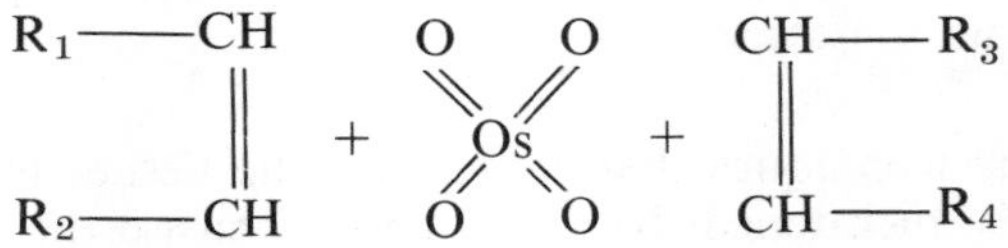

$$= \quad \begin{array}{c} R_1 \text{—CH} \\ | \\ R_2 \text{—CH} \end{array} \begin{array}{c} O \\ \diagdown \\ Os \\ \diagup \quad \diagdown \\ O \end{array} \begin{array}{c} O \\ \diagdown \\ \diagup \end{array} \begin{array}{c} \text{CH—} R_3 \\ | \\ \text{CH—} R_4 \end{array}$$

Protein or Fat Osmium tetroxide Protein or Fat

The action may, of course, be more complex than this, especially where fats are concerned, but the diagram is restricted to showing what happens to bring about fixation. Potassium bichromate acts in a somewhat similar way, by forming chrome bridges such as are formed in the process of tanning of hides. Similarly, formaldehyde makes methylene bridges (**–CH$_2$–**). The degree of consolidation is greater or less according to the fixative used, and its action may be insufficient. This is true of fixation in formalin, which is not always enough to prevent subsequent changes when for instance, the preparation is dehydrated in alcohol.

2 *Freezing*. Fixation by freezing consists of subjecting the material to a sudden, intense freezing, which brings all cellular activity to a stop. The rate of reduction of temperature needs to be extremely rapid, of the order of 5,000°C per second, so that the water that is in the cells will pass straight from the liquid state to an amorphous solid, and not into ice crystals, which would cut the protoplasm to pieces. For this reason very small objects (less than 0·25 mm across) are frozen by dropping them into a liquefied gas that has been kept at a temperature below its boiling point. This last condition is essential, otherwise a cushion of vapour will form round the specimen and prevent it from being frozen quickly enough.

We have no space to elaborate on the details of this method of fixation, which approaches most nearly to the ideal, in that no foreign substance is introduced into the cell. Hence the protoplasmic proteins are denatured as little as possible. The method, however, has the inconvenience of being awkward, and even more, of leaving the fixed tissues extremely delicate under the operations that we are about to describe.

Microtomy The techniques that come after the tissues have been fixed need to be mentioned, because they emphasise the fact that these later stages of preparation may often be the most damaging of all to the cell structures.

The purpose of the whole operation is to present the object to the microscope in the form of a thin slice, which may vary from a few microns for the light microscope to less than one tenth of a micron (often even one thirtieth or one fiftieth) for the electron microscope. Hence the specimen must be sliced into fine, or even ultra-fine sections, by using a microtome. Such thin sections can be cut only from materials that have suitable mechanical properties; since these are not the properties of normal cell contents, they must be embedded in some material suitable for sectioning.

The most usual embedding media are insoluble in water: paraffin waxes, 'epoxy' resins, methacrylates. To give adequate support, the medium must come into intimate contact with the object, and so the latter must be completely dehydrated, and then impregnated either with the embedding medium itself, or with some solvent that will mix completely with it. It is these processes of dehydration and impregnation that are so very liable to alter the cell structure. For example, if structures that have been inadequately fixed in formalin are afterwards dehydrated with alcohol, the latter may cause disastrous overfixation.

These disadvantages can be mitigated, to some extent, by dehydrating at a temperature close to the freezing point of ethyl alcohol ($-111°C$) (freeze substitution). Another technique, which is essential after fixation by freezing, is to dehydrate by subliming off the ice in a high vacuum (less the 10^{-5} mm of mercury), and at a very low temperature. This operation (freeze drying) requires complex apparatus, and even then does not always avert a slow, but catastrophic crystallisation of the clear ice. To guard against this possibility it would be necessary to keep the temperature down below $-130°C$, but then the vapour pressure of ice at that temperature is so low that the ice does not sublime, even under the lowest pressures that can be obtained with the best available pumps. The usual working temperature is $-80°C$, corresponding to a vapour pressure of 4×10^{-4} mm of mercury, since pumps will go down to less than 10^{-5} mm. Freeze drying is possible under these conditions.

When the object has been completely dehydrated it must be impregnated, either by a solvent of the embedding medium, or by the medium itself (for example, paraffin wax), or by one of the constituents (monomers) from which the embedding medium is derived by polymerisation (for example, some synthetic resins). For the light microscope it is usual to embed in paraffin wax, with a melting point somewhere between 45° and 65°C. Impregnation and embedding are carried out at a temperature very little above the melting point. Embedding media for the electron microscope are either plastics such as the methacrylates, or epoxy-resins such as the araldites, or epon, which solidify when the liquid monomer polymerises.

The actual sectioning technique or *microtomy*, is often less worrying for the cytologist than either dehydration or embedding. Microtomes used for making sections suitable for the light microscope carry the preparation at the end of an oscillating arm, which advances by the thickness of one section at each stroke. The embedded object is brought down upon the edge of a sectioning knife, which is extremely sharp, and the sections come off in the form of continuous ribbons, portions of which are then mounted on glass slides.

Electron microscopes require the use of ultramicrotomes (figure 4·6), which may work on a similar principle, or may advance the object at each slice by thermal expansion of the supporting rod. In any event an ultramicroscope must get rid of all mechanical joints, replacing them by springs or by some other device, because the mechanical tolerances are of an order of magnitude greater than the thickness of the sections that are to be cut. Similarly, the knife edge that cuts the section must be free from the minute irregularities that are present on any metal edge, and so the ultramicrotome uses knives of *glass*, which are made very simply by cutting thick glass strips in such a way as to obtain edges with an angle of 40° or 50° through the thickness of the glass (figure 4·6). Diamond knives made in a similar way have a high degree of polish.

The sections, which are extremely fragile, are received on a water surface in a tiny hollow on one side of the knife itself. Under a binocular microscope the sections are transferred to the special

4·6 Top Ultramicrotome equipped with a binocular microscope for estimating the thickness of the section by means of the interference colours.
Bottom A glass knife used for ultramicrotomy. a=thick glass plate to be cut into squares, and then into right-angled triangular knives; b=cutting edge of glass knife; c=water-trough attached to knife which collects the sections.

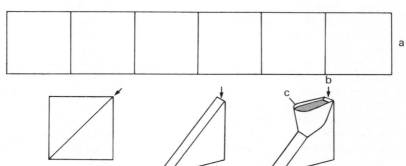

a

b

c

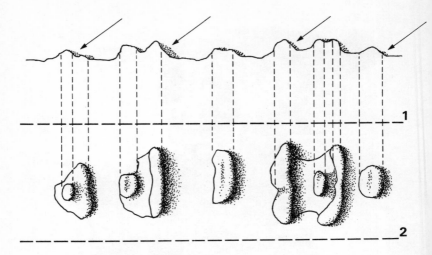

4·7 The principle of oblique metallic shading.
1 A noble metal vaporised under an electric arc, and projected
at a shallow angle on to the surface to be studied.
2 Object viewed at right angles under the electron microscope,
when the oblique shading increases the contrast.

specimen grids used for the electron microscope, which are little
circles of net, about 3 mm across, and of very fine mesh, and
covered with a supporting film of either plastic or carbon.

Sections for the light microscope are then rinsed clear of their
embedding medium by a suitable solvent, passed through the
alcohols to a medium suitable for staining, and then stained by
whatever technique is appropriate to the tissues to be studied.
Finally, they are generally mounted permanently between the slide
and a cover-slip, in some such medium as Canada Balsam.

Sections for the electron microscope may be examined direct, or
they may be artificially made more contrasty to the electron beam
by treating them with compounds containing heavy atoms which
are opaque to electrons. This time the embedding medium is usually
left intact, unless one wants to examine structures that are very
transparent to electrons, when the medium is removed, and the
bare, irregular surface of the object is exposed. On to this surface
is then deposited a metallic film, by evaporating the metal electrically
and projecting it at an oblique angle on to the surface of the section.
The metal builds up on one side of the irregularities, just like drifting

snow, and when this is exposed to the electron beam the metal throws a shadow, and shows up the irregularities in relief (figure 4·7).

The electron microscope The electron microscope has made it possible to examine cell structures down to an order of size and resolving power far beyond that of the light microscope. Since about 1950 this technique has resulted in a great resurgence of general cytology, and we shall have to bear these advances constantly in mind during what follows.

1 *The principle*. The work of L. de Broglie showed that when a beam of electrons is accelerated in an electrostatic or a magnetic field it behaves as if it had a definite wavelength, which depends on the speed of the electrons, hence upon how much they are being accelerated. In the field produced by several thousand volts this wavelength is much shorter than the wavelength of visible light. By designing 'electronic lenses' capable of refracting these beams of electrons, and forming images comparable to those of a light microscope, one might hope to take advantage of the very short wavelength, and thus make a microscope which had exceptional resolving power. Such 'electronic lenses' can be made, and used to make an image of those parts of the object which allow electrons to pass through and diffract them. As in the light microscope, the image formed by the first lens is then magnified again by a second lens, and usually by a third again. The final image can either be observed on a fluorescent screen or recorded photographically.

2 *Construction*. The 'optical system' of an electron microscope is enclosed in the column (figure 4·8).

The electron gun has a source of electrons, usually a tungsten filament heated electrically, and some system by which the electrons are accelerated. The latter consists of a cathode, pierced by a hole through which the electrons emerge, and an anode. The potential difference between anode and cathode provides the accelerating force, and may be between 50 and 100 kilovolts.

The condenser is the first electronic lens, and serves to concentrate the beam of electrons on to the object, which is mounted on the special support already mentioned (the circle of mesh), and can be moved about by outside controls.

The objective is an electronic lens with the same function and the same importance as the objective lens in a light microscope. This lens provides the first image, which forms the object for the second lens.

The intermediate lens serves to magnify the image already produced by the objective.

The projector lens is the fourth electronic lens, and gives the final image, again magnified, which can be observed on the fluorescent screen, or photographed.

Each electronic lens has its own control system, by means of which the magnification can be varied, and the final image focused on the screen. This can be examined with the naked eye, or with a binocular microscope attached to the column, or a camera attachment can be swung into place.

In addition to the column, with its 'optical system', the electron microscope has a console containing the various circuits which provide the high voltage needed to accelerate the electrons, stabilise the various electrical forces, and pump out the column to the high vacuum needed before the electrons can perform their function.

This last requirement, that the interior of the microscope shall be at a high vacuum, is one of a number of factors which impose limitations on the practical use of the electron microscope in biology, and which we must now consider.

3 *The electron microscope in cytological research.* As we have just seen, specimens in the electron microscope are exposed to extremely low pressures, and this automatically dehydrates them. This condition nullifies almost all observation of living cells under the electron microscope, since any cell that will tolerate such a dehydration without being killed must be in a state of suspended animation.

In contrast to visible light, which easily passes through most of the constituents of protoplasm, electrons (even when they are accelerated by about 100,000 volts) have very poor powers of penetration. This means that the preparation must be extremely thin. Electronic images begin to show useful detail when the section has been cut down to a thickness of about 1,000Å, but if the remarkable resolving powers of the electron microscope are to be utilised it is usually necessary to cut sections less than 300Å thick.

The kinetic energy of the electrons when they have been shot at great speed out of the electron gun of the microscope, is partly converted into heat energy when the electrons strike an obstacle, such as the specimen grid bearing the specimen. This can result in a rise of temperature that has been estimated to be as much as

70

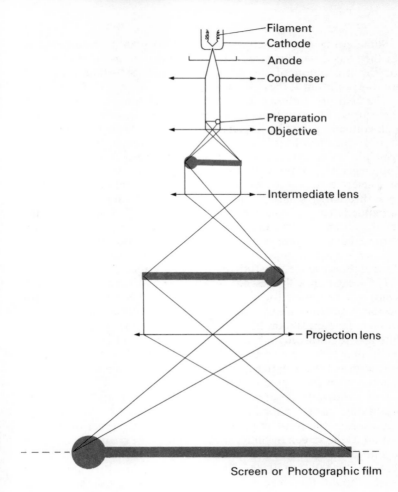

Filament
Cathode
Anode
Condenser

Preparation
Objective

Intermediate lens

Projection lens

Screen or Photographic film

4·8 Diagram of the column of an electron microscope.

500°C under normal conditions, in spite of the use of grids and other supports that have a high thermal conductivity. This heating may alter the structure of the preparation, and one of the reasons for leaving the embedding medium intact is to give some protection against this heat. Some embedding media are better than others for this purpose: polyester, for example, is better than methacrylates (Kellenberger and others).

71

Some electron microscopes are provided with a cooling system for the object, but this mechanical complication, useful though it is for the protection of the specimen, introduces other problems, notably pollution of the column and of the environs of the specimen.

The heat production can be minimised by using a narrow beam of electrons, few in number (low intensity of emission), but driven by high voltages. Actually the electrons that pass through the preparation produce less heat than those that are stopped by it, and this principle has been made use of in a huge microscope constructed at Toulouse by G. Dupouy. By using voltages of the order of a million to accelerate the electrons, Dupouy has been able to make them pass through a small plastic cell in which living bacteria were suspended in an aqueous medium. This was the first time that living cells had been observed under the electron microscope. At least some of these bacteria were still able to divide after the experiment, and thus we are led to hope that we shall ultimately be able to use the electron microscope for studying living protoplasm.

The image on a fluorescent screen, besides being impermanent, is not good enough for cytological research, but happily photographic emulsions are extremely sensitive to cathode rays (electron beams). This means that the image can be made permanent, and thus provide not only a durable record, but one that shows more detail than can be observed directly on the fluorescent screen. Furthermore, the negative can be enlarged, sometimes very greatly, and may then show up even finer structures.

Thus, instruments currently in use, operating under optimum conditions, have a resolving power of less than 5Å; with average preparations the resolving power is about 10Å. Direct magnification on to the screen or on to photographic film is capable of going beyond 200,000 diameters, and in current practice generally lies between 20,000 and 50,000. Two points that are 10Å apart, and which should therefore theoretically be distinguishable in the image, appear with a separation of 0·1 mm when the image has been magnified 100,000 times. If the photographic negative is then enlarged by five, as is generally possible for good negatives, these two points will now lie half a millimetre apart, and will be visible to the naked eye.

Cytochemical techniques The methods briefly described so far have been applicable to morphological study and the description of the constituents of the cell, but the most recent progress in cytology has

72

come from the combination of these observational techniques and those of modern cytochemistry. The latter is now becoming complex, and we have space for only a few general ideas.

1 *Isolation of cellular organelles.* From 1941 onward, A. Claude and his colleagues developed techniques by which cellular organelles could be separated out in measurable quantities, thus making possible the detailed analysis of the principal cell structures. These methods were first applied to animal cells (liver of the rat), and then to plant materials by Martin and Morton. The operative details ought really to be studied for each kind of cell.

Broadly speaking, the technique consists of 'pounding' the tissue in a kind of mixer in the presence of a liquid that is either isotonic or very slightly hypertonic. This produces a homogeneous pulp, or homogenate, which is then subjected to gradually increasing centrifugal force, in carefully regulated doses, separating out particles

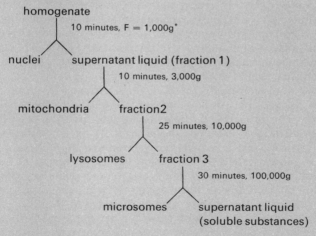

Table 2 An example of fractionation of a homogenate of rat hepatic cells

homogenate

    10 minutes, F = 1,000g*

nuclei   supernatant liquid (fraction 1)

        10 minutes, 3,000g

mitochondria   fraction 2

            25 minutes, 10,000g

lysosomes   fraction 3

                30 minutes, 100,000g

microsomes   supernatant liquid
                  (soluble substances)

* g = acceleration due to gravity; F = centrifugal force

which have a decreasing 'coefficient of sedimentation'. First to settle out are intact cells and gross particles of cell debris, then nuclei, plastids – if the tissue contains any – the mitochondria, and finally the lightest particles, to which Claude gave the name microsomes. All that then remains of the homogenate is a 'supernatant liquid', which contains only particles that are very much smaller than the rest, and of course soluble substances.

By way of example, table 2 shows the sequence of operations as applied to the tissue that is perhaps the most studied of all by this method – the liver of the rat (after de Duve). This technique, which is actually a very delicate one, has undergone many refinements, such as sedimentation in a density gradient. The homogenate is placed at the top of a tube which contains a solution of sucrose, the concentration of which increases from top to bottom (the 'density gradient'). By this means a single centrifugation will separate particles with coefficients of sedimentation very close to each other.

The ability to separate the cellular organelles has made possible great progress in our knowledge of the chemical composition and enzymatic activity of the principal constituents of the cell. We shall often be mentioning these results.

2 *Autoradiography.* In recent years the progress of cytochemistry and cellular physiology has received an astonishing impetus from *autoradiography*. The principle of autoradiography is that living cells are induced to ingest those molecules that will act as precursors for the particular biological syntheses that one wishes to study, and that these molecules have been already provided with radioactive atoms. Atoms commonly used include tritium H^3, carbon C^{14}, sulphur S^{35}, phosphorus P^{32}, nitrogen N^{15} and many other artificial isotopes. The progress of these molecules can then be followed through all stages of the synthesis by tracking the radioactivity; they are said to be labelled and are referred to as *radioactive tracers*.

After allowing the necessary time for these tracers to become incorporated into the macromolecules of the cell, the tissues are fixed and sectioned by the usual methods. After spreading on to the object holder of the microscope – whether it is a glass slide for the light microscope or a wire mesh for the electron microscope – the preparation is coated with a photographic emulsion, and left in the dark long enough for the β-rays from the radioactive atoms to register on the emulsion.

The complete preparation is then developed like an ordinary

film, after which it may be stained if necessary. In the vicinity of those places where radioactive atoms are present in the cell the emulsion has formed silver grains, which are opaque to the electron beam. The distribution of these grains shows what has happened to the radioactively labelled molecules, and the number of grains gives some quantitative information.

This method, which has been improved and refined, makes it possible to follow the fate of the basic metabolic substances, and to trace the stages by which they are incorporated as macromolecules into the cell. Such information would have been difficult, if not impossible, to obtain by any other means, and we shall see several examples of this later.

3 *Enzymological techniques.* It is a matter of basic importance to discover the distribution of the enzymes that operate in the various organelles of the cell, and these enzymes, besides being very numerous, occur only in very small amounts. More or less ingenious techniques have been devised for detecting some of these in the places where they actually work, by providing the enzyme with some of the substrate on which it operates, and then estimating, *in situ*, the products of the enzymatic activity. As an example, various phosphatases, which hydrolyse organic phosphates (nucleotides, for instance) can be identified by providing them with an organic phosphate under normal operating conditions, especially the correct pH. The 'incubation' then produces phosphoric acid, or an inorganic phosphate, which can be precipitated as either silver or lead phosphate. These two metals give a granular, opaque precipitate that is easy to detect.

These techniques are still being developed, and apply to both kinds of microscope.

There are a great many chemical and physical methods that can be applied to cytology, and only specialist studies can do justice to them; we cannot do more than mention these few examples.

5 The cytoplasm

The cytoplasm is a fundamental constituent of protoplasm, and all the other components of the cell can be considered as immersed in it. Besides the nucleus, mitochondria, plastids, and so on, the cytoplasm contains paraplasmic inclusions, the most important of which are the vacuoles and the fat-soluble granules.

Cytoplasm is essentially composed of proteins, ribonucleic acids, and complex lipids (phospholipids), which form macromolecular systems, dispersed in an aqueous medium in which ions and a large number of smaller soluble molecules circulate. Among the latter are to be found the 'metabolites', or basic ingredients of the macro-molecules already mentioned, as well as energy-producing food materials such as sugars, which break down catabolically, and the by-products of their breakdown, such as adenosine triphosphate (ATP). The electron microscope has added enormously to our knowledge of cytoplasm, but certain important facts could not have been obtained except through the light microscope, and we shall start briefly with these.

The living cytoplasm

The physical properties of living matter, described in chapter 4, are particularly applicable to cytoplasm. It is remarkable that even today we can still describe these in the same terms that were applied in 1835 by Dujardin to his 'sarcode'. 'This substance', he wrote, 'has a completely homogeneous appearance, is elastic and contractile, transparent, and refracts light a little more than water, and much less than oil: absolutely no trace of any organisation can be detected in it, neither fibres, nor membranes, nor any sign of cellular structure'.

We shall see that in fact cytoplasm is organised, but on a molecular scale; and that it does contain fibres and membranes, but that these are for practical purposes invisible when the cytoplasm is observed, alive and in good condition, under the light microscope. It therefore behaves like an 'optically empty', hydrophilic colloid, the viscosity of which varies from point to point within the same cell, as well as according to the age and physiological condition of the cell.

The experiment of making a micropuncture, described earlier, shows that the cytoplasm has a surface tension sufficient to make any exudation assume a spherical shape (p. 50, figure 3·5). Furthermore, the cytoplasm that is extruded as a 'plasmasol' exhibits the phenomenon of superficial gelation, which re-establishes within the exudate the character of thixotropic heterogeneity (a fluid with a skin), which existed within the cell, and which is a characteristic of the living state.

Cytoplasmic movements

1 *Different types of movement.* Most plant cells are surrounded by a rigid cellulose cell wall. Within this envelope, the living cytoplasm usually shows traces of internal currents, which give the impression of a fluid passing along very fine tubules. Currents can be seen to flow in opposite directions, to come together and to divide. The currents carry along cytoplasmic inclusions, such as mitochondria, plastids and granules of fat, and may flow continuously, or be interrupted, or even have sudden starts and stops; but as long as the cell remains physiologically healthy there is no trace of Brownian movement. If Brownian movement does take place it is usually a sign that changes have begun which are liberating water into the cell system.

In highly differentiated plant cells, which possess a large vacuole, the cytoplasm immediately surrounding this is sometimes in motion over a wide area, in a kind of rotation about the vacuole, and against the cell wall. This happens so often that a name has been given to the phenomenon – cyclosis. As with the smaller currents within the cytoplasm, cyclosis carries along various cytoplasmic inclusions, and it has been pointed out that, without these inclusions, cyclosis itself might never have been detected.

Cytoplasmic movements also go on within 'naked' cells, that is, those that have no cell wall (myxamoebae, plasmodia, spores of certain algae). The flow and counterflow that can be seen in the plasmodial strands of Myxomycetes come into this category.

In addition to this, cells sometimes make 'amoeboid' movements, that is, they emit pseudopods as does *Amoeba* when it moves. Finally, cilia and flagellae, which allow both zoospores and some plant gametes to make swimming movements, are developments of the peripheral cytoplasm.

77

2 Mechanism of cytoplasmic movements.

(a) *Movements of plasmodia*. The mechanisms responsible for cytoplasmic movements are still a mystery, despite a great deal of study, much of it very able. Most of this work has been done on the plasmodia of Myxomycetes, and a long time ago the use of accelerated cinematography enabled Comandon and de Fonbrune to show that the plasmodial movement is rhythmical, and is the result of periodic contractions of the plasmagel which forms the outside of the plasmodium.

Kamiya succeeded in analysing these contractions by using a very ingenious apparatus, which applied opposite forces until the

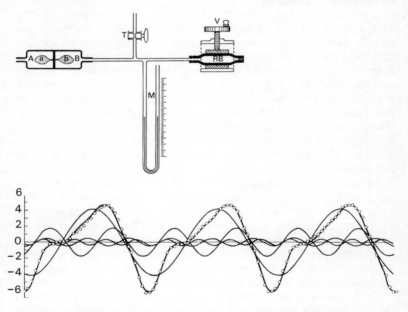

5·1 Top Apparatus devised by Kamiya for measuring the forces which cause movement of the plasmasol in a myxomycete plasmodial strand. **A** and **B** are two chambers separated by a plug of agar, impervious except where it is traversed by the plasmodesmata. M=manometer; RB=rubber bulb which can be squeezed in the vice (V); T=tap by which chamber B can be closed. **Bottom** Curve of variation of the motive force using the above apparatus over a period of 3 minutes. The curve can be resolved into a series of harmonics (thin lines), showing that the movement is polyrhythmic. The ordinates are pressures in cm of water.

contractions were neutralised (figure 5·1). Kamiya was able to produce inside compartment B, every five seconds, a rise (or fall) of hydrostatic pressure which exactly neutralised that which was causing a current of plasmasol to flow in the plasmodial strand. These variations of pressure were recorded, and produced a curve that was complex, but could be analysed into a number of simple sinusoidal curves. Thus it seems that the cytoplasmic movement is a combination of a number of simple periodic rhythms, caused by multiple local contractions of the plasmagel (figure 5·1).

Little is known, still, about the cause of these contractions. More recent research by Kamiya and his colleagues has shown that the necessary energy is obtained from the adenosine triphosphate (ATP) that is produced by cytoplasmic glycolysis, and not from phosphorylative oxidation in the mitochondria. This means that the cytoplasm must contain contractile proteins with the action of an ATP-ase. In actual fact several biochemists have succeeded in extracting from the plasmodia a protein that resembles the myosin in muscle, and which is able to hydrolyse ATP, like an ATP-ase. This protein has been named myxomyosine.

(b) *Movements of cyclosis.* Within cells that have a cell wall, the internal movements of the cytoplasm could equally well be explained in terms of local contractions of the cytoplasm, but such contractions have not yet been clearly demonstrated. Nevertheless when isolated droplets of protoplasm were examined against a dark background the cytoplasm showed fine fibrillae in motion in the opposite direction to that of nearby cytoplasmic particles (Jarosch 1957).

A process of alternate contraction and expansion of the macro-molecules might be invoked to explain the general movement of cytoplasm, but then it would be necessary to find fixed points to which the forces could be applied. It is tempting to look for such points, on the one hand in the interface between plasmagel and plasmasol, and on the other among the ever-changing bonds between one macromolecule and another in the cytoplasm (figure 5·2).

This hypothesis is supported by certain experimental facts, which show that thixotropic heterogeneity (plasmasol/plasmagel) is indispensable to the movements of cyclosis. Thus, anaesthetics suppress cyclosis and at the same time destroy the division into plasmagel and plasmasol, either by causing the cytoplasm to gel completely (CO_2) or to become completely liquid (ethyle oxide). Furthermore, if living cells (leaves of *Elodea*, for instance) are subjected to heavy hydrostatic pressure, the thixotropic equilibrium is displaced towards the liquid phase, and Brown and Marlsand have stated that when liquefaction is complete, cyclosis ceases. This is not caused by death of the cells, because if the pressure is gradually reduced, thixotropic heterogeneity is re-established, and the movements begin again.

Cytoplasmic movements are affected by various environmental conditions: light, temperature, osmotic variations, etc. The movements themselves are a constant expenditure of energy, but they are an inseparable part of the life of the cell. Probably they have a basic function in the transport of raw materials, the removal of waste, and the continuous renewal of the cellular constituents, all collectively known as the 'turnover' of the cell.

Cytoplasmic changes Characteristic changes take place in the cytoplasm when the cell becomes moribund and dies. These changes were followed under the ultramicroscope by Mayer and Schäffer (1908) in animal cells, and were discovered in plant cells by Becquerel and by Guilliermond.

The first symptom of decline is that the cytoplasm ceases to be 'optically empty', and takes on a milky appearance, while Brownian movement makes its appearance and takes the place of normal cyclosis. The diffractive particles, which are responsible for these

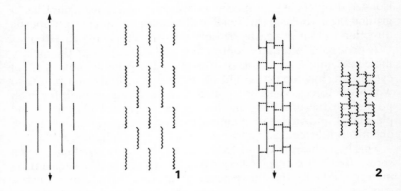

5·2 Possible effects of contraction of protein molecules.
1 In a true sol, where the molecules are not bonded to each other, and where there is no aggregative effect.
2 In a system such as a plasmasol, where intermolecular cohesive forces occur. If these act in unison, contraction may result.

appearances, are not yet visible under the microscope, even against a dark background. If the changes continue, then the particles soon become visible, and the 'milky' appearance is succeeded by a 'snowy' one, and growing flocculent masses appear as the cytoplasm coagulates.

Once the changes have progressed to the 'snowy' stage they are irreversible. What we have already said about the physical properties of living matter suggests that this stage is accompanied by the release of bound water from the macromolecules, and its conversion into free water, which in its turn is liable to alter other constituents of the cell, notably the mitochondria.

In many cases the death of the cytoplasm is followed by general destruction of the cell, quite apart from any action of microbes. This phenomenon is called 'autolysis', and implies that the cell contains within itself all the enzymes needed for its own destruction. This prompts the obvious question how these enzymes are kept under restraint while the cell is alive. Several explanations have been offered. It is possible that some of these enzymes are held inactive in the living cell by a kind of blockage of their active sites. Another possibility is that they do operate when the cell is alive, and are continually destroying structures which cellular activity is continually renewing ('turnover'). This would account for part of the steady consumption of energy by the living cell, over and above what is needed for growth.

Finally, the work of de Duve and his colleagues has revealed the existence of cytoplasmic inclusions called lysosomes, containing numerous hydrolases which are capable of dissolving the entire cell. The enzymes are normally imprisoned within the plasmic membrane surrounding the lysosome, and thus their activity is under the control of the cell. This membrane is only about 50Å thick and it requires only slight alteration for it to release enzymes and dissolve the cell: for this reason de Duve called the lysosomes 'suicide-bags'. Necrosis of the cytoplasm inevitably brings about release of these enzymes, and so initiates autolysis.

It is now known that there are cellular ailments that are caused by alterations in the lysosomes. It seems that the cell must be always on the defensive against these substances, and that it harbours within itself the seeds of its own destruction. This is just one of many indications of how delicate, and constantly disturbed, are biological equilibria, kept in being always at the cost of a continuous expenditure of energy.

Cytoplasm under the electron microscope

The electron microscope has revealed that the apparently 'optically empty' cytoplasm in fact contains a number of characteristic structures, most of them of the nature of 'plasma membranes', and that one kind is formed from granules, the ribosomes. The systems of plasma membranes had been more or less recognised with the light microscope, but without being able to see any of the fine structure. They include the endoplasmic reticulum, the dictyosomes – collectively known as the Golgi apparatus – the cell membrane, the vacuolar membrane, or tonoplast (Hugo de Vries 1885). These various systems will be considered in order.

The endoplasmic reticulum This was first observed in animal cells by Porter, Claude and Fullam (1945), and later, in a generally similar form, in plant cells.

1 *Morphology.* The technique of making ultra-fine sections through cytoplasm, after it has been fixed in osmium tetroxide, reveals contours (or 'profiles') of certain narrow, elongated spaces. Each space is delimited by a dense narrow line, which is the cut section of a membrane separating the space from the general cytoplasm, or hyaloplasm (figure 5·3). Other profiles are less elongate, more elliptical, or circular.

The third dimension of these spaces – that is, their solid shape – can be established either by comparing the frequency with which particular outlines appear, or by fitting together a series of sections. It can then be proved that the elongate profiles are actually transverse sections of much flattened cavities, which have a surface that is very extensive in proportion to their cross-section. The very short profiles are likely to be cross-sections of tubules. Here and there among the sections, one will be found that shows signs of branching, or of changing from one profile to another (figure 5·6).

The internal space is generally transparent, and appears 'empty'. The membranes encompassing the internal space are about 50Å wide, while the flattened cavities, or saccules, vary from a few hundred Å to more than 1,000Å.

Finally, over some of the profiles the membrane is coated externally – on the side towards the hyaloplasm – with granules of 150–200Å in size, which are strongly osmiophillic. These granular

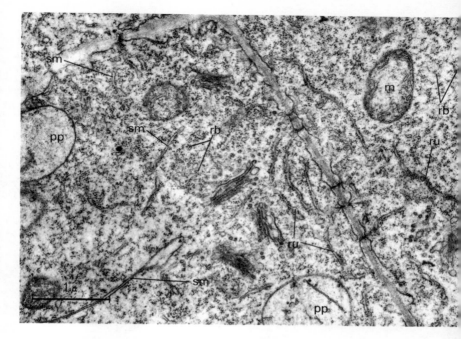

5·3 A root cell from *Cucurbita pepo* fixed in osmium tetroxide.
The cytoplasm contains both rugose (ru) and smooth (sm) profiles
of the endoplasmic reticulum (ER). Note that the hyaloplasm contains
numerous ribosomes (rb) – the so-called 'free' ribosomes, which are not
attached to the ER. m=mitochrondrion ; pp=proplastid (×20,000).

portions are the rugose or rough-surfaced endoplasmic reticulum,
while the portions without granules are the smooth-surfaced ER.
(Palade 1956) (figure 5·3). Palade and Siekevitz (1956) isolated and
examined granules from animal cells, and T'so and colleagues (1956)
did the same for plant cells, by homogenisation and differential
centrifugation. The granules are composed of proteins and ribonucleic acids, and it is the latter that give the grains the property
of taking up basic stains.

Fibrillar structures in the cytoplasm that take up basic stains
were described long ago by Garnier (1897), in glandular cells of
animals, and were named ergastoplasm. These structures can be
equated with the rugose ER, since the electron microscope has

shown that the ergastoplasm is actually part of the ER, both in animal and plant cells.

The ER was discovered in the cells of higher plants in 1957, and was soon located in many eurycaryote plants (plants with nucleus separated from cytoplasm by a nuclear membrane). It is thus a normal constituent of the cell, both in animals and plants, and can be found both in young, undifferentiated cells, such as those at growth points at the tips of shoots and roots, and in cells that have become differentiated into particular tissues. In plant cells where the cytoplasm is degenerating at the end of their period of differentiation (as in the pitted cells of the vascular system) the ER remains for long periods without any very significant changes. It ends up, however, as vesicles, which can change their shape and be assimilated with the other remnants of the cytoplasmic membranes.

2 *Relationship with nuclear membrane.* The electron microscope has brought to light the fine structure of the nuclear membrane, which is formed from two concentric plasma membranes, separated by a clear space, and perforated by a multitude of pores, which seem to make communication possible between the cytoplasm and the nucleoplasm (figures 5·4, 5·5, 5·6). The profiles of these membranes are identical with those of the ER, and the analogy between the two

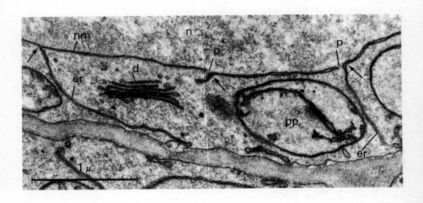

5·4 A meristematic cell of *Elodea canadensis* fixed in permanganate. nm = nuclear membrane pierced by pores (p) and continuous with the endoplasmic reticulum (marked by arrows) ; n = nucleus ; d=dictyosomes ; pp=proplastid. (×28,000).

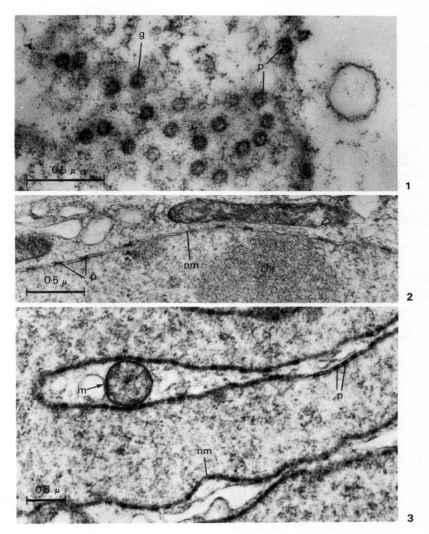

5·5 1 Pores (p) in the nuclear membrane (nm) of a vascular cell of
Cucurbita pepo in face view fixed in OsO_4, with an osmiophilic
central granule (g), as well as a peripheral series ($\times$ 40,000).
2 and **3** are profile views. chr=chromocentre ; m=mitochondrion
in a strongly lobate sinuosity of the nucleus. (**2**=30,000 ; **3**=20,000).

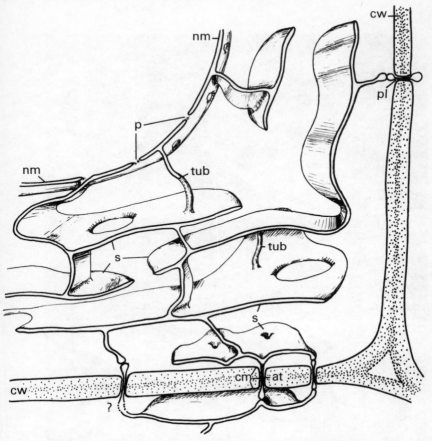

5·6 Diagram of the appearance of the ER and its relationship with the nuclear membrane (nm) and the plasmodesmata (pl). cm = cell membrane ; p = pores of the nuclear membrane ; s = sacculus and tub = tubules of the ER ; at = axial tract of the plasmodesmata ; cw = cell wall.

is confirmed by the discovery that they are connected together. In fact the outer membrane of the nuclear envelope leads into diverticula of the ER system, so that the internal spaces of the ER and of the nuclear membrane are continuous.

The nuclear membrane is thus shown to be a specialised part of the ER system, and so has affinities with the cytoplasm rather than with the nucleus.

The pores of the nuclear envelope, with diameters ranging from

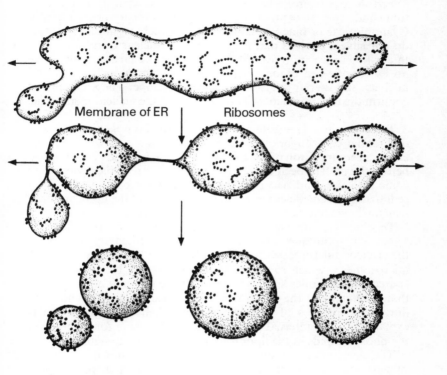

5·7 Microsomes resulting from
homogenisation of the cell.
The arrows to right and left
indicate the disruptive forces.

300–700 Å seem to be open when certain fixatives have been used
(for example, $KMnO_4$), but other, more effective fixatives have
shown them to be filled with a substance that is dense to the electron
beam (figure 5·5). Often a central granule can be seen, surrounded
by other granules at the periphery of the pore, leaving spaces between
them that seem bigger than is needed for the passage of the macromolecules that are involved when exchanges take place between the
nucleus and the cytoplasm.

87

The ER has been detected in an overwhelming majority of animal and plant cells that have been studied. After having first been described in cells from higher plants, the ER was seen in bryophytes, fungi and algae. In contrast it is lacking in Protocaryotes – bacteria, Cyanophyceae or blue-green algae, all of which, it should be noted, do not have a nucleus that is defined by a nuclear membrane. It is interesting to see, moreover, that among the animal cells which have no ER are the red blood corpuscles of mammals, which have no nucleus, and therefore also no nuclear envelope. These exceptions confirm the functional identity of the ER and the nuclear membrane.

3 *Biochemistry*. The same techniques of homogenisation and differential centrifugation have made it possible to work out the chemical composition of the ER system. These methods were applied before the ER had been discovered, or the electron microscope had come into use, and had resulted in isolating a precipitate with a sedimentation coefficient much lower than that of the mitochondria, which Claude had named the 'microsome fraction'.

To elucidate the nature and function of the microsomes, the separation techniques needed to be supplemented by the use of the electron microscope. Palade and Siekevitz had showed that the microsomes – which to some extent appeared to be small spheres coated with granules similar to those of the ER – are nothing more than fragments of the ER, drawn out, nipped off, and pounded up during the process of homogenisation. Their spherical shape is explained by the internal attraction of the cohesive forces between the phospholipids in the lipoprotein membranes (see figure 5·7).

The electron microscope is also useful for monitoring the purity of sediments which are being purified by repeated suspension and centrifugation.

Chemical analysis of the microsomes shows that RNA is present in amounts which vary according to the nature and age of the tissues, and that holoproteins and phospholipids are present in comparable amounts.

The distribution of these basic substances can be investigated by disintegrating the membranes by means of a detergent, such as deoxycholate (Palade and Siekevitz). The individual granules that are thus produced can be precipitated by centrifuging at high speed (110,000 g). The analysis of the granules, already mentioned earlier, shows that they contain proteins and RNA in similar quantities. They are called ribosomes because they are rich in ribonucleic acids.

It is deduced from this that the membranes contain phospholipids, as well as that part of the proteins that is not incorporated into the ribosomes. This shows that the membranes of the microsomes, and therefore those of the ER, are lipoprotein membranes.

In addition, the microsomes have an important enzymatic activity that is difficult to define in a general way, because it seems to differ in different types of cell. To this extent we might say that the ER participates in cellular differentiation. In addition the distribution of the enzymes is certainly not uniform throughout the whole extent of the system, but varies from place to place. Part of the enzymes is localised on the membranes and part on the granules.

4 *Function.* The chemical composition of the ER system, as well as its morphology, give strong indications of its probable function. Ever since the earlier work of Caspersson in 1941, it has been shown time and time again that RNA always participates in protein synthesis, and the fact that the ribosomes attached to the ER are rich in RNA suggests that they are particularly active participants in the synthesis of proteins in the cytoplasm. This function has been demonstrated in several different ways, both in animal and plant cells, for example, by introducing amino acids marked with carbon C^{14} into germinating peas (T'so and Sato 1959). After allowing a minimum time for the amino acids to be incorporated, the plant tissue was homogenised, and the cellular constituents separated by differential centrifugation. It was then shown that the fraction to reach maximum radioactivity first was the microsome fraction, and that the uptake of amino acids was accelerated in proportion to the richness in ribosomes.

A second method was to induce the incorporation of these amino acids into microsomes in suspension in the test tube. If the system is also provided with substances that will supply the energy necessary for protein synthesis (ATP and GTP), the amino acid activating enzymes, and transfer-RNA, the suspension of microsomes is capable of synthesising proteins. Moreover it is possible to obtain the same syntheses starting from isolated ribosomes, both from plant cells such as germinating peas and brewers' yeast (Webster 1957) and from animal cells (Rendi and Hultin 1960).

We shall return to the functions of ribosomes later on, when we are dealing with ribosomes that exist in the hyaloplasm, and have no apparent connection with the ER.

Sometimes, at least, the proteins that are synthesised by the

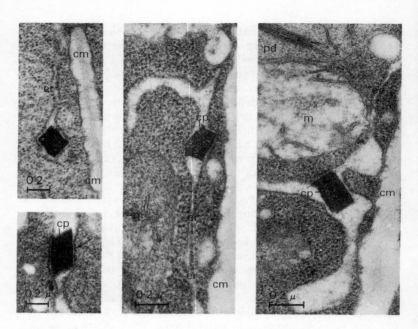

5·8 Crystaline proteins (cp) in the ER of young leaves of *Lens culinaris*.
m=mitochondrion; pd=plastid; cm=cell membrane. (×30,000 and ×45,000).

ribosomes of the ER are carried along through the cavities of the system, but they are not usually visible in preparations made for the electron microscope. We have, however, at least two examples of accumulations of protein that have been photographed in the ER. The first was obtained by G. Palade in pancreas cells from a guinea-pig, and studied in detail by this author and his colleagues. It emerges from this work that the ER synthesises and accumulates the proteins which form the zymogene granules in pancreatic cells. The ER transmits these granules to the Golgi apparatus, after which they are excreted through the acini of the pancreas.

The second example concerns the leaf parenchyma of germinating lentils, where Nougarède has demonstrated the accumulation of a protein which crystallises in the reticular cavities (figure 5·8).

Proteins are certainly not the only substances synthesised by the ER, but further precise information is lacking for plant cells; in certain animal cells, such as the interstitial cells of the testes, which produce steroid hormones, the smooth-surfaced ER seems to be the place where the sterols are manufactured (Christensen and Fawcett 1960). In all these biosynthetic activities, the behaviour of the ribosomes, and even more of the membranes, is still poorly understood. For instance, we do not know how the complicated proteins from the ribosomes are able to pass through the plasma membrane, as they must before they can accumulate in the cavities of the ER.

Finally, one or two examples, which so far have been worked out only on animal cells, have proved that the ER system functions as a circulatory system within the cell. It is very likely that it has a similar function in plant cells, and we shall see later on that the ER system may also make possible exchanges between one cell and another.

Ribosomes 'free' in the hyaloplasm After Palade had first described the granules associated with the ER, he discovered apparently similar granules lying in the general cytoplasm, without any obvious connection with the ER system. Similar 'free' ribosomes are also to be found in plant cells, especially when they are actively proliferating (meristematic tissues) (figure 5·3).

1 *Distribution in the plant cell.* The number of ribosomes scattered in the cytoplasm, and not associated with the membranes of the ER system, is related to the amount of meristematic activity of the cells, and the number per unit volume of cytoplasm decreases steadily during the progress of cellular differentiation. As the cell grows bigger, and then begins to age, the basophily (affinity for basic stains) and the RNA content of the cytoplasm (as estimated by the colorimetric method, using pyronine, as devised by Brachet), begin to diminish. Thus in differentiated plant cells the 'free' ribosomes are first to dwindle, while the ER generally retains those ribosomes attached to it.

2 *Biochemistry.* When the homogenate is subjected to differential centrifugation, after the mitochondria and then the microsomes have been deposited, there remains a supernatant liquid. If this liquid is centrifuged for a long time at high speed (more than 100,000 g) it is possible to extract from it a sediment which the electron microscope shows to be composed of granules similar to the ribosomes that are attached to the ER system. These are, in fact, ribosomes, and they have either been detached from the ER membranes by the operation of homogenisation or else they are the 'free' ribosomes of the cytoplasm. Their diameter varies between 150 and 300Å, and chemical analysis shows that they are ribonucleoproteins, analogous to the granules of the ER. On the average they contain 50–60 per cent of protein and 40–50 per cent of RNA.

Radioactive marking techniques have shown that this ribosomal RNA (r–RNA) is relatively stable, and that it makes up the greater part of the total RNA of the cell. Relationships between this form of RNA and the proteins of the ribosomes are still very little understood.

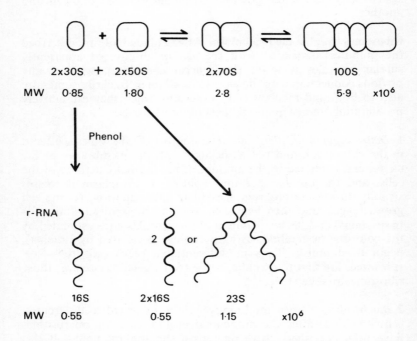

5·9 Diagram of the ultrastructure of ribosomes in *Escherichia coli*. The monoribosomes, with a sedimentation coefficient of 70S, are produced by the combination of 50S and 70S particles, which may also give rise to 100S particles. The lower part of the diagram shows RNA corresponding to 30S and 50S particles.

3 *Fine structure.* Even under the best conditions, the electron microscope does not show the fine structure of the ribosomes very precisely, but all the same it is enough to confirm the conclusions arrived at from differential centrifugation. It seems, in fact, that the coefficient of sedimentation of the ribosomes varies according to the method by which the granules have been extracted, in particular according to the concentration of magnesium ions. Thus, starting from *Escherichia coli* in a medium rich in Mg^{++} (concentration 1M), produces ribosomes with coefficients of sedimentation of either 70 S or 100 S; whereas if the medium is much weaker in magnesium ions, say only 0·1 M, then most of the ribosomes are either 50 S or 30 S. If the last batch is brought into suspension again, in a medium with a magnesium concentration of 1M, then it will spontaneously re-form 70 S ribosomes (figure 5·9).

These results have led to the theory that 'normal' ribosomes are made of two parts, 50 S and 30 S, associated together in granules with a sedimentation coefficient of 70 S. These granules, again, can join together in pairs, and a pair has a sedimentation coefficient of 100 S. Extraction by phenol produces an RNA of molecular weight of $1·15 \times 10^6$ from 50 S ribosomes, and RNA of lower molecular weight (550,000) from 30 S ribosomes. These forms of RNA are relatively stable, but their function is little understood.

On a different scale, ribosomal granules may have different

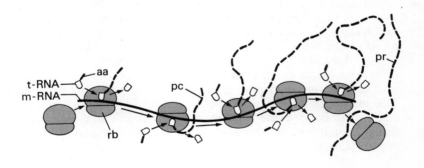

5·10 Diagram showing how ribosomes (rb) and associated particles function as polyribosomes during the synthesis of a protein.
aa = aminoacyl radical fixed on to the t-RNA ; pc = polypeptide chain in process of construction ; pr = protein already constructed and liberated after separation of the ribosome and the m-RNA.

93

dimensions according to the method, vigorous or gentle, by which the cell has been homogenised. Vigorous methods generally produce ribosomes of 70 S or 80 S, called monoribosomes, or isolated ribosomes. Gentler methods, such as 'osmotic shock' may produce particles with a sedimentation coefficient which indicates that they are aggregates of ribosomes, from four upwards: polyribosomes. The electron microscope has confirmed these deductions, and has shown that these groups of ribosomes are bound together by a fine thread which is sensitive to RNA-ase, and which therefore seems to be a form of RNA (Rich and others; figure 5·10).

4 *Function.* The following discoveries have mostly been made on animal cells, notably the reticulocytes of the rabbit, but they can be extrapolated to fit plant cells, where the hyaloplasm has been shown to contain ribosome groups very similar to the polyribosomes of reticulocytes (figure 5·11).

Suspensions of monoribosomes hardly incorporate any amino acids in protein form in the conditions described on p. 89 for ER ribosomes, whereas, in contrast, suspensions rich in polyribosomes obtained by gentle methods are very active. Rich and his colleagues concluded from this that the smallest unit that could take active part in protein synthesis must be an association between several ribosomes and one molecule of RNA, and that very likely the latter is a molecule of messenger-RNA, bringing from the nucleus the genetic information needed to direct the formation of one specific protein.

To this unit then comes transfer-RNA (t-RNA), bringing amino-acid residues that are needed to build up the polypeptide chain bit by bit (figure 5·10). The authors postulate that each ribosome then travels along the m–RNA from codon to codon (a sequence of three bases on the m–RNA), attaching the appropriate amino acid at each point of the polypeptide chain under construction (figure 5·10). This interpretation has so far been confirmed by experiment, and all the while becomes more and more plausible. For fuller details the reader is referred to specialist works on biosynthesis, such as Ingram (1966).

The hyaloplasm In young plant cells the cytoplasm seems to be densely and uniformly scattered with free ribosomes, which often obscure the infrastructures of the hyaloplasm. As the cell becomes more differentiated the hyaloplasm becomes less rich in ribosomes but those that remain tend to aggregate into groups,

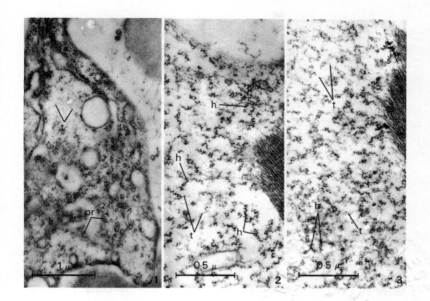

5·11 The cytoplasm of vascular cells in the process of differentiation, fixed in OsO$_4$.
1 A vascular cell. pr = ribosomes gathered into small groups, which probably represent polyribosomes ; t=fibrous thread of the hyaloplasm. (×16,500).
2 and **3** are pitted cells. Here and there along the hyaloplasmic threads the ribosomes gather into helices (h). (×30,500).

which may be polyribosomes, and which take on the shapes of clusters, or chains, or spirals. When the loss of ribosomes has advanced further, as in cells where differentiation has been accompanied by degeneration of the cytoplasm, ultra-fine sections under the electron microscope show a hyaloplasmic network of fibrillar texture, mostly irregular but some part of which may be helical. Such an appearance can be seen, for instance, in vascular elements from *Cucurbita pepo,* when they are in the course of differentiation, or in pitted cells (R. Buvat and N. Poux).

These fine fibrillae have a diameter of less than 50 Å, have little affinity for osmium tetroxide, and show little contrast by ordinary methods. It is tempting to suggest that they are the macromolecules of the main structure of the hyaloplasm, that is, of the living sub-

95

stance that remains outside all the membranous and granular structures revealed by the electron microscope (figure 5·11). It is probable that this fundamental substance is chiefly responsible for the movements of the cytoplasm. Its appearance corresponds quite closely with what we have said above about the physical structure of protoplasm.

In electron microscope pictures the free ribosomes that are visible seem generally to be borne upon the hyaloplasmic fibrillae, and to emphasise the helicoidal appearance of these in places. Such an arrangement recalls the pictures of ribosomes attached to m–RNA, obtained after extraction of an homogenate, but it is likely that the fibrillae that can actually be seen in ultra-fine sections are not RNA itself, which ought not to be visible under these conditions.

Still more cytochemical research is needed before the nature of the hyaloplasmic fibrillae is understood, although these are almost certainly protein structures. In fact it is difficult to explain cytoplasmic movements without the existence of a macromolecular system of proteins in the hyaloplasm. The resolving power of the electron microscope is certainly great enough for these macromolecules to be detected, even if they were dispersed, but it is not certain that the techniques of fixation and subsequent extraction are good enough to recover the whole of the protein. Anyway the state in which the proteins appear after fixation may be different from what it was in the living cell. It is surprising, for example, that no globulins are found in preparations examined under the electron microscope; possibly they are unfolded at the time of fixation. We shall have to hope that newer techniques of fixation, which avoid chemical action, will lead to a solution of these problems.

Microtubules. The use of glutaraldehyde as a fixative for the electron microscope has brought to light microtubular structures in the peripheral regions of the cytoplasm (Ledbetter and Porter 1963). These tubules have a diameter of about 200–250Å, according to species (figure 5·12), and transverse sections under high resolution show them to be built up from globular or fibrillar units with a diameter of 40Å. They usually lie in the immediate proximity of the cell membrane, and are more or less parallel to it; contacts exist between the two, though these have not yet been seen very clearly. The cell membrane seems to be interrupted in these areas of contact. Microtubules lie in the directions perpendicular to that in which the cell will grow. It has been suggested that the tubules may serve to

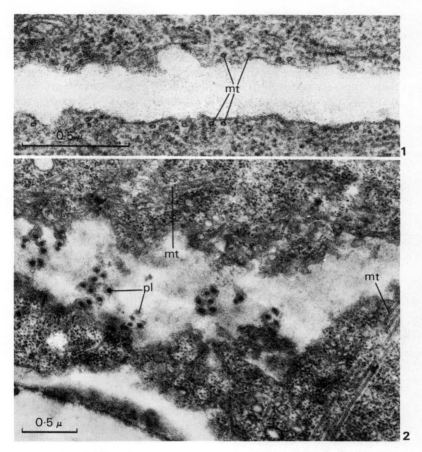

5·12 Microtubules (mt) in the peripheral cytoplasm of root cells of *Raphanus* (**1**) and *Cucurbita* (**2**) fixed in both glutaraldehyde and OsO₄. *Raphanus* is a transverse and *Cucurbita* a longitudinal section. pl=cross-sections of plamodesmata in the cell wall. (**1** = × 56,000 ; **2** = × 29,000).

convey towards the cell wall the materials needed for synthesis, and they may also have an influence upon the existence and direction of cytoplasmic movements (Ledbetter and Porter 1964).

The tubules are in every way plasmagel structures, analogous to the fibrillae of the chromatic spindle that functions during cell division (figure 8·10). They are not usually preserved after fixation by any agent other than glutaraldehyde.

The Golgi body We have already discovered that the 'optically empty' cytoplasm of the old authors contains one system of plasma membranes, which is partly associated with granules of ribonucleo-proteins, as well as a fundamental fibrillar network. The cytoplasm contains yet another system of membranes, the Golgi apparatus, which is practically invisible in the living cell, and which was the centre of much controversy long before the electron microscope was invented. This early history must be run through briefly before we can go on to recent developments.

1 *The Golgi body in classical cytology.* It was in 1898 that Golgi described in nerve cells from an owl, a network of very fine filaments which had the property of reducing silver nitrate. Golgi's 'internal reticular apparatus' was soon discovered in many animal cells, and became known as the 'Golgi apparatus'. Silver-fixing structures of this nature took so many different forms, however, that many cytologists questioned whether there was such a thing as a single 'Golgi apparatus'. Later on, silver impregnation was replaced by impregnation with osmium tetroxide, and using this method Duboscq and Grassé (1933) showed that a multitude of Protozoa had organelles that were distinct from all the other cellular con-stituents. They appeared as discs or crescents which took up the metal (chromophilic) while the surrounding space was transparent (chromophobic). These elements were given the name of *dictyo-somes*, and were regarded as components of the Golgi apparatus. A quarter of a century later these same dictyosomes were rediscovered in electron microscope pictures, when their ultrastructure could be studied, but it can be imagined how difficult it was to prove a connection between these dictyosomes and the internal reticular apparatus described by Golgi, and what arguments they led to.

The application of techniques of metallic impregnation with silver or osmium led Guilliermond and his pupils to deny the existence of the Golgi apparatus. Guilliermond (1935) showed that these techniques, used on a great diversity of plant tissues, produced opaque figures which could always be interpreted as ordinary constituents of the cell – mitochondria, vacuolar precipitates, patches of fat-soluble substances, and so on – altered almost beyond recognition by the treatment they had received.

Actually these structures were much more bulky than the real dictyosomes, which remained undetected. However, Bowen (1928) had described, in plant cells fixed in osmium tetroxide, tiny rodlets, or flattened granules, which he called 'osmiophilic platelets'. Today it seems likely that these objects, difficult to distinguish from mitochondria, were in fact dictyosomes. In the same way Hovasse (1937) had studied unicellular algae, and had recognised the existence of dictyosomes analogous to those studied in Protozoa by Duboscq and Grassé. Nevertheless the majority of cytologists continued to deny the existence of the Golgi apparatus in plant cells, right up to the time that the electron microscope demonstrated its existence (Buvat 1957, Perner 1957).

2 *Ultrastructure of the dictyosomes.* The ultrastructure of dictyosomes was worked out as soon as the techniques of fixation and ultramicroscopy were perfected by the introduction of the electron microscope into cytology. This ultrastructure was first described in animal cells (Grassé, Carasso and Favard 1955–6), and then found to be almost identical in plant cells.

A dictyosome is built up from a pile of flattened cisternae, which have an almost circular outline, and a diameter of about 1–3 μ. These hollow discs are formed from a membrane analogous to that of the ER system, and about 40–50Å thick. The space inside the cisternae is 60–100Å thick, and the space between to adjacent cisternae is about the same (figures 5·13, 5·14). In most animal and plant cells each dictyosome contains 3–8 cisternae, but in Protozoa and some algae this number may reach 20 (figure 5·15). Generally the total thickness of a dictyosome works out at around 0·1 to 0·3 μ, which is just about the limit of resolution of the light microscope.

The cisternae of dictyosomes may have a very sinuous outline, because they are continually forming vesicles, which break off and are released into the cytoplasm. These Golgi vesicles are retained for a time in the vicinity of the dictyosome by a lattice of fine tubules, which links them to each other and to the cisternae (figure 5·16) (Mollenhauer). In sections cut at right angles to the surface of the cisternae, most are curved into the arc of a circle, and the vesicles are more fully developed on the concave face (figures 5·14, 5·15).

This very characteristic ultrastructure makes it impossible to confuse the dictyosomes with any other constituents of the cell, and its discovery finally convinced all cytologists that the Golgi apparatus really did have an independent existence.

99

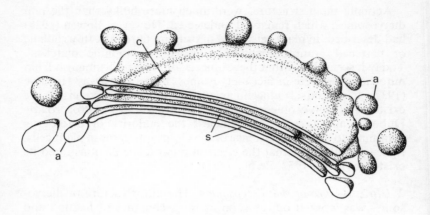

5·13 Diagram of a dictyosome. s = flattened sacculus, nearly circular in section but giving off vesicles (a) extending into the cytoplasm; c = constriction of saccule.

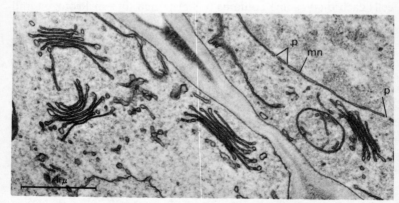

5·14 Ultra-thin section of dictyosomes in a meristematic cell of *Elodea canadensis*, fixed in potassium permanganate (× 20,000).

It was not long before dictyosomes were found in all the vascular plants, as well as in bryophytes (Heitz 1958), and in algae (Chardard and Rouiller 1957), but there was a long delay before they were found in fungi, where they are rare (Moore and McAlear 1962).

On the other hand, just like the ER system, the Golgi apparatus is lacking in Protocaryotes (bacteria and blue-green algae). So it seems that an entire system of cytoplasmic membranes (ER, nuclear envelope, dictyosomes) is completely lacking in the last group.

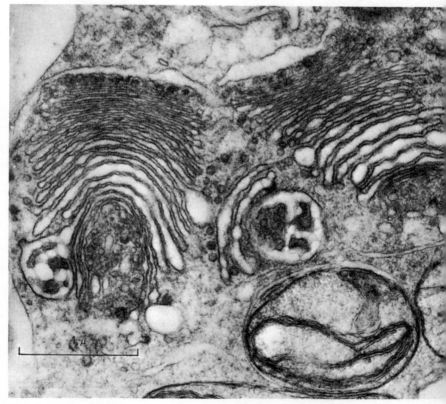

5·15 Dictyosomes from the brown alga *Himanthalea lorea*, comprising a score of saccules and showing a definite polarity. (× 31,500).

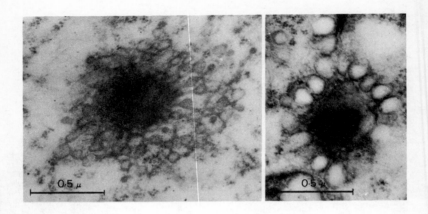

5·16 A dictyosome sectioned along the length of the saccules. Peripheral chambers can be seen leading off from the saccules, to which they are linked by tubular stalks. (Fixed in glutaraldehyde). (×39,000).

3 *Biochemistry of the dictyosomes.* The chemical composition of dictyosomes remained uncertain until Kuff and Dalton (1958) devised a technique by which these organelles could be isolated from the epididymis of a rat. More recently Morré and Mollenhauer (1964) succeeded in isolating plant dictyosomes from onion leaves and cauliflower inflorescences.

In the first place these researches showed that dictyosomes are resistant to the processes of homogenisation and centrifugation, and the sediment, after fixing and sectioning, contains dictyosomes that seem identical with those that can be seen in the living cytoplasm. There must, therefore, be some substance which ensures the cohesion of the cisternae. Mollenhauer (1965), using a short method of fixation with glutaraldehyde, demonstrated the existence of this substance, which is different from the cytoplasm surrounding the dictyosomes.

Analysis of sediments of dictyosomes shows that the membranes which form the cisternae have the nature of a lipoprotein, and as in ER membranes, proteins and phospholipids are present in about equal quantities. On the other hand, in contrast to the ER, the dictyosomes are very poor in enzymes, which mainly consist of alkaline and acid phosphatases. The existence of acid phosphatase in plant dictyosomes has been confirmed by cytochemical means applied to them when they were *in situ* in the cytoplasm. N. Poux

(1963) showed that this enzyme is found mainly, if not exclusively, in those cisternae nearest to the concave face, and this explains the polarity that is implied by the concave–convex structure.

As for the content of the Golgi vesicles, this seems to vary in different kinds of cells, and may include proteins, glucosides and – in plants – various polysaccharides, gums and resins. We shall mention this again later on, when we discuss the morphological signs of dictyosome activity. *

4 *Function of the Golgi bodies.* Study of the chemistry and enzymology of the dictyosomes has not revealed their functions as it did for the ER system, and the role of the dictyosomes was chiefly inferred from the morphological changes that their activities brought about.

The earliest observations were those of Mollenhauer, Whaley and Leech (1960), who showed the part played by dictyosomes in the shedding of the cap cells of the maize root. When the cell walls thicken in readiness for splitting, the dictyosomes emit a profusion of vesicles, which make their way through the cytoplasm, growing all the while, and apply themselves against the cell membrane. The material in the vesicles, after being rendered opaque with potassium permanganate, can be detected on the other side of this envelope, in the pectocellulose layer, which it causes to thicken before splitting occurs.

Since this work was done, plant cells have provided several examples of participation by the Golgi apparatus in the construction of pectocellular cell walls. This occurs during differentiation of the sieve tubes of the phloem, and the vascular elements of the xylem. When the 'nacreous membrane' of the sieve tubes is being elaborated, the numerous dictyosomes of the cytoplasm produce around themselves Golgi vesicles of varying sizes, which move towards zones of thickening of the membranes. In the same way, among the future elements of the vascular system, the emission of vesicles by the dictyosomes is sometimes so intense that the cytoplasm takes on an alveolar appearance. These vesicles are excreted, by a process still little understood, into the space where the membrane is in process of thickening (Buvat 1964) (figure 5·17).

The secretion of mucus on the surface of the leaves of the sundew (*Drosera*) brings into play a similar activity of dictyosomes (Schnepp 1961), and the same thing happens in pollen tubes and in trichocysts in the course of growth (Sievers 1963).

All these examples seem to show that the Golgi apparatus

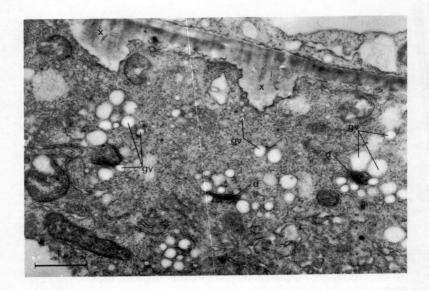

supplies the glucides necessary for the building-up of pectocellulose membranes, or for adapting them to special purposes,
functions which are peculiar to plant cells. Yet the structure of
dictyosomes is so remarkably similar in animals and plants that it
seems likely that there are other functions common to both types of
cell.

In fact in animal cells it has been shown that dictyosomes may
temporarily store substances that have been manufactured in some
other part of the cell, and simply transport and excrete them. This
happens to granules of zymogen from the exocrine cells of the
pancreas (Caro and Palade 1964), and to the oily droplets that may
be absorbed by the villi of the intestinal wall. These droplets, after
having been led through the ER system, are taken in charge by the
Golgi apparatus, and transported to the opposite pole of the cell,
where they are dumped into the chyliferous spaces (Palay and
Karlin 1959).

When all these morphological details are added to the fact that
dictyosomes are poor in enzymes, it seems very likely that their
function is confined to transport of substances that they have not
manufactured, carrying these either to places where they accumulate,
or to excretion.

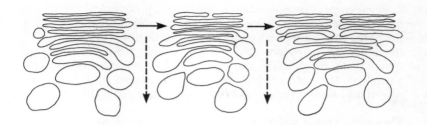

5·17 A young vascular element of *Cucurbita* in the course of differentiation with many Golgi vesicles (gv) surrounding the dictyosomes (d), as well as scattered in the cytoplasm. Some of these accumulate in the vicinity of structures (x) that are being built-up. (×27,000).

5·18 Diagram showing the way in which dictyosomes reproduce by the formation of saccules *de novo* at one pole, followed by vesiculation, and then dispersal from the opposite pole.

5 *Origin of the dictyosomes.* Since dictyosomes are found in the majority of cells, we may ask how they survive during cell division. There is as yet no definitive answer to this question. Their survival is not even a certainty, since it is quite possible that they have a short life, and are subject to a rapid 'turnover'.

On the other hand, we have seen that their form, and their biochemical character, show a polarity, which is accentuated in the Protista, and in the algae. In these groups the dictyosomes possess a great many cisternae, which might come into being at one pole and disappear by vesiculation at the other (Grassé 1959). This method of renewal of the cisternae, incidentally, provides a way in which the dictyosomes may be duplicated: two new cisternae – or several – may appear in place of one (figure 5·18), and may give rise to an equal number of dictyosomes, after the older cisternae have disappeared.

It seems possible, in addition, that entirely new dictyosomes may appear in certain circumstances, notably in the phragmoplast which arises after karyokinesis (see p. 231), and which – in plant cells – is responsible for the construction of the membrane between the two daughter cells. This membrane makes its first appearance in the shape of minute 'pectic vacuoles', which fuse together to form the middle lamella of the membrane. It has now been proved that the

Golgi apparatus furnishes the essential part, if not the whole, of this material. Dictyosomes appear very rapidly, and in great number, in the phragmoplast while it is still in a gel state, not yet penetrated by the maternal cytoplasm, although a little while before there was no sign of them. Nevertheless it is very difficult to say positively that not a single Golgi cisternum has been able to penetrate into the spindle region and more precise research is needed to settle this question.

The cell membrane and the relationship between different cells

1 *Evidence of its existence.* It has long been known that every mass of protoplasm is always surrounded by a very thin envelope, which heals quickly if it should be punctured or cut. The existence of this envelope can be directly demonstrated in 'naked' cells such as amoebae, by gripping it with a micromanipulator, pulling it out, and stretching it. It then comes away from the cytoplasm, and forms a fine thread that is no longer elastic (Seifritz 1918).

In ordinary plant cells, surrounded as they are with a more or less rigid pectocellulose cell wall outside the plasma membrane, the cell membrane can be made visible by the technique of plasmolysis. If the cell is put into a solution that is hypertonic to the contents of

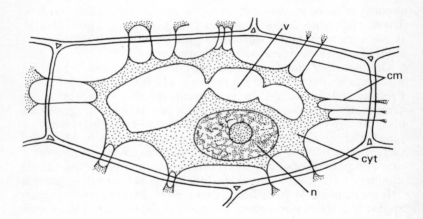

5·19 A plasmolysed plant cell. The cell membrane becomes visible as it withdraws from the cell wall, except where it adheres at certain points—the plasmodesmata. cyt=cytoplasm ; n=nucleus ; v=retracted vacuole ; cm=cell membrane.

the vacuole, the cell loses water, and its protoplasm shrinks away from the cell wall, carrying the pellicle with it (figure 5·19). Nevertheless the latter remains attached to the cell wall at certain points, and the shrinkage from these points gives rise to fine threads that consist of the cell membrane. Sometimes along the length of these filaments remain fine droplets of cytoplasm that have separated from the main body.

The cell membrane is much too thin, however, for its detailed structure to be visible under the optical microscope, and only physico-chemical evidence has made it possible to infer that it contains proteins and fats. Thus, the fact that the cell membrane is rich in fats is suggested by the following: if a tiny drop of water is placed on the surface of a plasmodium of a Myxomycete (figure 5·20), it remains there without spreading until it evaporates, whereas a drop of oil is rapidly absorbed. Conversely, a drop of water injected into the cytoplasm disappears rapidly, while a drop of oil remains unchanged for a long time.

If this experiment indicates that the cell membrane is rich in fats, a study of its surface tension shows it to be closer to a colloidal protein than to a lipid surface. Hence the cell membrane must also contain protein.

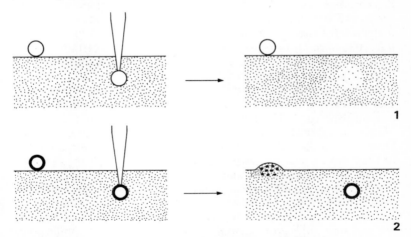

5·20 Experiments with a plasmodium of a myxomycete, to show that the cell membrane is lipophilic and hydrophobic whereas the cytoplasm is not.
1 A water droplet remains intact against the cell membrane, but diffuses rapidly into the cytoplasm.
2 The opposite happens with a droplet of oil.

2 *Fine structure.* If ultra-thin sections are examined at points where the cytoplasm is believed to have been well-preserved, and the cell membrane is seen exactly in profile, it takes the form of two fine lines which are dense to the electron beam, separated by a clear space (a technique giving contrasty fixation is necessary) (figure 5·21). The thickness of each dense layer is in the neighbourhood of 25Å, varying according to the type of cell, and sometimes to which side of the membrane is considered; the clear layer is about 30Å thick, so that the total thickness of the cell membrane may be 75–90Å, sometimes more. These dimensions are those measured after the cell membrane has been fixed, embedded, and sectioned with the ultramicrotome; the thickness of the cell membrane in the living cell may possibly be even greater.

The tripartite structure of the cell membrane is easily visible in preparations that are made by modern techniques, and afterwards studied with a good electron microscope. J. D. Robertson postulated this as the structure of plasma membranes in general, and gave it the name of a 'unit-membrane' (see p. 38). However, this structure is only rarely visible in the membranes of the ER system, or of the dictyosomes, among others, even in the kind of preparation that shows the structure up well in the cell membrane. As we have already seen, these plasma membranes appear to be even finer than the cell membrane (40–60Å). Thus it is by no means certain that the various types of membrane have the same structure, or, if they do, then they react differently to the same fixatives.

All the same it sometimes happens, though only exceptionally, that the ER and the dictyosomes show evidence of tripartite membranous structures. This fact suggests that the molecular architecture of these membranes undergoes variations and rearrangements, and a knowledge of these changes must be of great importance in the study of their mechanical operation, in relation to permeability, and the passage of substances from one side to the other.

Stoeckenius (1959), and Lucy and Glauert (1964) studied artificial models made from fat and water, and showed that films analogous to the unit-membranes could be transformed into micelles with their hydrophobic poles grouped at the centre and their hydrophilic poles on the periphery (figures 5·22, 5·23). When this had happened the tripartite structure no longer existed. Perhaps this process can take place reversibly in the cytoplasm at times when it is necessary for substances to be able to pass from one side of the membrane to the other.

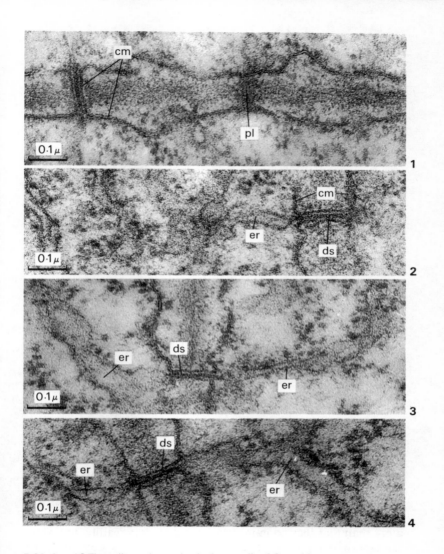

5·21 **1** and **2** The cell membrane (cm) of root cells of *Cucurbita* — tripartite and continuous through the plasmodesmata (pl). **3** and **4** The axis of these plasmodesmata is occupied by a dense substance (ds), which is continuous with the diverticula of the ER in the two adjoining cells. (Fixed in OsO₄). (×100,000).

109

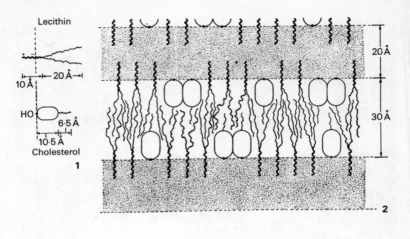

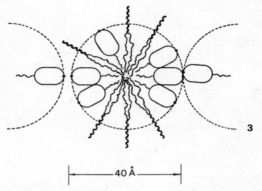

3 *Ultrastructure of the plasmodesmata.* The pectocellulose wall of plant cells is pierced by numerous very fine canals, the plasmodesmata, which it is tempting to regard as favoured routes for exchanges between the cells, enclosed as they are by the paraplasmic cell wall. The average diameter of these canals is less than 0·05 *μ*, and this is too small for study with the light microscope, which shows no more than that they contain structures that stain readily, but which are otherwise unknown. From first principles there seem to be two possibilities: either the cytoplasm of the two cells is continuous through the plasmodesmata; or each cell keeps strictly to itself, and the two cell membranes touch without fusing.

The latter alternative recalls the synapses of the nervous system,

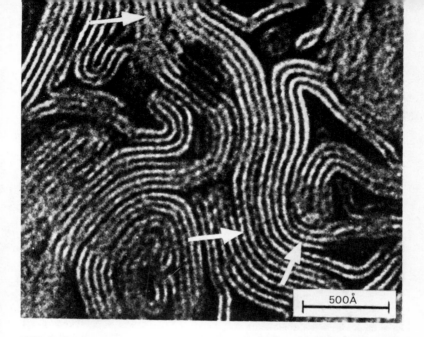

5·22 Left 1 How phospholipid and cholesterol molecules arrange themselves in tripartite lamellae and into networks (micelles) when in an aqueous medium.
2 Possible arrangements of these molecules into bimolecular folds, which are part of the structure of muscles. **3** A micellary arrangement.

5·23 Above View of a preparation of lecithin and cholesterol in ultra-thin sections after negative staining. The arrows indicate places where there seem to be globular sub-elements. (×450,000).

and following upon extensive researches into intercellular communication, several cytologists have put forward the hypothesis that a synaptic structure should be found in ordinary plasmodesmata, and that it would assure that the cells remain morphologically autonomous.

The advent of the electron microscope made it possible to study the ultrastructure of plasmodesmata in greater detail, and threw doubt on the synaptic theory. On the contrary, electron microscope pictures of favourable longitudinal sections of plasmodesmata showed that the cell membrane was diverted to form a lining to the intercellular canal, in the same way as it lined the cell wall, and that it joined on to the cell membrane of the next cell. In other words there is perfect continuity between the cell membranes of two adjoining cells, along the length of the plasmodesmata (figure 5·21).

Thus the cell membrane forms a fine cylindrical casing inside the intercellular canals. In the narrow lumen of this cylinder the electron microscope reveals the existence of an axial filament of extreme fineness, each end of which is dilated and communicates with diverticula of the ER systems of the two cells (figure 5·21). Thus not only the cell membranes, but also the ER membranes maintain continuity between the cytoplasms of two plant cells, even though each is surrounded by a cell wall. Fixation in permanganate, which is particularly helpful in showing up plasma membranes, clearly shows that diverticula of the ER system systematically reach out towards the plasmodesmata (figure 5·24).

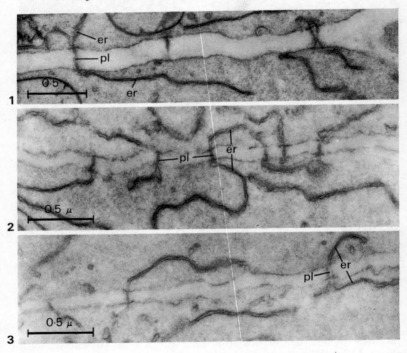

5·24 Relationship between the plasmodesmata (pl) and the ER. After fixation in permanganate, diverticula from the ER are constantly to be found reaching the openings of the plasmodesmata. (**1** = ×30,000; **2** and **3** = ×34,000).

The space between the ectoplasmic lining and the axial filament is extremely narrow, and after contrasty fixation, shows up very densely under the electron microscope. This space probably maintains a continuity of the hyaloplasm, enough to ensure the passage of certain macromolecules from one cell to the other. Yet this transit has never been clearly seen.

The discovery of the fine structure of plasmodesmata has important consequences for cell physiology, since the plant cell can no longer be thought of as an autonomous morphological unit, shut up inside its cell wall like a prisoner in a 'cell' in the ordinary sense. The cytoplasm of the many cells in a plant tissue is physiologically continuous, and so bears more resemblance to the plasmodia of Myxomycetes, or to the 'siphon' structures of many Algae and Siphomycetes than to an animal cell.

Thus the cell wall is no longer to be seen as a prison ('cell') separating one protoplast from another, but rather as a skeletal support for an internal medium which permeates the entire plant, and through which circulate metabolites, water, ions and the products of cellular activity. This function in addition to the mechanical importance of the cell wall in growth, is important in the morphology and in the characteristic habit of the plant, which results from the equilibrium between the turgidity of the cell contents and the resistance of the cell walls.

In conclusion, it is known that plant viruses can only pass from one living cell to another, and that a zone of dead cytoplasm is an obstacle to this. It would be impossible for a virus to pass through the cell wall. The plasmodesmata, and the ultrastructure that is revealed by the electron microscope, allow a free passage to the viruses, whereas a synaptic arrangement would seem to present an obstacle to them.

Nevertheless we shall see later that in certain circumstances macromolecules can be absorbed by living cells even though these may be entirely surrounded by a complete cell membrane.

4 *Deformations of the cell membrane resulting from cellular activity.* Over most of its surface the cell membrane is normally applied closely to the cell wall, due to the turgidity of the cell contents, but occasionally the activity of the cytoplasm disturbs this contiguity. The cell membrane then comes away locally from the cell wall, and forms small pits, or more or less elongate invaginations. The cavity thus created may appear 'empty', that is, entirely transparent in fine,

or ultra-fine sections, or it may be seen to enclose various globular, tubular or reticulated structures (figures 5·25–5·27).

In most cases these morphological phenomena are difficult to interpret with certainty, and we can do this successfully only when the activity of the cell is clearly defined: for example, when it is visibly adding to its cell wall.

(a) *Deformations associated with elaboration of the cell wall.* In the course of differentiation of the phloem or of the xylem it is easy to recognise young sieve cells, or young vascular elements in the course of differentiation, and to confirm that the elaboration of the sieve cells, and of the ornamentations of the secondary membrane of the future vascular system is in progress. It may then be shown how irregularities in the surface of the cell membrane result in local excretion of substances derived from the cytoplasm and passed into the cavities of membranes in the vicinity of places where the cell wall is undergoing thickening (figure 5·17).

On p. 103 we saw that some or all of this material is carried out to the cell membrane by vesicles originating from the Golgi apparatus, but it is still an open question how these vesicles – or at any rate their contents – pass through to the other side of the cell membrane. The process that would seem to be simplest morphologically would be if the membrane of the vesicle were to anastomose with the cell membrane (figure 5·25), but the structures of these two membranes are generally different, and they are of different thicknesses. Such a mechanism could not operate without complicated rearrangements of the Golgi membranes.

Certain electron microscope pictures suggest that perhaps there are other mechanisms. The surface of a great variety of different cells shows, here and there, splits in the cell membrane, in several places close together. The fragments of the cell membrane close up again on themselves into small spheres which are recognisable because of their tripartite membrane (figure 5·26). Vesicles or other constituents of the cytoplasm may be mixed in with these, and then the cell membrane heals itself behind these, expelling them and their immediate surroundings into the parietal space (figure 5·25). This mechanism would explain how small precursor molecules may build the pectocellulose organisation of the cell walls outside the protoplasm, yet still remain within its control. It still remains to be proved, however, that these appearances are not produced, or at least exaggerated, by fixation.

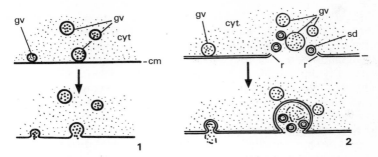

5·25 Theories on the secretion of substances contained in the Golgi vesicles.
1 By anastomosis of these vesicles with the cell membrane (cm).
2 By rupture (r) of the cell membrane, which then reunites, expelling
both its own spheroid debris (sd) and the material in the Golgi vesicles.

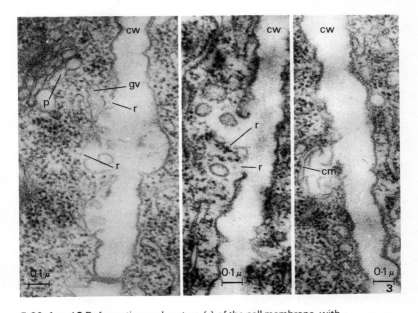

5·26 1 and **2** Deformation and rupture (r) of the cell membrane, with
the formation of characteristic minute spheroids.
3 A local reformation of the cell membrane (cm) may cut off some of these
spheroids and their immediate surroundings from the main body of the cytoplasm.
d = dictyosomes; gv = vesicles, probably Golgian, in the vicinity of a tear in
the cell membrane ; cw=cell wall. (Root cells of barley fixed in OsO_4). ($\times$ 55,000).

115

(b) *Pinocytosis*. In 1937, Lewis, using microcinematography, showed that macrophages in *in vitro* cultures were capable of ingesting droplets of liquid from the culture medium by means of invaginations of the cell membrane, the invagination being subsequently nipped off, and moving off as a vesicle into the interior. These droplets moved towards the nucleus, growing smaller all the time. After this first observation, the same phenomenon was detected in a variety of animal cells, where it seems to be a normal occurrence, analogous to phagocytosis, or the ingestion of solid particles.

This process, called *pinocytosis*, has still not been directly observed in living plant cells, and there was no question of this happening so long as we believed that the cell membrane is tightly pressed against the cell wall by turgidity. Nevertheless several experiments have been made that strongly suggest that pinocytosis does happen in plants. For example, according to J. Brachet (1956), onion roots immersed in a solution of ribonuclease will absorb this enzyme and it is then to be found inside the living cells, forming a complex of macromolecules with its substrate, before it begins to change the latter. It would seem, therefore, that the enzyme has been able to pass through the living cell membrane with its macromolecules still intact.

Jensen and McLaren (1960) confirmed this fact, using historadiography. Molecules radioactively marked with C^{14} or H^3, penetrated into root cells of onion or of barley, even though they came from proteins such as ribonuclease, lysozyme, haemoglobin, some at least of which are supposed to hydrolyse only poorly. It is tempting to invoke pinocytosis to explain such a penetration. Now the electron microscope has shown ectoplasmic invaginations in plant cells, as well as in a variety of animal cells, and it is very likely that these indicate pinocytosis (figure 5·27). All the same, the fact that electron micrographs are entirely static means that before we conclude that pinocytosis does take place in plant cells, we ought to wait for evidence from living cells, or for showing radioactive tracers actually making their way to the interior by this process.

5 *Functions of the cell membrane*. The cell membrane is one of the most fundamental structures in the cell. Whether or not the cell is surrounded by a cell wall permeable to all kinds of liquids and solutions, the cell membrane is not only the barrier which prevents penetration of undesirable substances, but it is even more important because it stands between the cell and the outside world. The very survival of the cell depends primarily on how it reacts to

116

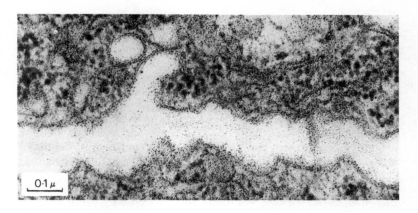

5·27 Formation of liquid-filled hollows and pinocytosis in root cells of *Hordeum sativum*, fixed in OsO_4. ($\times$ 90,000).

the chemical and physical conditions of the surrounding medium.

Physiologists have been studying for a long time the permeability of this fine membrane and difficult researches are still going on. The osmotic properties are those of a semipermeable membrane, that is, one which is permeable to water and small molecules, but not to most molecules *in solution*. Yet only a small part of the properties of the cell membrane can be explained by osmosis. Many molecules can traverse it easily (urea, glucose), while others that are much smaller are stopped. This phenomenon has been called selective permeability, but giving a name to the phenomenon does not explain how it happens.

In a general way fat-soluble (lipophilic) substances penetrate more easily than water-soluble (hydrophilic), but exceptions to this rule are glucose and water itself. This is explained away by supposing, on the one hand, that the phospholipid molecules of the middle of the membrane are hydrated, and on the other by assuming some kind of chemical affinity between the glucose and the molecules of the membrane, which happens to facilitate the incorporation and penetration of this sugar ('facilitated permeability').

In theory such membranes should have a very low permeability to ions, since these are not lipophilic. However, important exchanges of ions do take place through the cell membrane, even against gradients of diffusion. The passage of ions must therefore require an expenditure of energy, and it is within the cell membrane itself

117

that the work of absorption and transport is carried out. It is evident that mechanisms of this kind are a characteristic of the living state, and cannot be explained by simple physical models. It is thanks to the process of *active transport* that living cells are able to accumulate substances that exist outside at a lower concentration than inside, for example, iodine and bromine by brown algae, sucrose by the roots of sugar beet, etc.

The energy necessary for this process is provided by ATP, and so it must be supposed that the cell membrane contains definite structures that possess enzymes, including ATP-ases. For details of active transport the reader is referred to specialist authors such as Lehninger (1965).

On the other hand we have seen that the cell membrane is able to absorb macromolecules, probably by pinocytosis (certainly so in animal cells and Protista). Perhaps these processes of mechanical absorption involve mechanisms as complex as those of active transport? In fact it must be assumed that certain macromolecular substances (proteins, essentially) have the power to provoke an invagination of the cell membrane, by means of which they are ingested. It is probable that certain particular points on the surface of the cell membrane are sensitive to a substance, or to a group of related substances with a common structure.

The proof of this does not really belong to the domain of cytology, but it does show that the complexity that surrounds the phenomenon of permeability of the membrane is matched by an equal complexity of molecular structure. It is the latter that results in a mosaic of specific permeable sites, borne on a common framework of lipoprotein molecules.

So there is much still to be clarified about the structure and functioning of the cell membrane. In conclusion it might be mentioned that these complexities have been studied in membranes of bacteria. The surface of many bacteria will reduce potassium tellurite, forming a precipitate, opaque to electrons, on those sites where there are present the enzymes and electron carriers which bring about the chemical reduction. These oxydo-reduction sites seem to be perfectly well defined, and their number is constant for each strain of bacteria (van Iterson, A. Ryter).

The vacuoles The vacuolar apparatus is essentially the place where the accumulation takes place of the hydrophilic paraplasmic products that have been either manufactured or ingested by the

118

plant cell. Even though they contain this paraplasmic material, the vacuoles are still cytoplasmic constituents intimately concerned with the state of being alive, since they are separated from the cytoplasm by a fine membrane. This tonoplast is the counterpart of the cell membrane, and it forms the inner barrier of the cell.

The development and the importance of the vacuolar apparatus are particular characteristics of plant cells, on the same footing as the cell wall and the plastids. Most of what we know about this subject has been obtained by use of the light microscope, and from looking at living cells.

1 *General aspect of vacuoles in mature cells.* The vacuolar apparatus is usually the most bulky constituent of well-differentiated plant cells. Typically it consists of one single large vacuole, of such a size that the cytoplasm and its inclusions are pressed against the cell wall like a fine film, which is thickened only in the corners of the cell, and anywhere where it happens to contain inclusions that are themselves bulky, such as the nucleus and the plastids. This vacuole is often crossed by cytoplasmic tubules, inside which are to be found a variety of organelles, being carried along by the process of cyclosis (figure 1·5).

2 *Discovery of the tonoplast.* The fact that vacuoles had their own membranes was demonstrated a long time ago by de Vries (1885), who gave them their name of tonoplasts. De Vries' experiments to isolate the vacuole started by treating cells that were not too old with eosine. This stain is toxic, and penetrates into the cytoplasm, progressively killing and staining it. De Vries followed this process, which first affected the outside layers of the cytoplasm, and then approached nearer to the vacuole. When the stain had almost reached the vacuole the cell was plasmolysed by means of a hypertonic solution. The vacuole could be seen to shrink, then to become detached from the dead cytoplasm surrounding it, and remain floating in the cellular cavity that was thus created. When the cell was now placed in pure water the vacuole began to swell, and it was possible to make it burst, thus showing it was surrounded by a membrane.

Since the electron microscope came into use the reality of the tonoplast has been amply confirmed and shown to be a plasma membrane analogous on the one hand to the cell membrane, and on the other hand to the membranes of the ER system. Like the latter,

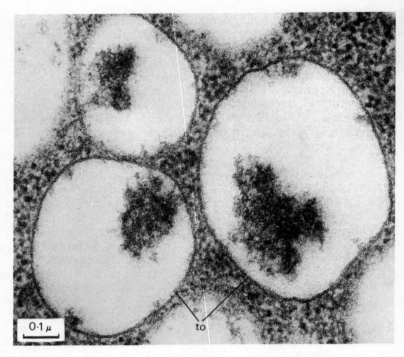

5·28 Vacuoles in meristematic cells from the root of *Hordeum sativum*. The tonoplast (to) shows a delicate tripartite structure similar to that of the cell membrane shown in figure 5·27. (Fixed in OsO₄). (×95,000).

the tonoplast is often thinner than the cell membrane, with a thickness of 50–70Å, but here and there a tripartite structure can be detected (figure 5·28).

3 *The vacuolar contents.* In living cells that have become differentiated, the general content of the vacuoles is optically empty, more fluid and less refringent than the cytoplasm. Such vacuoles, however, may sometimes contain well-defined inclusions, notably crystals such as calcium oxalate, or granules, which on rare occasions may be fatty. Scales from lily bulbs have even been found to contain 'sterinoplasts', concretions of sterides (Mirande, Reilhes). These inclusions are exceptional, and the vacuolar contents are essentially in the form of dissolved substances.

Cells from rapidly growing parts of the plant (meristematic cells) have several vacuoles with their contents more concentrated and less fluid. One effect of this is to bring the refractive index of the vacuole close to that of the cytoplasm, thus making the vacuoles very difficult to see until after the cell has been vitally stained.

Typical vacuoles always contain colloidal proteins, the particles of which are negatively charged under normal physiological conditions. Vacuoles contain a wide variety of different chemical substances, and the existence of a negatively charged colloid is perhaps the one factor that they all have in common. Thus, vacuoles are different from the truly 'living' constituents of the cell, such as mitochondria or plastids, in that they have no chemical unity.

The following are the chief categories of vacuolar substances.

(a) *Mineral substances:* mineral salts; chlorides (NaCl), iodides (in seaweeds and *Laminaria*); nitrates (which may accumulate in certain 'nitrophilic' plants such as Chenopodiaceae and Urticaceae); inorganic phosphates.

(b) *Acids and organic salts:* malic acid, and calcium malate; oxalic acid, potassium hydrogen oxalate $(COO)_2KH$ (in sorrel), tri-hydrated calcium oxalate $(COO)_2Ca.3H_2O$, crystallised into tetragonal crystals in the form of pyramids or prisms, or druses, or monohydrated calcium oxalate forming monoclinic crystals of a needle or tabloid shape. Oxalates are very widely distributed among plant cells, and highly poisonous.

(c) *Glucides:* glucose, generally in very small quantity; fructose, rarely abundant (except in the pulp of fruits); sucrose, which sometimes accumulates when it is the form in which the glucides are being stored, as in sugar beet or sugar cane; maltose (as in *Mercurialis*); inulin, a polysaccharide of high molecular weight, which is in colloidal solution in the vacuoles of certain roots such as chicory, where it is the sugar reserve.

In addition to these mono- and di-saccharides, the vacuoles may accumulate 'heterosides', one example of which is the tannins, extremely widely distributed among plants. Anthocyanic pigments, which in nature colour the vacuoles carmine, violet or blue, and oxyflavone pigments, which produce a yellow colour, may be present either in the free state, or combined with sugars into heterosides. The tannins and the vacuolar pigments are phenolic compounds, and many other heterosides which are present in vacuoles of plant cells have a chemical nature which gives them practical

121

applications, such as in medicine; an example is the cardiotonic glucosides found in *Digitalis*.

(d) *Proteins and their derivatives.* In addition to the electro-negative colloid, the vacuoles sometimes accumulate other proteins by way of reserves, in those tissues which are concerned either with reproduction or with the perennial life of the plant. This happens, for example, in the sap wood of trees in autumn (the phloem, the cambium and the early wood), as well as in seeds in process of maturation. We shall return to the latter example later, to talk about aleurone grains, which are derived from vacuoles that are rich in proteins and dehydrated.

The vacuoles of certain plant species contain concentrations of a variety of products derived from the degradation of proteins, the best known of which are the alkaloids. These nitrogenous bases are common in particular families of plants such as Solanaceae (atropine, hyoscyamine) or Papaveraceae (morphine). Their pharmacological importance will be familiar to every reader.

Sometimes the vacuoles also contain amino acids and amides, particularly in young plants that are in the process of germination. The former can exist only in small amounts, because any accumulation rapidly becomes toxic; whereas amides are more readily tolerated, and can sometimes become abundant (as, for example, asparagine in the lupin).

Thallophytes have often been said to contain 'metachromatin', a substance believed to be a phosphoprotein, which could be precipitated by coloured dyes, thus giving a red precipitate with certain blue dyes, such as toluidine blue or cresyl blue.

4 *Vital staining of the vacuole.* We have seen (p. 60) that it is possible to stain the living vacuoles by using alkaline stains, that is, those in which the colour-producing ion is the positive ion, or cation. The build-up of such a stain in the vacuole is brought about by its fixation by the electronegative colloid present there. The following description of the sequence of events is taken from the work of Guilliermond and Gautheret (1939) (figure 5·29).

In a yeast cell cultured in a liquid to which neutral red has been added, the vacuole passes through the following stages: (1) On entry, the colour-bearing positive ion is neutralised by particles of the colloid, which flocculate into fine red granules, highly refringent. (2) The colour ions in excess (more than needed to neutralise the colloid), become adsorbed on to the granules, which both makes

122

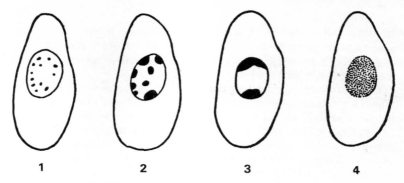

5·29 Successive stages in vital staining of the vacuoles of yeast (*Saccharomycodes ludwigii*) with neutral red.
1 The coloured ions are fixed by the vacuolar colloid, which they neutralise and precipitate. **2** The precipitate grows by adsorption of more ions of the colorant, and by fusion with others. **3** The precipitate attaches itself to the tonoplast. **4** The precipitate finally dissolves in the vacuolar liquid, which becomes uniformly stained.

the granules electropositive and increases their bulk. (3) The surface tension of the granules is at first high, but diminishes, and as this happens the granules aggregate into a deeply coloured precipitate, which settles alongside the vacuolar membrane. (4) The precipitate now dissolves in the vacuolar liquid, which assumes a uniform colour, clear rose-pink.

This sequence of events applies only if the pH of the vacuole is somewhere near neutrality. Very alkaline vacuoles stain uniformly in one step; on the other hand very acid vacuoles do not dissolve their precipitates. For instance, if vacuoles contain tannins these form stable combinations with the coloured ions of the stain, and these stable compounds precipitate.

The ability to stain a living cell thus depends on how rich in protein the vacuoles are. Some cells exist which contain liquid enclaves similar to vacuoles – and which have been regarded as a special kind of vacuole because they do not take up vital stains. Possibly this is because these vacuoles have no electronegative proteins.

5 *Modification during cellular differentiation.* At the tips of stems and roots there are growing points, or primary meristems, where active growth is going on, and here the cells that are proliferating do not have the large vacuoles that are to be seen in the cells that have

123

become differentiated. Usually the vacuolar apparatus of the growing cells is invisible, partly because the vacuoles are so small, and partly because their contents have a refractive index very close to that of the adjacent cytoplasm.

Rare exceptions exist to this rule, and vacuoles may be found which are conspicuous because they already possess pigments. This is true of cells from the teeth of young leaflets of roses at the time of opening. These vacuoles, which have a natural colour due to anthocyanin pigments, were studied by Guilliermond as long ago as 1913. In the cells that are least strongly differentiated the vacuoles are numerous, and filamentous in shape, resembling mitochondria. As the cells become more differentiated, the vacuoles enlarge, become globular, press one against another, and end up by merging together into the single large vacuole that is characteristic of adult cells.

A very similar course of development can be traced in growing root tips, thanks to vital staining. Cells from the zone which the older authors regarded as being the initiatory zone of growth, and which today are known to be almost inactive, have many small globular vacuoles – in the roots of wheat and barley, for instance. It is the cells surrounding this zone that are the least differentiated (the most meristematic), and which are proliferating most rapidly. These cells have a vacuolar apparatus that is reticulate, with a few diverticula here and there (figure 5.30_{1-2}). Neutral red staining shows this network faithfully at the very beginning of the staining process, but very soon provokes it to begin swelling.

In cells that are a little further out than this zone of maximum proliferation, the vacuolar network has more globulose diverticula, but remains in evidence between them, and joins them together (figure 5.30_3). Higher up the root the cells enter into the first phase of differentiation, which is characterised above all by a process of growth. The vacuolar apparatus of these cells breaks up into a multitude of tiny spherical vacuoles, brightly and uniformly coloured with the neutral red (figure 5.30_4). Still further away from the meristem, among the cells that are beginning to elongate, the vacuoles have become larger so that they are pressing on each other (figure 5.30_5), and pushing the cytoplasm and the other protoplasmic constituents such as the nucleus away to the periphery of the cell. These vacuoles take on a paler pink colour than the others, and are at the beginning of the stage of precipitation provoked by the dye.

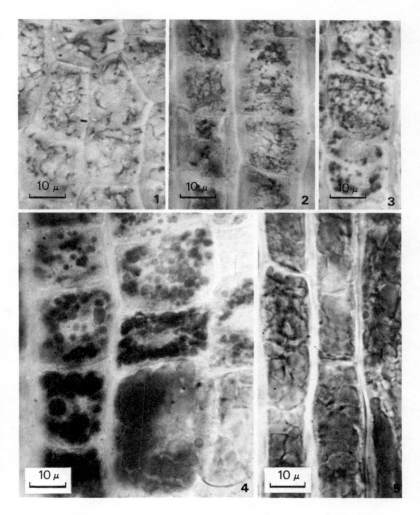

5·30 Evolution of the vacuoles, starting with meristematic root cells of wheat vitally stained with neutral red (×950).

1–3 The stain reveals a vacuolar apparatus that is fully reticulate.

4–5 As soon as differentiation starts, these vacuoles develop into small vesicles which become individual globules, continue to grow, and press one against the other until they coalesce into one large vacuole. This, in turn, compresses the cytoplasm and nucleus against the cell wall.

Finally, the vacuoles merge into one enormous liquid-filled space, which stains pale pink in neutral red, and which produces precipitates analogous to those described above as being produced in yeast cells.

While all this is going on, and while the volume of both the overall cell and of its vacuolar spaces is increasing, there is no apparent growth in the amount of living substance. It seems that the growth of the cell at this stage, which is essentially an elongation, is brought about by the development of the vacuolar apparatus. We shall meet other examples of this later on.

To summarise, the first stage of cell-differentiation, starting from the primary meristematic cells, is a process of growth and bringing into action of the vacuolar apparatus. It would be an over-simplification, however, to assume that the enormous vacuole thus produced has finished its development, and now we shall look more closely at changes taking place in the vacuole after differentiation of the cell.

6 *Post-differentiation changes in the vacuole.* Although the last phase of cell-differentiation, the phase of specialisation, principally concerns constituents other than the vacuoles, the latter are not usually static. A few examples will illustrate this.

(a) *Vacuolar aggregation.* These phenomena are reversible processes of transformation of the vacuole into a large number of small ones, recalling the condition of the vacuolar apparatus in meristematic cells. It is interesting to note that this phenomenon was seen by Darwin, long before the idea of the vacuole had arisen. In the course of his famous studies of carnivorous plants, Darwin realised that changes of this kind took place in the cells of the pedicel of the tentacles of *Drosera*, at times when these tentacles had caught prey in the mucus covering the head, and were digesting it. The vacuolar changes seemed to be concerned on the one hand with exchanges of water (or of aqueous solutions) between the vacuoles and the cytoplasm, and on the other hand with the passage of a current of liquid through the cells.

At the beginning of this process, the cytoplasm takes in liquid, while the vacuolar volume decreases, so that the vacuoles now become more dense than the cytoplasm, the reverse of the original condition. Moreover, the arrangement of the resultant small vacuoles is said to be polarised (Mangenot 1930).

(b) *Transformation into aleurone grains.* As the seeds ripen, most of the cells of the embryo, as well as those that form the reserve

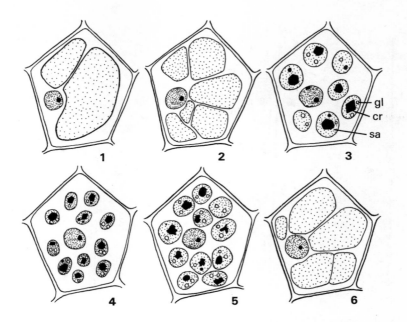

5·31 The development of vacuoles in the albumen of seeds of the castor oil plant.
1–3 Dehydration as the seed matures, with the original vacuole being broken up
and its contents precipitated; sa = amorphous substance of a protein nature;
gl = globule of inositol hexaphosphate; cr = crystalline protein.
4 Cell from the albumen of a ripe seed with its vacuoles transformed into
aleurone grains. **5–6** Rehydration when the seed germinates; the aleurone grains
revert to being liquid-filled vacuoles.

tissues, stock up their vacuoles with proteins, and sometimes with
other reserve substances (for example, inositol hexaphosphate in
seeds of the castor-oil plant). At first these products exist in a
colloidal state, but with the desiccation that accompanies the
process of maturation, these substances become concentrated, and
end up as solid inclusions. While this is going on, the original
vacuole splits up into smaller, globular spaces, and each of these
becomes solidified into an aleurone grain (figure 5·31).

Aleurone grains have a characteristic structure, a little like that
of starch, and Guilliermond (1908, 1933) distinguished three types.
The first type is composed of rounded or ovoid grains, each of
which is made up of a fundamental, amorphous matrix of a protein

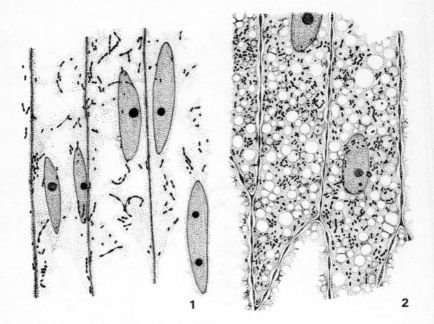

5·32 Cambial cells of *Robinia pseudacacia*.
1 Observed in June, when the cytoplasm forms an
envelope surrounding an enormous vacuole.
 2 In October, when the vacuolar apparatus is broken up into innumerable
tiny globular vacuoles. In addition, the radial cell walls are thickened, and
the mitochondria are more granular.

nature, in which are embedded various inclusions: a single crystalloid, protein in nature, though crystalline, together with one or more spherical corpuscles, the globoids, which mainly consist of inositol hexaphosphate (Posternak 1905). This type is widely distributed, and is found, for instance, in the seeds of the castor-oil plant, and of Cucurbitaceae, where the aleurone grains may be bigger than the nucleus. Sometimes the globoids in their turn enclose vacuolar substances such as calcium oxalate.

The second type of grain is generally smaller, and contains many tiny globoids, but no crystalloids, with the same amorphous protein matrix. An example is the aleuroid layer in grasses. Finally, the aleurone grains in Leguminosae generally belong to yet a third type, small corpuscles consisting simply of an amorphous protein mass. In other families, such as Umbelliferae, these grains may

128

contain crystals of calcium oxalate, but they are neither crystalloid nor globoid.

When moisture starts the seed germinating the aleurone grains absorb the water, swell, and become fluid. Moreover, they are once again capable of being stained with neutral red. The matrix is the first to dissolve, and sets free the crystalloid and the globoids, which soon disappear. The contents of these new vacuoles are at first concentrated, and have a tendency to form into a network; then they become globulose, grow as they become more dilute, and finally take on the appearance of the large vacuoles of cells in the course of differentiation.

(c) *Seasonal variations.* The cells of those organs that persist from year to year undergo seasonal variations, which sometimes involve the vacuoles. This is true of the living cells of trunks and branches of trees, especially of the cells of the cambium. When they are active in spring, the cambial cells have a big central vacuole, which is traversed by multiple rods of cytoplasm, which are unstable and changeable. In autumn, a little before the leaves of deciduous trees begin to fall, the cambial cells become quiescent, and build up reserves; their vacuolar apparatus breaks up into thousands of tiny vacuoles, which give these cells an alveolar appearance. A reverse process takes place when the sap begins to rise in spring (figure 5·32).

These reversible changes may resemble the phenomenon of vacuolar aggregation, which we described earlier, but they are of a totally different duration. They bear more resemblance to the start of the formation of aleurone grains, especially by their preliminary enrichment with substances drawn from the yellowing leaves, which are taken into reserve.

(d) *Instantaneous variations.* Alongside the relatively slow variations just described, the vacuoles may undergo sudden modifications at times during the life of the cell, afterwards returning to their previous state. Thus, going back to the cambial cells of trees (*Robinia*, for example, or maple), I. W. Bailey (1930) and A. M. Catesson (1964) have stated that the vacuolar apparatus is very unstable, and may pass from the single vacuole state to an appearance of having been 'shattered' into innumerable droplets, or into a reticulated state. Eventually the many tiny vacuoles fuse together again into the original big one. These changes, too, have the look of vacuolar aggregation, but so far they have not been associated with any particular transits of materials through the cell.

Comparable processes occur in yeast cells, which normally possess one single spherical vacuole, relatively large and stable. Nevertheless, Guilliermond noticed the outline of the vacuole suddenly becoming irregularly sinuous, bulging and contracting. This went on for several minutes, after which the cell recovered its previous stability. At other times the vacuole became elongate, stretched out, and broke into minute fragments, which afterwards reunited; sometimes the vacuole abruptly shot out long and slender processes, which it afterwards retracted.

The cause of these changes is not known, but it seems as if the shape of the vacuole changes in response to movements of the cytoplasm. Thus, during winter, the vacuoles in the cambial cells of the maple (*Acer pseudoplatanus*) continue in their dispersed phase only as long as there is no cyclosis. As soon as a slight warming-up causes cytoplasmic movements to begin again, the globulose vacuoles change into a reticulated system, or else they become more or less joined together into a continuous vacuolar apparatus (A. M. Cateson 1962, 1964).

7 *Special kinds of vacuole.* Many plant cells contain vacuoles of two types, for example they may have vacuoles that are rich in tannins alongside vacuoles without any. This is so in cells from the epicarp of the young fruits of *Rubus*, which has anthocyanin-stained vacuoles of different colours. Rectractile cells from the Sensitive Plant (*Mimosa sensitiva*) have one large, central vacuole that contains tannins, and peripheral vacuoles that do not. Epidermal cells from the petals of *Hibiscus syriacus* have vacuoles with a red pigment, side by side with others coloured violet.

Specialised vacuoles are common, especially in flowers and fruits. Although tannin-bearing cells with only one kind of vacuole have tannoids based on gallic acid, others sometimes have tannoids based on pyrocatechol.

8 *Origin of the vacuole.* Most of the information just given was originally obtained with only the light microscope, combined with observation of the living cell. Recently, however, the electron microscope has given some assistance in clearing up particular problems, among which is that of the origin of the vacuoles.

What we have just described shows that vacuoles arise by splitting up of pre-existing vacuoles, but it is strongly suggested by a variety of observations that vacuoles can also arise *de novo* in the cytoplasm. Thus, when yeast cells are dividing, it often happens that the vacuole of the mother cell takes no part in providing a vacuole for the daughter cells, which are at first without one. Later on a vacuole makes its appearance (Guilliermond 1926). In the same way no vacuoles are visible at the growing extremities of mycelial filaments of *Saprolegnia*, but at some distance from the end, globular spaces begin to appear. They can be stained with neutral red, they grow, and they fuse with the axial vacuolar canal of the hyphae, which has a siphon structure. Thus, new tiny vacuoles are continually coming into being near the tips of the hyphae, apparently spontaneously (Guilliermond 1933, p. 324).

These young vacuoles are extremely small when they first appear, and the light microscope is not powerful enough to show whether they have inframicroscopic precursors. It might be imagined that the cytoplasm would first synthesise the hydrophilic colloid of the vacuole, and that later vacuoles would form round small masses of this colloid, and would become liquid-filled when the colloid became hydrated. Dujardin (1835) said that cytoplasm had the ability of 'se creuser de vacuoles', and this process would be explained by the above process. Electron microscope studies convinced Mühlethaler (1958) that vacuolar membranes could come into being as secondary developments round such watery spaces in the cytoplasm, but all the same the vacuoles that we have traced from their earliest origin in primary meristems have already been surrounded by a plasma vacuolar membrane from their most undifferentiated stage.

For instance, in meristems of roots, where vital staining shows up a fine vacuolar network, ultra-fine sections can be cut and studied under the electron microscope. These show, among the numerous cut sections of the ER system, various globular or star-shaped profiles, which have a close resemblance to the ER system, but which also contain some substance that is opaque to electrons, and is surrounded by a plasma membrane similar to those of the ER (figure 5·33). The development of these spaces in places further away from the tip of the root, proves them to be thin sections of young vacuoles, which must be genuinely reticulated right from the start. In the course of this development, the space enclosed by the plasma membrane grows, and its opacity diminishes, an indication that its contents are becoming diluted. What goes on in the living cell could be reconstructed from the electron microscope pictures by putting them together to form the third dimension.

So far it has proved impossible to obtain the substance that is opaque to electrons, without having it surrounded by its membrane. The electron microscope pictures strongly support the view that the young vacuoles originate in certain parts of the ER system, which separate off and follow their own development, accumulating the vacuolar colloid in their interior.

All this does not exclude the possibility that vacuoles might also arise spontaneously in the cell. One might mention, for example, the sudden appearance of vacuoles in their most undifferentiated state in the phragmoplast of cells that are in telophase (see p. 231). There, too, the opaque spaces are surrounded by a membrane from the beginning (figure 8·13).

Moreover, the origin of the vacuolar colloid itself is unknown. All that is known is that the membrane surrounding it generally does not possess ribosomes, but is similar to those of the smooth part of the ER (see figure 5·3).

Whenever a profile in the electron microscope pictures can be identified as belonging to a vacuole, it is extremely rare for it to be obviously connected to typical profiles of the ER system. Thus we are still very uncertain what are the relationships between the vacuoles and the ER system, but relations seem to exist, at least sporadically. It is tempting to suggest that products built up in the ER system may then be transferred to the vacuoles, and stored there.

Profiles of vacuoles often have fringed or flattened processes which are visible under the electron microscope (figure 5·33). Some of these are clearly artefacts, caused by a loss of water at the time of fixation, and by deformations occurring subsequently, but others seem to be natural phenomena. They perhaps represent vestiges of links between the ER system and the vacuole. These processes themselves have some tendency to make contact with each other, reminding us of the tendency of vacuoles to merge together. We are also reminded of the sudden changes of shape that can be seen in living cells (see section 6, d).

9 *Function of the vacuole.* We have stated above that the vacuoles are the chief places where the hydrophilic substances of the cell accumulate. In addition to the hydrophilic proteins, one of which is the vacuolar colloid, the substances stored by the vacuole are either reserve materials, such as sucrose, inulin, and the constituents of the aleurone grains, or else substances involved in the processes of secretion and excretion. The significance of the latter is not always clear: for example, the role of the heterosides and alkaloids.

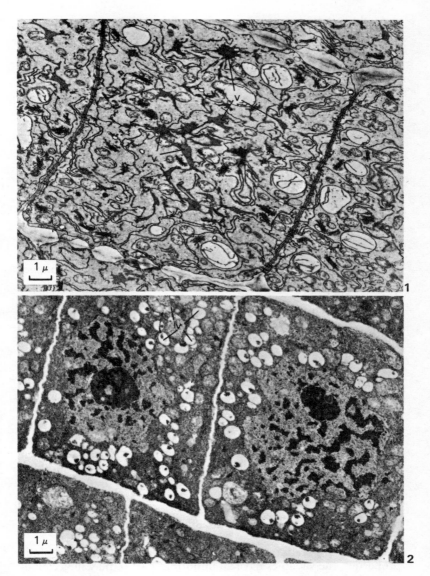

5·33 Electron micrograph of vacuoles (v) in meristematic root cells of barley.
1 Fixed in permanganate ; **2** fixed in OsO₄ (× 5,500).

133

Insoluble substances may also collect in the vacuoles, where they either crystallise or precipitate. We have seen how one such substance is calcium oxalate, which is particularly insoluble, and which forms crystals of various different types. So it looks as if the vacuoles can gather together substances that are either useless to the cell, or positively harmful to it, and in default of being able to excrete these to the exterior, the cell is able at least to separate them from the protoplasm. The very special case of the laticifers, or latex vessels comes into this category. Latex is a hydrophobic product, a terpene hydrocarbon, which is passed into the vacuoles, where it forms an emulsion. Another remarkable contribution of these vacuoles is to receive grains of starch which were built up in plastids, and have been released when the plastids degenerated (see chapter 8).

Phenol compounds (various tannoids, vacuolar pigments) are among the compounds that are most widely distributed among the vacuoles of plant cells, where they apparently have an anti-toxic role. It is found, for example, that cells with a high content of tannin can tolerate vital staining for a much longer time, before changes set in, than adjacent cells of the same tissue that have no tannin.

Vacuoles have a very important role to play in water balance – and probably that of many other substances – between the cell and its surrounding medium. It looks as if the system of vacuoles plus tonoplast and cell membrane operates effectively as an osmometer with a semipermeable membrane. These properties give the vacuoles an important mechanical role in controlling the rigidity of plants, and determining the state of turgidity. Normally the cell is able to adjust the tonicity of its vacuolar liquid to be slightly higher than that of its surrounding medium.

As a result of their mechanical properties, the vacuoles participate in cellular growth. We have seen already that when cells first begin to differentiate, starting from the primary meristem, their initial growth is mostly confined to the vacuoles. The pressure that these exert upon the protoplasm, and through it upon the cell walls, supplies the motive force of cell growth. How the membrane responds to this force is dictated by its structure and mechanical properties, which in their turn are affected by several other growth factors.

Germinating seeds take up water and, because of their hydrophilic properties, the vacuoles have an important part to play in germination. Moreover, those vacuoles that arise out of the aleurone grains are the sites of an intense activity of hydrolases, which split up the big molecules into smaller ones, and thus increase their osmotic pressure and add to the force of water intake. The work of N. Poux (1963–5) has identified *in situ*, in electron microscope pictures, several phosphatases which operate upon the aleurone grains in the process of hydration, and upon the vacuoles that result from this.

The mechanical function of the vacuoles is again of prime importance in the growth of pollen tubes. The germination of a pollen grain, in fact, is accompanied by an enormous increase in volume, without any appreciable increase in protoplasm, and this is made possible by the development of a huge vacuole.

In brief, the mechanical importance of vacuoles explains why they have been so extensively developed among the plants. Vacuoles are one of the constituents that are responsible for the most characteristic properties of cells and organisms of the plant kingdom. Even though the vacuoles must be classified as paraplasmic because of the nature of their contents, yet their physiological importance, and their various functions both on the level of the cell, and on higher organisational levels such as that of tissues, all contribute to making them more than just a reserve store. Because they have a part to play at every instant of the life of the cell, vacuoles should truly be classified as part of the living cell.

6 Mitochondria

Mitochondria or 'chondriosomes' are granular or filamentous protoplasmic organelles scattered throughout the cytoplasm. In animal cells they form a homogeneous group, and this is also true of the mitochondria plant cells once they have become differentiated. In meristematic plant cells, however, which are in active proliferation, the mitochondria are mixed up with other constituents which resemble mitochondria, but which develop into plastids as the cell becomes differentiated. Because of this resemblance, to which we shall later return, some cytologists have considered that mitochondria and plastids must be related organelles, and have given them the collective name of chondriomes (Guilliermond); those who do not accept this affinity restrict the name chondriomes to the mitochondria and call the plastids plastidomes (P. Dangeard).

Some aspects of the living cytoplasm and its changeability The mitochondria were not discovered until long after the nucleus and the plastids because they are difficult to see in the living cytoplasm, and were destroyed by the acid and alcoholic fixatives used by cytologists of the old school. Although the refractive index of mitochondria is in fact very little greater than that of the general cytoplasm, they can actually be seen with good modern microscopes if the material is suitably chosen, and properly illuminated.

When the mitochondria have been made visible they appear either as grains (mitochondria in the strict sense of Benda 1897), or as short, bacilliform rods, or as longer, sinuous filaments (called chondriocontes by Meves in 1907). They show up as a very clear grey against the paler cytoplasmic background, with a breadth of about $0.5\,\mu$, and a length that easily reaches to $10\,\mu$.

These corpuscles are dragged hither and thither by the cytoplasmic currents, and their shape is continually changing. They thus behave with the consistency of a semi-fluid, though one that is more viscous than the plasmasol. Any deformations undergone by the mitochondria are more or less reversible (Guilliermond 1933) (figure 6·1).

Observation of living mitochondria demands certain special precautions, because these organelles are very sensitive to variations

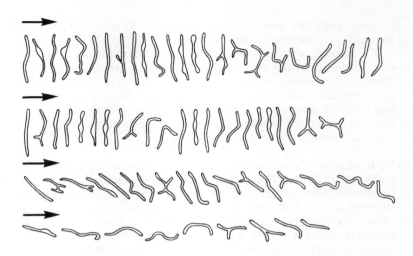

6·1 Successive deformations of a mitochondrion of *Saprolegnia* observed in the living state.

in the surrounding medium. If observations are too prolonged the cell eventually suffers from the artificial conditions imposed upon it, and the mitochondria are generally the first organelles to be affected. What happens is usually more or less the same thing, described by Prowazek under the name cavulation. The short forms, the rodlets and mitochondria, swell up into hollow spheres, and their surface layer becomes more highly refringent. Each of the elongated chondriocontes forms itself into a series of similar vacuoles, which separate from each other, and then press together into an alveolar mass.

Cavulation is generally an irreversible phenomenon, and is a prelude to the death of the cell, but there are changes in the mitochondria which can be provoked and which are reversible. Some cells are more resistant than others in this respect. For instance, the mitochondria of the root cells of chicory or *Scorzonera* are considerably changed both in size and in shape by the action of pure water. After an initial swelling phase, they show a tendency to join together end to end, in long filaments, or even into perforated sheets. If the cell is returned to a normal, isotonic solution, over a period of several hours the mitochondria return to normal (Buvat 1948). Similar changes can be brought about either by high or low

137

temperatures, and these changes are reversible provided that they have not gone too far (Genevès 1955).

The intensity of cytoplasmic movement also influences the shapes of mitochondria. An active cyclosis tends to break up the mitochondria into small pieces. On the other hand, any trace of free water reaching their surface is taken up, lowers their surface tension, and tends to cause them to unite into elongate mitochondria. Thus they are seen to respond to every factor which alters the physico-chemical equilibrium within the cytoplasm.

Vital staining The mitochondria in living cells can be stained with Dahlia Violet, Methyl Green 5B, and Green Janus B. The last is the one most commonly used, and produces a light, blue-green tint, which may not last long, because the mitochondria themselves reduce the molecules of dye. If this decolorisation does not take place, then the pigment quickly brings about cavulation. This change is quickly followed by changes in cyclosis, and the cell dies.

So it seems that mitochondria take up living stains only very briefly before they undergo irreversible changes. It is for this reason that this type of staining has been called 'sublethal' rather than truly 'vital' (Guilliermond 1933, p. 76). Guilliermond tried to culture *Saprolegnia* (aquatic siphomycete fungi) on media to which Green Janus B had been added. In a weak dose (less than $3 \cdot 5/10^{-5}$) the fungus reduced the colorant, and went on developing without being stained; at heavier doses (more than 4×10^{-5}) it ceased to grow. Dahlia Violet and Methyl Green are even more toxic. It will be recalled that the same author cultured the same fungus on a medium stained with neutral red, the vacuolar apparatus being vitally stained, and observed its complete development.

Fixation Once it was realised the mitochondria were so fragile, cytologists devised special mitochondrial fixatives, containing neither acid nor alcohol, and designed both to preserve the mitochondria and techniques to stain them. Mitochondrial fixatives contain mixtures of neutralised formaldehyde, potassium bichromate, chromic acid, corrosive sublimate, osmium tetroxide, and so on. To round off the fixation it is usual to give an after-treatment to fix the fats, which are abundant in mitochondria, by making them insoluble.

Mitochondria fixed in this way can be stained black with Iron Haematoxylin, or purple with Altmann's Fuchsin, and then they

138

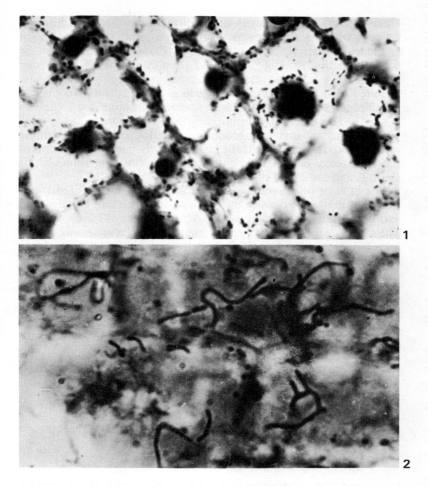

6·2 Mitochondria as seen under the light microscope by Regaud's technique.
1 Stem of tomato. (×1,000). **2** Old phloem cells of *Robinia* (×1,500).

can be clearly seen in fairly thin sections (0·5 to 3 μ), in the same shapes that they had when alive (figure 6·2). Sometimes it can even be distinguished that the mitochondria are built up from strings of shorter elements, recalling the way in which they are assembled and broken down.

Ultrastructure The discovery of the ultrastructure of mitochondria was one of the early successes of the electron microscope, as soon as the techniques of fixation (osmium tetroxide buffered and made slightly alkaline to pH 7–7·5) and of ultramicrotomy had been developed. A mitochondrion, whatever its shape, is always surrounded by a double envelope, which is formed from two plasma membranes separated by a narrow space of about 100Å (figures 6·3–6·5). The external membrane is regularly convex, as a rule, whereas the internal membrane has tubules, or 'villi' extending inwards into the interior; or the protuberances may take the form of flattened folds, or lamellae, which may sometimes be branched, or sinuous and are called cristae.

The interior of the mitochondrion is occupied by a ground substance of moderate density, the stroma, in which can be seen here and there granules which resemble the ribosomes of the cytoplasm. The stroma also usually presents one or more clear spaces, which for a long time were thought to be defects of fixation, but which are probably natural, because it has recently been demonstrated that they contain a strand of DNA. In ultra-thin sections the majority of 'profiles' cut through either cristae or villi appear as if isolated in the stroma, suggesting that whatever connection they may have with the internal membrane must be a slender one. In the mitochondria of most plant cells the cristae and the villi are sinuous, and point in all directions.

The fact that both components of the double membrane are continuous separates the contents of the mitochondrion into two distinct phases: one that lies between the membranes, and the other the stroma, inside the inner membrane, with its folds. The two phases appear of different densities under the electron microscope.

The fine structure of mitochondria is substantially the same in animal cells as in those from plants.

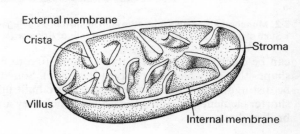

External membrane

Crista

Stroma

6·3 Diagram to show the ultrastructure of a mitochondrion.

Villus

Internal membrane

140

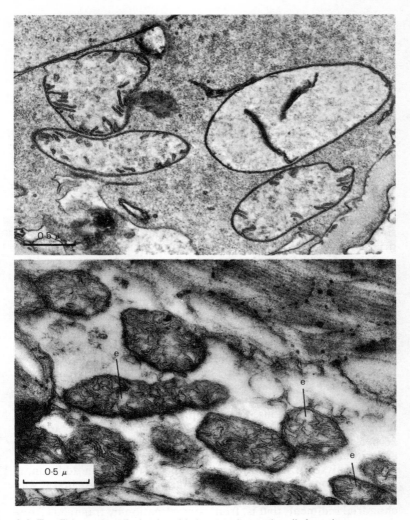

6·4 Top Thin section of mitochondria from meristematic cells from the growing point of *Elodea canadensis*, fixed in permanganate (×27,000).

6·5 Bottom Mitochondria from differentiated, chlorophyll – containing cells of *Elodea canadensis* containing many cristae. Note the clear space (e), which is probably the region where the mitochondrial DNA is to be found. (×34,000).

Biochemistry Ever since the beginning of this century it has been known that mitochondria are rich in fats, because of the ways in which they react to fixation with acids and alcohols, and to staining (Regaud, Fauré-Premiet, Mayer and Schaeffer). The authors just mentioned had shown that 'mitochondrial' fixatives worked because they were oxidising agents, and converted the unsaturated fats into hydroxilated acids which were not very soluble in the usual fat solvents. This treatment made sure that any cell organelle containing such fats was well preserved.

On the other hand the low refractive index of mitochondria, as well as the residues that were left when they had been altered by treatment with acids and alcohols, all led to the conclusion that they must also contain protein compounds. This was confirmed by Giroud (1921) for animal and by Milovidov (1928) for plant cells.

The use of indicators of the oxidation – reduction potential (rH) showed that cellular oxidation is particularly active in mitochondria, and that they contain systems which facilitate the transfer of electrons. Green Janus B is the indicator most commonly used for this purpose. The mitochondria are equally active in reducing tetrazolium salts, producing precipitates of formazan.

Later on the techniques of homogenisation and of differential centrifugation, by providing measurable quantities of pure mitochondria, made it possible to analyse them in detail, both organically and enzymatically. These studies were carried out both on animal and plant cells, and confirmed that the mitochondria in the two kingdoms were of the same nature, and that, by inference, they probably had the same infrastructure. According to this analysis, 70–80 per cent of the dry weight consists of proteins and fats in about equal proportions. For example, mitochondria from germinating peas (*Pisum sativum*) contain 30–40 per cent protein and 25–38 per cent fat. The fats are essentially phosphoaminolipids, such as lecithins (Lewitt 1954).

The analysis of mitochondrial sediments reveals, in addition, a small RNA content (1–6 per cent) and traces of DNA. At first it was thought that the nucleic acids came from impurities in the mitochondrial sediment, that is, from contamination by fragments from the ER system, or nuclear debris. However, the nucleic acids were still present even in sediments that had been carefully purified under the electron microscope. Furthermore, both DNA and RNA have been detected *in situ*, cytochemically, in fine sections studied under the electron microscope (Nass, Nass and Afzelius 1965).

142

Finally, purified suspensions of mitochondria show enzymatic activities, and these are both varied and highly characteristic. It is possible in fact, to obtain in the test tube every stage of the Krebs cycle (a cycle of tricarboxylic acids) by adding suitable solutions of the appropriate substrate to suspension of pure mitochondria. Mitochondria also contain all the substances which act as hydrogen (or electron) transfer agents (carriers) during the various oxidations and phosphorylations that make up the process of respiration (nicotinamide-adenine dinucleotide, or NAD; flavoproteins; cyto-chromes a, a_3, b, c, etc ...). Naturally the enzymes and coenzymes that work with the carriers are also present (coenzyme A, hexokinase, malic and succinic dehydrogenases, cytochrome reductases, oxy-dases, notably cytochrome c oxidase, phosphorylases, etc). Mito-chondria also contain vitamins, notably vitamin C, or ascorbic acid, which is also a hydrogen carrier.

Location of various chemical constituents When the ultrastructure of the mitochondria became known, it was natural to want to know where the various chemical components were located in this ultra-structure, but this investigation has so far mostly been applied to animal mitochondria (Watson and Siekevitz (1956) on rat liver; Green and others (1959) on cow's heart).

The technique consists of breaking up the mitochondria either with a detergent (deoxycholate), or by ultrasonic vibrations, and then isolating the fragments of membrane by centrifugation. It then appears that the bulk of the fats are located on the membranes, along with the proteins. These membranes are therefore lipoproteic, like the ER membranes and the dictyosomes.

The membranes also hold the greater part if not the whole of the enzymes and electron carriers, and so it seems that all the substances that participate in the oxidation-phosphorylation processes are to be found on the membranes (Watson and Siekevitz 1956).

The work of Green and his school, which we cannot dwell on, important though it is, because it deals with animal cells, has led to the conclusion that the mitochondrial membranes contain thousands of macromolecular units which have the capacity to transfer electrons from succinate or NADH, which are formed in the Krebs cycle, to molecular oxygen. The study of these macromolecular particles, which are known as ETP ('electron-transport particles') has been pursued down to the molecular level, and has shown that they com-prise four molecular complexes, and a total of eleven different

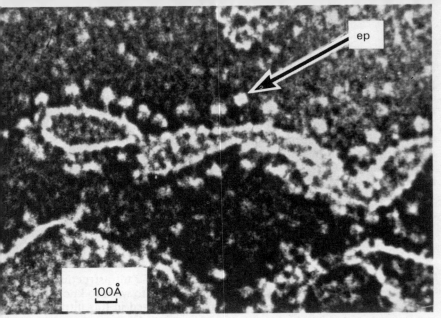

ep

100Å

6·6 Oxysomes on the cristae of mitochondria segregated by ultrasonic vibrations and prepared by negative staining. ep=elementary particles. (×500,000).

protein molecules. All these are joined together by specific lipids, different from the phospholipids of the membrane.

It is now known that the majority, if not all, of the electron carriers are the same in plants and animals, and it is very important that studies of plant mitochondria should be made, on a par with those made on animals by Green and his colleagues.

Using the technique of negative staining, H. Fernandez-Morán took mitochondria from the heart cells of ox, disrupted them by ultrasonic vibrations, and found that the internal face of the inner membrane, including its folded parts (cristae) was covered with tiny spheres, about 100Å in diameter, and attached to the membrane by a stalk which arose from a small base in the thickness of the membrane (figure 6·6). Like Green, we are tempted to locate the oxydo-reduction systems just described on these particular structures, which have been called elementary particles or *oxysomes*. It is still disputed, however, whether this view is correct; it is all the more reason for wanting to find similar structures in plant cells.

Physiology In spite of all the efforts of cytologists, the physiological

144

function of the mitochondria remained unknown until 1940, when the separation techniques devised by A. Claude provided a means by which the biochemical composition of mitochondria could be analysed, and their physiological potentialities in the test tube could be estimated. This proved so fruitful that today the mitochondria are among the best understood of all the organelles of the cell. Their functions may be summed up as principally respiratory, and the following experiments show how this conclusion was reached.

1 *Breakdown of glucose.* Suspensions of mitochondria in isolation make use of ATP for the phosphorylation of glucose (Laties 1951). This activity is not a function exclusive to mitochondria, since it goes on in the cytoplasm, the plastids and even the nucleus. In the mitochondria it results in production of the pyruvate ion, and this anaerobic phase of respiration is called *glycolysis*. ATP is produced also.

2 *Tricarboxylic acid cycle.* Millerd, Bonner and their colleagues (1951) showed that suspensions of mitochondria oxidise pyruvate, and do so more actively if the medium is enriched with malates. These suspensions have a similar oxidising effect on citrates, ketoglutarate, and succinates, showing that they possess all the enzymes necessary for the Krebs cycle. The cofactors needed for the Krebs cycle are also present, provided that the mitochondria have been extracted in the presence of phosphate.

It has been established that the Krebs cycle, which controls the oxidation of pyruvates into CO_2 plus hydrogen, takes place only in the mitochondria.

3 *Electron transport.* The same is true of the chain of hydrogen transporters (or electron carriers) which are associated with systems which involve the Krebs cycle. Such carriers collect up the hydrogen (or the electrons) liberated by the oxidation of pyruvate, and pass it on to its final acceptor – molecular oxygen. The intermediate stages of this transfer consist of a whole chain of oxidation-reductions, which can be briefly summarised as follows (cf. Hackett 1959):

succinate **1**   **3**

     →flavoproteins - - - →cytochrome *b* - - - →cytochrome *c* - - - →

NADH   **2**   **4**

    - - - →cytochrome *a* - - - →cytochrome a_3 - - - → O_2

4 *Phosphorylative activity.* As electrons are transferred along the above chain there is a progressive fall of potential, which is expressed as a release of energy in steps, at each transfer. Part of this energy is taken up by phosphorylation reactions, in which ADP (adenosine diphosphate) combines with an inorganic phosphate ion to form ATP (adenosine triphosphate), that is, to form phosphate bonds that are 'energy-rich'. In fact it is known that each of the steps 1, 2, 3 and 4 above yields one molecule of ATP, the energy from which can be used either for biosynthesis or for any other cell process for which energy is needed. The coupling of respiratory oxidation and oxidative phosphorylation makes the mitochondria the indispensable carriers of energy within the cell.

5 *Other oxidative activities.* It has been said that the mitochondria contain ascorbic acid, or vitamin C. This substance, too, is a hydrogen transporter, so it seems that there must be other oxidation-reduction systems in the cell besides the one we have just described. No other systems have yet been found, however, and the role played by ascorbic acid in the mitochondria is unknown.

6 *Synthetic activities.* It has recently been worked out in what form DNA and RNA occur in the mitochondria. It looks as if the RNA is produced by the DNA, in a manner recalling the action of messenger-RNA in the cytoplasm, coded by the DNA of the nucleus. We are forced to conclude, therefore, that the mitochondria are active in protein synthesis in much the same way as is the cytoplasm, and that they make use of part of the ATP that they themselves have produced. As more and more is known of the ultrastructure of the mitochondria, it seems likely that they also synthesise complex lipids, but where this goes on is not yet determined.

A further point is that, in some cells at least, the life of the mitochondria is quite short, and to accomplish such a 'turnover' it would seem that they must renew themselves fairly frequently. The mitochondrial RNA may perhaps have an essential part to play here, as a carrier of information, but this is difficult to study.

Evolution during cell differentiation The earlier workers knew that cells in active growth (meristematic cells) contained mitochondria, granular and bacilliform, that were very small and very numerous. In certain tissues these became elongate during the process of differentiation, and formed chondriocontes; this is very obvious,

146

for example, in the hyphae of many fungi when they are growing (*Saprolegnia:* Guilliermond). Yet there is no lack of exceptions to this rule and, moreover, we have seen that changes in the environment can provoke changes in shape of the mitochondria. In many tissues the shape of the mitochondria depends on the physiological state of the cells; thus leaf cells that are actively engaged in photosynthesis often have their mitochondria in the form of grains or short filaments, whereas the relatively quiescent cells of tissues that are engaged in building up reserves have the majority of their mitochondria as long chondriocontes. But in any event, differentiation does not bring about the accumulation of paraplasmic products in the mitochondria – with rare exceptions, when proteins are formed – as we shall see is the case in the plastids.

All the same, mitochondria do evolve, at least on an ultrastructural scale, during the differentiation of the cell. In meristematic cells the mitochondria are poorly provided with cristae and villi, and these are generally very short and peripheral in position. The material of the stroma is abundant, but of very low density (figure 6·4). Those cells, which differentiate into photosynthetic cells with chlorophyll, and intense biochemical activity, have mitochondria in which both the number and the length of the cristae have become considerable (figure 6·5). In contrast, in the mitochondria of reserve tissues, where physiological activity has dropped, the ultrastructures are often reduced to villi only, and these are very poorly developed. Lund, Vater and Hanson (1958) have established a relationship between the abundance of lamellae, the number of mitochondria in one cell, and the intensity with which oxidative phosphorylation is going on in the cell (from a maize root). The maximum respiratory activity, which is to be found at the end of the zone of cellular elongation, coincides with maximal development of the mitochondrial cristae.

Origin The fact that actively dividing cells keep a reasonably constant number of mitochondria implies that these organelles possess the necessary mechanisms, not only to multiply, but to maintain their numbers in equilibrium. The question whether mitochondria can arise *de novo* in the cytoplasm has been debated a great deal, without reaching any conclusion, but it is certain that existing mitochondria can divide transversely into two new ones. This operation, by drawing out and nipping off, can be observed in living cells, but it is not known whether any other methods exist. It is odd, for example, that numbers of mitochondria appear suddenly

147

in the phragmoplasts of cells that are in process of division, at the end of telophase, just before the phragmoplast passes from the gel state (when it is not penetrated by the cytoplasm) into the sol state (cf. p. 231). It is questionable whether these mitochondria come directly from the maternal cytoplasm, since in ultrastructure they have a distinctly juvenile appearance. From the beginning they resemble in every way the mitochondria from ordinary meristematic cells.

Equivalents of mitochondria in Protocaryotes All living cells of higher organisms, both animals and plants, possess mitochondria. Bacteria and blue-green algae do not, but they contain structures that can be stained with Green Janus B, and which reduce the salts of tetrazolium, producing a precipitate of formazan. These structures are sites of oxidation-reductions, and in this respect they resemble mitochondria. Only after the introduction of techniques of fixation and embedding, specially modified to suit bacteria (Kellenberger, Ryter and Sechaud 1958) could these structures be studied under the electron microscope. It was then discovered that they consisted of clumps of villi, much folded upon themselves, and having continuity with the cell membrane of the bacterium. In ultra-fine structure they suggest the cristae of mitochondria, but they are not surrounded by the double membrane that is characteristic of the mitochondria of higher organisms.

In fact these structures, which are called *mesosomes*, are special regions of the cell membrane, which are particularly well developed in many gram-positive bacteria (figure 6·7, *Bacillus subtilis*: Van Iterson and Leene: Ryter), and in several gram-negative bacteria of certain groups (Caulobacteria; Poindexter and Cohen Bazire 1964). The rest of the gram-negative bacteria generally have nothing more than individual diverticula of the cell membrane (as in *Escherichia coli*) or else they are without mesosomes altogether.

Nevertheless, these bacteria possess sites where oxidation-reductions are going on, as can be shown by culturing them in the presence of potassium tellurite (Van Iterson and Leene; Ryter), which is reduced to form a precipitate of either TeO or metallic tellurium, both of which are opaque to electrons, and so mark the site in question. By this method it has been shown that these sites are in contact with the cell membrane itself, and that all the cells from one strain of bacteria may contain the same number of them, perhaps genetically determined (Ryter). In ultra-thin sections these

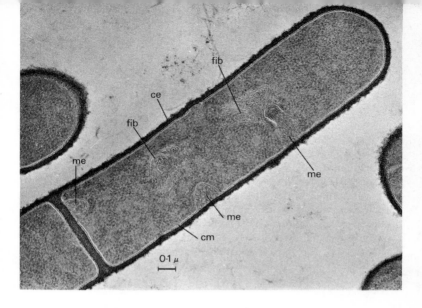

6·7 Thin section of *Bacillus subtilis*, a gram-positive bacterium. Visible are the mesosomes (me), contorted tubules which issue from the cell membrane (cm), two nuclear tracts of fine fibrillae (fib), and the cell envelope (ce). (×45,000).

sites appear as finely granulose areas, without ribosomes, but showing some structure in the shape of very tiny rods which are difficult to distinguish (Van Iterson and Leene 1964).

The blue-green algae are probably similar, but they are still awaiting detailed study; it is known, however, that these organisms also possess oxidation-reduction sites which perform the functions of mitochondria (Niklowitz 1958).

It seems, therefore, that in these Protocaryotes (bacteria and blue-green algae) the cell membrane itself makes up for the lack of the other membrane structures that are characteristic of the cytoplasm of higher organisms (Eucaryotes), not only the mitochondria, but the ER system, the nuclear membrane and the dictyosomes. We shall now go on to see that this applies to the plastids as well.

149

7 Plastids

Plastids are peculiar to plant cells, and are mainly found in the living cells of green plants. Nevertheless P. Heim (1947–9) described organelles in fungi that look like chromoplasts, and which contain inclusions of carotenoid pigments, sometimes in a crystalline form.

Plastids, like mitochondria, are scattered throughout the cytoplasm, and can be divided into three categories, according to their pigmentation. The most important are the chloroplasts, which are especially rich in chlorophyll, but which also contain carotenoids. The latter are the predominant, or even the only pigments, in the chromoplasts. Finally the leucoplasts have no pigment at all.

Let us consider the three types in turn.

Chloroplasts

Chloroplasts are the only cellular organelles to contain chlorophyll. The general shape of chloroplasts will now be considered briefly. Later we shall consider their ultrastructure, chemical composition, and their main functions.

Shape In the green cells of higher seed plants, as well as in most Pteridophytes, the chloroplasts are lenticular granules, more or less flattened, and a few microns in diameter (often $3–6\mu$ across and about 2μ thick). Each cell contains a large, but apparently indefinite number of these (figure 1·5), usually scattered throughout the cytoplasm, but if the cytoplasm becomes pressed against the cell wall then the chloroplasts are orientated with their biggest surface against the cell wall, causing the cytoplasm to bulge wherever they lie. Sometimes the chloroplasts are more numerous around the nucleus, but they may also be carried along in cyclosis, in spite of their being thicker than the peripheral layer of cytoplasm.

Certain Pteridophytes, such as *Selaginella*, have only one single plastid in their meristematic cells, and one, two, or a small (definite) number in their differentiated cells (Emberger 1923). In Bryophytes the cells usually have an indefinite number of chloroplasts, which may be ellipsoidal or lenticular: an exception is the genus *Antho-*

150

ceros, in which every cell contains just one plastid, cup-shaped and several microns in diameter.

Chloroplasts are extremely diverse among algae. Thus, the assimilating tissue of the thalli of Pheophyceae and of Rhodophyceae contains a great many plastids of changeable shape, and of a size comparable with that of the plastids of vascular plants. Moreover, these plastids are coloured with supernumerary pigments, brown, or red, which may completely mask the green of the chlorophyll. In many green algae (in the broad sense) and among Bacillariophyceae (diatoms), the number, shape and size of the chloroplasts are often specific. These plastids, or chromatophores, are helpful for the identification of genera and species, because they are characters that are easily seen.

Only a few examples need be given (figure 7·1). The cells of *Chlamydomonas* have only a single chromatophore, which is cup-shaped; every cell of *Zygnema* or of *Cosmarium* (Conjugatophyceae) contains two chromatophores which are either star-shaped (*Zygnema*) or lobed (*Cosmarium*); the cells of *Draparnaldia* (Chaetophorales) and those of *Ulothrix zonata* (Ulothricales) have one

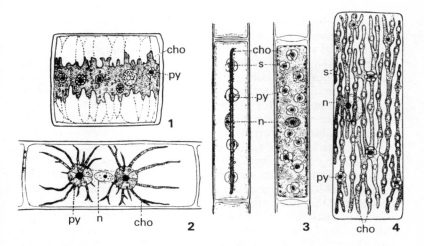

7·1 Shapes of chromatophores (cho) in several algae.
1 Annular in *Ulothrix zonata.* **2** Star-shaped in *Zygnema.*
3 Lamellar in *Mougeotia,* seen in profile and in full face. **4** Reticulate in *Oedogonium.* s=starch ; n=nuclei ; py=pyrenoids.

151

single annular plastid, with more or less toothed edges; the chromatophore of *Mougeotia* (Conjugatophyceae) is a perforated flat plate, nearly as big as the longest dimension of the cell; finally the species of *Spirogyra* are easily identified because their cells contain one or two chromatophores that are helicoidal, with strongly undulating edges.

Most of these chromatophores contain either one or several granules of a protein nature, called pyrenoids, around which starch grains are massed.

Finally, many algae, particularly the mobile forms, have a bright red spot of a carotenoid pigment on the surface of their chromatophore. This stigma is an organic photoreceptor, and is responsible for the phototactic properties of these algae.

Structure The elucidation of the fine structure of chloroplasts has been the subject of a great deal of effort over a considerable period of time, and cytologists have used the resources of biochemical and biophysical analyses at their disposal to the utmost limits of their potentialities. Let us look first at what was learned before the electron microscope came into use.

1 *Results before the electron microscope.* The idea that chloroplasts are heterogeneous is a very old one, and can be found in descriptions even by the original discoverers of these organelles. In fact A. Meyer (1883) and A. Schimper (1885) mentioned that the plastids contained granules of chlorophyll. For a long time these granules remained poorly known, probably because the best available techniques for staining chloroplasts rendered them a uniform colour. Nevertheless, these 'chlorophyll granules', which became the grana of present day terminology, were seen by Heitz in 1932, and made visible again in the delicate observations of living cells made by Doutreligne (1935). Heitz then took up the study again, and showed that the grana themselves are tiny lenticular inclusions, $0.3-2\mu$ in diameter, and contain the greater part, if not the whole, of the chlorophyll.

In 1937 the study of the fine structure of the grana was tackled with the aid of the fluorescence microscope, which confirmed that the chlorophyll was located in the grana (Metzner). Use of the ultraviolet microscope (Menke 1940) and the polarising microscope (Frey-Wyssling and Steinmann 1948, among others), demonstrated that the grana seen in profile had a laminated structure, and this structure was confirmed by Strugger (1951) by the technique of using potash to make the grana swell. In addition this author noticed that the grana are borne on lamellae which extend across the whole diameter of the plastid ('Trägerlamellen'), and also brought to light the existence of a membranous envelope (the plastid membrane).

This picture of the structure of a chloroplast is already elaborate enough, but it needs to be observed step by step with the electron microscope, as is in fact being done at the present time.

2 *Ultrastructures under the electron microscope:*

(a) *First observations.* For some time it had been possible to obtain chloroplasts in the form of a suspension, separated from the cells, and these suspensions were among the first biological material that was examined under the electron microscope. This was before techniques of fixation and ultra-thin sectioning had been perfected. The first pictures to be published seem to have been those of Kausche and Ruska (1940), and of Menke (1940). They were taken from chloroplasts that had been isolated and dried on to the stage of the microscope, and were repeated many times afterwards. In these pictures the grana could be seen, either intact, or smashed up in the process of extraction. The shattered grana were seen to be

7·2 Granum of a chloroplast of *Aspidistra*, disintegrated by the isolation technique, and completely desiccated on the stage of the electron microscope. In this way it can be seen that the grana are built up from discs stacked like piles of coins.

built up from a series of discs, piled up on each other like a heap of coins (figure 7·2). So the laminated structure of chloroplasts was confirmed straight away, and this was again seen when photographs of very thin sections became available.

The first 'new look' pictures were obtained in 1953 by Finean, Sjöstrand and Steinmann, working with *Aspidistra elatior*; they made it possible to measure the thickness of the granar lamellae (about 70–80Å) and that of the space between them, which was about the same. These figures were finally confirmed when freshly obtained chloroplasts were examined under x-rays.

Thus electron microscope pictures accumulated quickly, and it was soon realised that the arrangement of the lamellae in the chloroplasts varied according to the systematic position of the various green plants examined. Here are the main types, beginning with the higher plants.

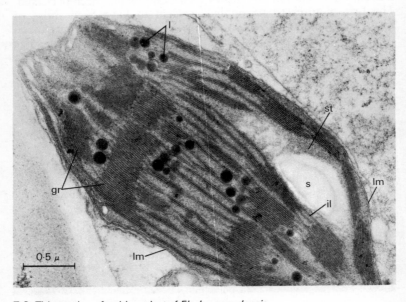

7·3 Thin section of a chloroplast of *Elodea canadensis* fixed in glutaraldehyde + OsO_4.
lm = limiting membrane ; gr = grana ; l = fat globules ;
il = isolated lamellae in intergranar space ;
s = starch granule surrounded by the stroma (st). (× 27,000).

(b) *Chloroplasts of vascular plants*. With few exceptions, the chloroplasts of the higher plants belong to one relatively uniform type (figure 7·3).

Like mitochondria, chloroplasts are always contained within a double membrane, of which the outer membrane is usually regularly convex, while the inner membrane (separated from the outer by a narrow space, about 100Å) may extend as folds into the stroma, especially in young plastids. The interior of the chloroplast is laminated into a great many lamellar membranes, of the same appearance as the plasma membranes of the cytoplasm, and as the two membranes which surround the plastid. These lamellae are all alike, and in transverse section their profiles are always associated two-by-two. By tracing out these profiles to their ends it is found that the lamellae are really a great number of flattened saccules, enclosing a clear space which is therefore separated from the

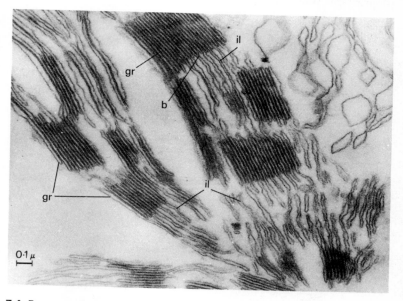

7·4 Fragment of a chloroplast from maize after having burst in a hypotonic medium. A thin section, cut after fixing in permanganate, shows the relationship between the piles of grana (gr) and extensive areas of plastidial lamellae (il), which are portions of double lamellae isolated in the intergranar zones. b=bifurcation of a double lamella. (×40,000).

155

ground substance of the plastid (figure 7·4). The diameter of these saccules may be almost as great as that of the plastid, though others may have a much smaller diameter, and then they are mostly either piled together in a heap, or stacked against one of the bigger kind. This is how the grana are built up from grana discs.

Between the profiles of grana can be seen other profiles of double lamellae, isolated in the stroma, which represent 'overflow' regions from the greater saccules. These long profiles are frequently interrupted (figures 7·3–7·5) and when the biggest saccules are seen in face view they are pitted with numerous holes.

This system of lamellae thus constitutes 'granar spaces' in which the membranes are heaped, and 'intergranar spaces' where the membranes are only in pairs. In the granar spaces it may happen that the two membranes of a pair are derived from one saccule folded back upon itself, or doubled by a flattened invagination of its own edge (figure 7·5). When this process has taken place on one of the big

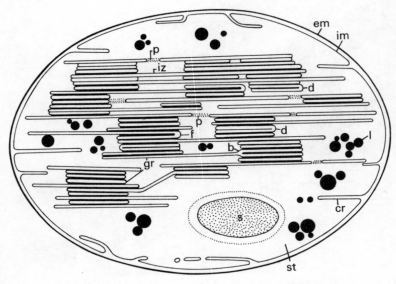

7·5 The ultrastructure of a chloroplast. s=starch enclosed in stroma ; b=bifurcation of lamella ; cr=crista ; d=duplication of a thylakoid by peripheral invagination ; gr=grana ; iz=intergranary zone ; l=lipid droplets ; em=external membrane ; im=internal membrane ; p=pores in lamellae (intergranary zones) ; f=folding of lamellae, which increase the area of the grana ; st=stroma.

156

saccules, it appears in a section as a bifurcated profile (figure 7·5). These complications of detail do not invalidate the description given above, and the 'grana' structure is always produced by paired membranes, isolated or heaped together.

Recently a terminology has been invented to describe these structures. The hollow discs, or flattened saccules, which when grouped together form the grana are called thylakoids (Menke). Weier and his colleagues have christened the spaces that are formed by two associated membranes 'partitions' etc ... The whole assemblage of lamellae is bathed in a ground substance, the stroma, which is fluid on the whole, though after fixation for the electron microscope it shows a granular and fibrillar structure. In the stroma are to be found, usually in quite large amounts, granules that take up osmium, and have a lipoid nature. Finally, if the plastid manufactures starch, then the starch grains will be found in certain vacuolar spaces, but lying in the stroma itself, outside the granar lamellae, and without any membrane surrounding them.

(c) *Chloroplasts in green flagellates.* Green flagellates contain many chloroplasts, all relatively small. In *Euglena gracilis,* for example, the chloroplast, inside its double membrane, contains a score of parallel lamellae, which run the whole length of the chloroplast, and are often of irregular outline (Wolken and Palade 1953). Other species show profiles with groups of four dense lines, with the two middle lines denser than the outer pair. When these profiles are traced to their extremities (Gibbs 1960) it becomes obvious that the four lines represent three saccules, and the two denser inner lines are really two surfaces pressed closely together. The same plastid may contain several groups of three saccules, with here and there groups of 2, 4 or 5.

Other flagellates, less rich in chlorophyll, – such as the Chrysomonad *Chromulina psammobia* (Rouillet and Fauré Fremiet 1958) have two chloroplasts with giant saccules, more or less isolated from each other, running through them. One of these plastids contains a stigma, a patch immediately beneath the membrane of the plastid where fatty granules rich in carotenoid pigments are laid out in a single layer.

The lamellae in these chloroplasts are indeed hollow saccules, but do not aggregate into granar zones and intergranar zones. Either they remain isolated, or they are irregularly paired, or again, they are paired with every surface facing another one. Such a structure is said to be agranar in contrast to those that we described earlier.

157

(d) *Chloroplasts in algae.* The algae are a particularly numerous and diverse group, and the diversity that they show in the gross structure of their chloroplasts is also reflected in their ultrastructure. Many green algae have agranar chloroplasts analogous to those of *Euglena,* which contain either heaps of giant saccules, often as many as a score (Characeae, many Conjugatophyceae), or else groups of from two to five saccules, like the flagellates studied by Gibbs (figure 7·6). The latter structure is the one found in *Fucus* (von Wettstein) and *Laminaria* (C. Berkaloff) and related seaweeds, and it could be interpreted in terms of 'giant grana', in which the lamellae were uniformly differentiated over their entire surface (figure 7·8).

In certain *Chlamydomonas* (Volvocales) and a few Conjugato-phyceae, at least when they are in a suitable physiological state (Drawert and Mix 1961), the groups of lamellae form into more or less well-defined granar zones (to a slight extent in *Cosmarium lundelli,* and more completely in *Micrasterias papillifera*) (Chardard and Rouiller 1957). In contrast, in the chloroplasts of Rhodophyceae in general, and in Chrysophyceae, the thylakoids are giant, and often follow the outline of the surface of the plastid, but they are isolated in the stroma, or form only irregular groups (figure 7·9).

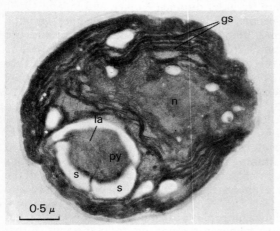

7·6 Thin section through a cell of *Chlorella,* showing the agranar plastid, which consists of giant saccules heaped up in from four to twenty groups (gs). py = pyrenoids surrounded by plaques on which starch (s) accumulates; n=nucleus; la=lamellae traversing the pyrenoid. (× 20,000).

In many species that are responsive to light the chloroplast – or one of these, if there are several – bears a stigma formed from one or more layers of spherical globules that are rich in a bright red carotenoid pigment. When there are several such layers these are generally separated by lamellae (*Chlamydomonas*: Sager and Palade 1957) (figure 7·7).

Finally, the chloroplasts of algae often contain pyrenoids with starch grains built round them. These appear under the electron microscope as areas of ground substance, moderately dense, and homogeneous: in Phaeophyceae they show little structure, but in Rhodophyceae and in green algae they are seen to be traversed by a number of lamellae, or with tubules that are connected to the lamellae. In the pyrenoids of *Chlorella*, for example, these lamellae would contain chlorophyll (Leyon 1953). The starch grains appear as clear areas, which are sometimes arranged geometrically round the pyrenoid (figure 7·6).

(e) *Chloroplasts in Bryophytes.* The chloroplasts of Bryophytes, for the most part, are more or less of a granar type (Manton 1957; Heitz 1958).

(f) *Chlorophyll-bearing structures in Protocaryotes.* Proto-caryotes have neither plastids nor mitochondria, yet those blue-

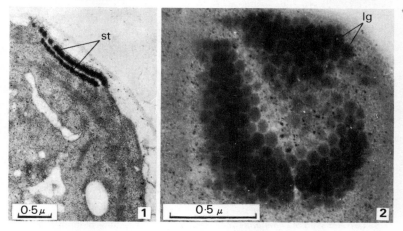

7·7 Thin section through the stigma of *Chlamydomonas*.
1 A section perpendicular to the surface of the stigma (st). (×17,000).
2 An approximately tangential section. It can be seen that the stigma consists of two layers of lipid globules (lg). (×45,000).

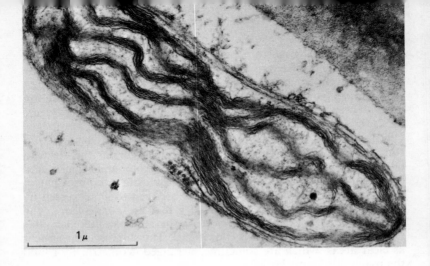

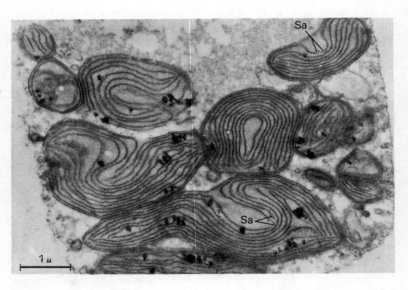

7·8 Top A plastid of *Laminaria saccharina*, containing systems of three very flattened saccules, which touch each other at places. (× 29,000).

7·9 Bottom Plastids of *Rhodomela* (Rhodophyceae) with isolated saccules, of which the extremities (sa) can be seen (× 18,500).

green algae and bacteria that are capable of photosynthesis possess chlorophyll. What structures do these organisms have to take the place of chloroplasts?

The first researches to be carried out with the aid of the electron microscope used techniques of fragmentation and centrifugation, and these made it possible to isolate the particles which carry the photosynthetic pigments (Calvin and Lynch 1952; Pardee and others 1952). The results were difficult to interpret, and our knowledge in this field did not progress far until techniques were devised for fixing the Protocaryotes, and thus made it possible to study them in detail in ultra-thin sections.

The ultrastructure proved to vary in different species, but in any event the pigments were always localised in some system of cytoplasmic membranes. In blue-green algae the chromatoplasma, that is, the coloured cytoplasm surrounding the central region of the nucleus, contains lamellae that are more or less sinuous, but lying roughly parallel to the surface of the cells (Niklowitz and Drews 1956–7 on *Phormidium*; Shinke and Ulda 1956, Fuhs 1958; Drawert and Metzner 1958, Lefort 1960 on *Oscillatoria*). According to Lefort these lamellae are built up from two dense layers, 30–40Å thick, separated by a clear space of about 100Å. Each of the dense layers is perhaps complex within itself, but the lamellae do not seem to be divided into granar and intergranar types.

Hence the Cyanophyceae, lacking chloroplasts, do have comparable pigments disposed in lamellar systems which lie directly in the cytoplasm. Recent studies in the cytology of bacteria raise the question of whether or not these lamellae in the Cyanophyceae have any communication with the cell membrane.

Photosynthetic bacteria, on the other hand, have been found to have several different kinds of structure, sometimes in the same genus. For example, *Rhodospirillum molischianum* has pigments on lamellar invaginations of the cell membrane (figure 7·10), and these lamellae are applied to each other, back to back, to form lamellar systems that are sometimes of great importance (Hickman and Frenkel 1965). These authors have also described *Rhodospirillum rubrum*, from which pigmented globular particles called chromatophores, can be extracted by fragmentation. These are invaginations of the cell membrane which are rounded in form, and not lamellar. At the end of one of these ectoplasmic depressions swellings appear, which become pinched off to form small groups of chromatophores (figure 7·11). These structures are not present in young cells. Cohen

Bazire and Kunisawa (1963) have shown, on the other hand, that in certain bacteria the abundance of these vesicles is in proportion to the chlorophyll content.

Biochemistry

1 *Analysis of isolated chloroplasts.* Long before general techniques had been devised for isolating cellular organelles, chloroplasts had been isolated from leaves by pounding them with sand in a mortar, followed by suitable filtration. Such a method made no claim to

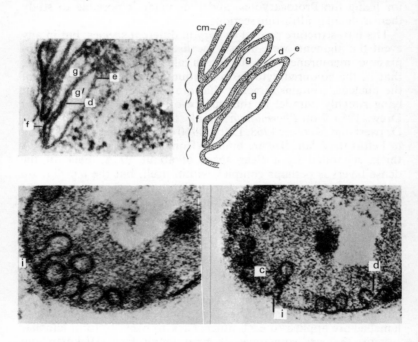

7·10 Top Electron micrograph and diagram of *Rhodospirillum molischianum*, a purple photosynthetic bacterium which has a cell membrane (cm) with peripheral lamellae (e). These lie back to back in pairs (d) and carry the pigment. f=invaginations of the cell membranes; g=internal spaces of invaginations. (×106,000).

7·11 Bottom *Rhodospirillum rubrum*, a species in which pigments are borne in vesicles, or chromatophores (c) which, like in the above, arise as invaginations (i) of the cell membrane; d=double invagination. (left ×83,000; right ×60,000).

162

give a chemical analysis of the chloroplasts, but it was observed that the results varied remarkably little whatever the details of separation technique. Nowadays extracts can be monitored under the electron microscope, and their purity guaranteed. The consensus of a great many tests is that the chloroplasts are specially rich in protein compounds and in phospholipids. For example, Comar (1942) found the following composition for chloroplasts from spinach leaves, expressed as per cent dry weight: proteins 54, lipoids 34, chlorophyll 5 and ash 7.

The chloroplasts also contain much smaller amounts of carotenoids (particularly carotin and xanthophyll), as well as RNA (Brachet 1959) and DNA (Ris and Plaut 1962). The protein and mineral ash fractions embody the constituents of numerous enzymes which participate either in the process of phosphorylation (absorbing energy from light and using it to power chemical reactions), or in 'obscure' reactions of photosynthesis, such as the ribulose cycle. Thus chloroplasts contain several electron carriers: nicotinamide-adenine-dinucleotide-phosphate (NADP), a flavoprotein, a cytochrome of group b, cytochrome f, an iron-protein compound (ferredoxine), oxydases, peroxydases (catalase) and hydrolases (phosphorylases, amylase, invertase, etc.).

The fats present in chloroplasts are predominantly phosphorylated lipids which may function either structurally (building up the lamellae) or metabolically, playing an important role in photosynthesis. Some are neutral fats such as the galactosyl-diglycerides, but many act either as acids alone, or – like the lecithins – as acids at one moment and alkalis at another. One of the most important of these lipids, quantitatively and physiologically, is phosphatidyl-glycerol (figure 7·12), which is found along with lecithins, phosphatidyl-ethanolamine, phosphatidyl-inositol and others.

Chloroplasts, like mitochondria, also contain quinolic compounds, which probably play an important part in the transfer of electrons, and which are known under the general name of 'coenzyme Q'. These are benzoquinones, which differ from each other mainly in the number of isoprenoid residues that are borne by the carbon atom 6 (from 6–10, hence the names co-enzymes $Q_6 \ldots Q_{10}$) (figure 7·12). Vitamins of group K, which are substituted quinones, are also found in chloroplasts.

The operation of the chloroplasts also demands a supply of inorganic phosphates, from which they produce ATP.

The chloroplasts are therefore extremely active and complex

7.12 Top Formula of phosphatidyl-glycerol. **Bottom** Formula of coenzyme Q.

organelles in photosynthetic cells. Apart from the origin of the energy, which in this case comes from light, the chloroplasts have much in common with mitochondria in that they involve oxidation-reduction systems, as well as phosphorylation, and work through chains of electron carriers.

2 *Location of chemical constituents.* One of the first questions that was asked when the ultrastructure of the chloroplasts was investigated was: where is the chlorophyll? Metzner (1937), Heitz and Maly (1953) showed that the chlorophyll is principally located in the grana, if these are present. Their observations demonstrated that at least the chlorophyll is associated with the lamellae of the plastid, and chemical analysis showed that these lamellae have a lipoprotein nature, like the other cytoplasmic membranes. The exact relationships between the lamellae and the chlorophyll

164

remain to be decided, but several pieces of work have been concerned, on the one hand, with the surface developed by the lamellae, in areas where they are linked together in pairs, and on the other hand, to estimate how many molecules of chlorophyll are contained within one chloroplast. Wolken and Schwertz (1953), working with agranar plastids from flagellates, and Thomas and his colleagues, studying both granar and agranar plastids, have arrived at about the same order of magnitude for the extent of the surface of granar lamellae (counting both surfaces where they lie together) on the one hand; and on the other for an estimate of how much area would be needed for the attachment of the tetrapyrrolic ends of the molecules of chlorophyll. The two together suggest that chlorophyll is disposed in a monomolecular layer over each of the lamellar surfaces that take part in this association ('partitions' of Weier *et al*).

Attempts were then made to work out molecular orders, taking into account the lipid and protein nature of the membranes, and the existence of a hydrophobic pole in the molecules of chlorophyll. There is a hydrocarbon chain 'phytol' ($C_{20} H_{39} OH$) (figure 7·13), which is able to combine via Van der Waals' bonds with the hydrophobic poles of phospholipids. The same applies to carotenoid molecules, which are equally hydrophobic.

To progress beyond this point requires the use of the electron microscope, in conjunction with techniques which would allow the molecules to be seen and recognised while they were still *in situ* on the lamellae. Several sets of experiments on these lines have been attempted, but so far nothing much has come out of them. The first experiment made use of negative staining on fragments of lamellae isolated from burst open plastids, or torn apart, and by this method obtained pictures of the surface-relief of the lamellae. Park and Pon (1963), studying the chloroplasts of spinach, discovered a large number of particles packed close together, which they called *quantasomes*, and suggested that the lamellae might essentially be no more than aggregations of these. A quantasome might measure 120Å by 60Å, and was itself built up from four smaller particles.

Analogous granules, but of sizes varying in different species, have been found on the plastids of algae (Giraud 1963), and it was thought for a time that these were the ultimate units of photosynthesis, analogous to electron-transporting particles isolated from mitochondria by Green and his colleagues (cf. p. 143). However, the correct interpretation of the molecular and physical structure, as well as the physiology, of quantasomes is still very

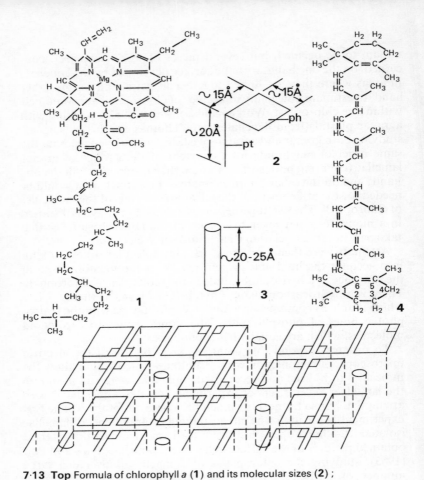

7·13 Top Formula of chlorophyll *a* (**1**) and its molecular sizes (**2**);
ph = porphyrin head; pt = phytol tail.
The molecular diagram (**3**) and formula (**4**) of carotene.
Bottom The assumed distribution of the pigments along the plastidial lamellae.

much in doubt. A different set of experiments, making use of freeze
etching, gives little support to the idea that quantasomes are photosynthetic units. The general idea of this technique is to freeze either
the whole cell, or organelles isolated from it, very rapidly, and then
to cut from the solid block a section that shows multiple breaks on
a microscopic scale. A replica of this surface is taken, using a plastic,
and this in turn is shadowed with vaporised metal at a known

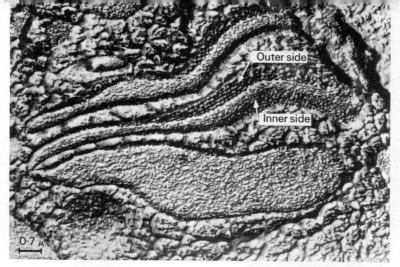

7·14 Lamellae of a chloroplast as seen under the electron microscope after freeze-drying. Note the difference in appearance between the inner surfaces with isolated granules, and the outer surfaces with their granules associated in small groups. (× 80,000).

oblique angle (cf. p. 68). It can then be studied under the electron microscope, and will show the ultrastructure of the surface.

When this method is applied to the breaks of chloroplasts it gives a surprising amount of information about the surfaces of the lamellae, and has the advantage of avoiding the denaturing effects of normal fixatives. Mühlethaler and his colleagues (1963) used this method to demonstrate the existence of globular particles with a diameter of about 60 Å, on the surface of the lamellae. The lamellae themselves formed one continuous membrane, probably lipoid in nature, 40 Å thick, and covered with tiny pits in which the granules were located. On the external surface of the lamella (the one facing the adjoining thylakoid) the particles were in groups of four, or in a mass that had a crystalline texture (figure 7·14). On the inner surface, on the other hand, particles of the same appearance and size lay in isolation, or irregularly scattered.

These particles look like globular proteins, and are about the right size. They could be either structural proteins in association with lipids, as in the other plasma membranes, or they could be enzymes taking part in photosynthesis; or, of course, they might be both at once (figure 7·15).

After freeze-etching, the lamellae seem to be thicker than those

167

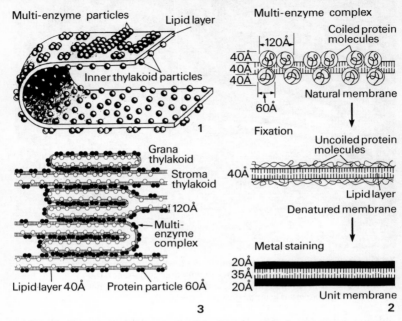

7·15 Diagrammatic interpretation of the ultrastructure of lamellae in chloroplasts, from the results obtained by freeze-drying.
1 Fragment of thylakoid bearing groups of particles on its outer face and isolated ones on its inner face.
2 Transverse section after freeze-drying (proteins in globular form) and after fixation (proteins assumed to be uncoiled).
3 Structure of the granular areas; black = external particles, white = internal particles.

measured in ultra-thin section, following fixation. The authors suggest that this may be because the process of fixation unrolls the globular proteins, and spreads them out on the surface of the lipid membrane, where they are necessarily thinner than they were as globules (figure 7·15).

The particles described by Mühlethaler and his colleagues are, therefore, smaller than the quantasomes of Park and Pon, and furthermore, they seem to be solely molecular proteins, and not photosynthetic units. Finally, pictures taken after freeze etching give no information about chlorophyll, or carotenoid pigments. So it is really quite difficult to know how to fit these various pictures together into a coherent plan of the molecular structure of the lamellae of plastids.

Leucoplasts

Location Chloroplasts are not produced in those parts of a plant that develop in the dark, and sometimes not in tissues exposed to the light: for example the epidermis of hyacinths, irises and *Ficus*. In these organs the plastids remain colourless, and they may or may not accumulate starch, according to the species of plant, and to the tissue concerned. Thus the parenchyma cells of roots, once they have become differentiated, contain such leucoplasts, which are called amyloplasts when they contain starch. In other root cells, such as those of many Chicoraceae (*Cichorium*, *Scorzonera*), where the glucide that forms a reserve is inulin, which accumulates in the vacuoles, the leucoplasts contain no recognisable paraplasmic structures.

In certain exceptional circumstances chlorophyll may be produced in the absence of light: examples occur inside the seeds of *Pinus* and *Citrus*, and in the phloem of various trees, where chlorophyll is formed even though the branch is covered with an opaque periderm.

Leucoplasts in living tissues Guilliermond (1933, cf. p. 143 *et seq.*) described at length the appearance of living leucoplasts in a variety of cells from the epidermis of leaves, of flowers, and of bulb scales. In particular he stressed their similarity to the mitochondria, in respect of their low refractive index, their mobility, and their changes of shape. Often they are filamentous organelles looking like chondriocontes, but perhaps a little bigger (figure 7·16), and they may undergo deformation by becoming undulating, or by emitting temporary processes, or by local and reversible dilatation.

Leucoplasts are quite as fragile as mitochondria and, like them, can undergo cavulation (cf. p. 137). This may happen even under the best physiological conditions, in Ringer solution, if examination under the microscope is too protracted. They can be stained, 'sublethally', by vital stains suitable for mitochondria, such as Janus Green, Dahlia Violet and Methyl Violet.

In many tissues with no chlorophyll, leucoplasts become noticeable when they build up starch grains, which often excessively swell the leucoplast (figure 7·20). Swelling of this degree may stretch out the ground substance of the plastid until it forms a thin skin round the starch grain, but the properties of the substance are not thereby modified, as are the properties of young plastids when they begin to secrete chlorophyll: nor does the fragility of the leucoplast change when treated with substances that affect mitochondria.

7·16 Studies of a living leucoplast showing successive deformations in the course of cytoplasmic movements.
1 From the epidermis of the bulb scales of *Allium cepa*.
2 From a bulb of *Asphodelus cerasifer*.

These facts have been confirmed by studying what happens when leucoplasts are fixed and stained, showing that they are physico-chemically similar to mitochondria. These were the reasons why Guilliermond was led to think that leucoplasts are a special category of mitochondria, genetically distinct, and peculiar to green plants. This view has been partially confirmed by study of their ultrastructure.

Ultrastructure The ultrastructure of leucoplasts has been studied systematically ever since the electron microscope came into general use in cytology (Caporali 1958–9), and many leucoplasts, with or without starch, have been noticed incidentally when ultra-thin sections were being studied. Their general appearance recalls that of mitochondria, but of much larger size, and bounded by a double membrane, as are the chloroplasts, too. The internal membrane extends into villi and cristae analogous to those of the mitochondria, though these are generally longer, and less numerous (figure 7·17). The stroma is finely fibrillar and granular.

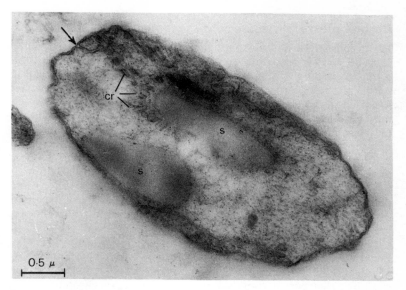

7·17 Ultrastructure of a starch-bearing leucoplast from the root of *Lens culinaris*, showing the two membranes and the cristae (cr) arising from the inner membrane. s=starch. (×22,500).

Leucoplasts are distinguished from mitochondria by their size, which is intermediate between that of mitochondria and that of chloroplasts. The stroma of leucoplasts also contains lipid granules that are rarely found in the mitochondria of higher plants.

Finally, when starch is accumulated it forms lumps within vacuoles of a type that is generated within the stroma, but has no boundary membrane (figure 7·17). The starch grains may grow very big, and distend the substance of the plastid until this is stretched into a thin skin, sometimes drawn out into a caudiform appendix. Either one starch grain or several may be produced inside the one leucoplast, depending on the species of plant and the tissue concerned; that is, the starch grain may be simple or composite.

Here and there in leucoplasts have been found accumulations of very fine granules which seem to be phytoferritine, a reserve protein containing iron (Caporali 1959; A. M. Catesson 1966). We shall be returning to the leucoplasts when we deal later with starch, and with the differentiation of plastids in general.

171

Chromoplasts

Plant cells often contain pigments other than chlorophyll, which may be yellow, red, blue or violet, and which fall into two categories according to their chemical nature and to their localisation within the cell. We have seen above (p. 121) that some of these are localised in the vacuoles: these are the phenolic heterosides, which may be blue, violet or purple-red (anthocyanin pigments) or they may be yellow (oxyflavone pigments). The remaining pigments, red or yellow, which are exclusively found in the plastids, either alone, or along with chlorophyll, are always carotenoids, either isomers or substitution derivatives of carotene, $C_{40}H_{56}$, a hydrocarbon with paired double bonds (formula p. 168, figure $7 \cdot 13_4$). Whether these pigments are present by themselves, or whether they mask the green of the chlorophyll by their abundance, the plastids in which they lie are called chromoplasts.

Location Chromoplasts may develop in a variety of plant cells, whether these grow in the light, or in darkness: it is known, for example, that carrot roots accumulate crystals of carotene in the plastids of parenchyma cells. However, it is in flowers and fruits of the higher plants that chromoplasts are most frequent. They form particularly in the mesophyll and epidermis of the perianth, in coloured bracts, and in the pericarp and mesocarp of fruits.

Appearance in living cells W. Schimper (1883) and A. Meyer (1883) pioneered the study of chromoplasts, which were extensively studied by Guilliermond (1919) in many living cells. The diversity of form of the plastids themselves was exaggerated by variations in the state in which the pigment existed.

The chromoplasts of *Lilium pomponium*, for example, are globular organelles, like the chloroplasts, and enclose coloured globules that are apparently fatty, with the carotenoid pigment dissolved in them. The same is true of epidermal cells from many flowers, but sometimes the globules are too small to be separately distinguishable under the light microscope, and the colour seems to be diffused through the chromoplast. This is so in chromoplasts from the petals of yellow tulips, containing xanthophyll, though in other respects these chromoplasts have a filamentous shape, like long chondriocontes (figure $7 \cdot 18_3$). In the epidermal cells of the flowers of *Iris germanica* these 'chondriocontes' swell locally, or they may build up

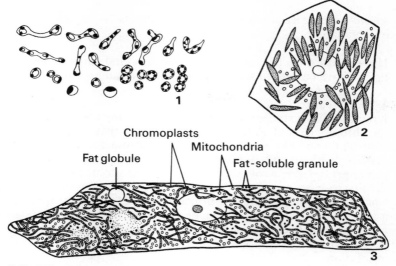

7·18 Different views of chromoplasts *in vivo*.
1 From the fruit of *Asparagus officinalis* (pigment dissolved in lipid droplets).
2 From the flower of *Amaryllis lutea*, with fusiform chromoplasts.
3 From a tulip flower (pigment diffused in the plastids in the form
of chondriocontes).

into great masses of apparently uniform colour. Analogous conditions can be found in various fruits, such as *Asparagus* seeds, where too, the pigment is dissolved in the fatty globules (figure 7·18₁).

In other species the pigment crystallises, forming needle crystals throughout the mass of the plastid as, for example, in the epicarp of the tomato or in crystalline plates more or less contorted in shape, as in carrot roots.

Finally certain cells from flowers (*Amaryllis*, figure 7·18₂), or from fruits (*Capsicum, Solanum capsicastrum*) contain chromoplasts in the shapes of spindles, crescents or changeable rhomboids, in which the pigment is fairly uniformly distributed. The condition in which carotenoid pigments are present in these plastids has been worked out only recently, with the help of the electron microscope (Frey Wyssling and Kreutzer).

Almost all differentiating chromoplasts pass through a period during which they accumulate starch grains, but by the time their differentiation is complete they contain hardly anything other than fatty droplets and carotenoid pigments. The chromoplasts of *Daucus carota* are one case where the starch persists to the end of cell differentiation.

Ultrastructure A few examples of the first and third categories listed above have been studied under the electron microscope.

1 *Chromoplasts with dissolved pigments.* Frey Wyssling and Kreutzer (1958) studied the development and the ultrastructure of the chromoplasts of *Ranunculus repens*. These may be globular or lenticular and, like other plastids, are surrounded by a double plasma membrane. The inner membrane extends into a few scattered prolongations, cristae or villi, projecting into a stroma that has a low density to electrons, and which is obviously weaker than it was when the cell was young. The principal contents of this stroma are a large number of osmiophilic globules, most of them compressed into a layer that lies almost continuously round the periphery of the plastid. These are the droplets which contain pigment (xanthophyll) in solution.

The chromoplasts of *Spartium junceum* (figure 7·19), studied by A. Lance-Nougarède (1964) have an analogous structure. This author has shown that the chromoplasts of *Chrysanthemum segetum* degenerate considerably at the end of their differentiation; cristae and villi disappear, and then the stroma itself becomes thinned down to the point where nothing is left but strings of fatty globules surrounded by the remnants of the plastid, reduced to its outer skin, which fits round them.

2 *Chromoplasts with pigment on lipoprotein fibrillae.* Chromoplasts with their pigment fixed on to bundles of fibrillae in the form of hollow rods have been described in the fruits of *Capsicum annuum* by Frey Wyssling and Kreutzer, and in the pericarp of the fruits of *Solanum capsicastrum* by Steffen and Walter (1958). The axis of these elements, after fixation with osmium tetroxide, is actually less dense to electrons than is the thin wall of the hollow rod itself. Frey Wyssling and Kreutzer state that the carotenoid pigment is held in this way in the cortex of the fibrillae.

7·19 1 Ultrastructure of chromoplasts of *Spartium junceum* where the xanthophyll is dissolved in lipid globules (l). cr = remains of cristae. Note the impoverished stroma. (× 32,000).
2 Chromoplast from *Capsicum annuum*, where the pigment is fixed in fibrillar lipoproteins (fl). (× 24,000).

174

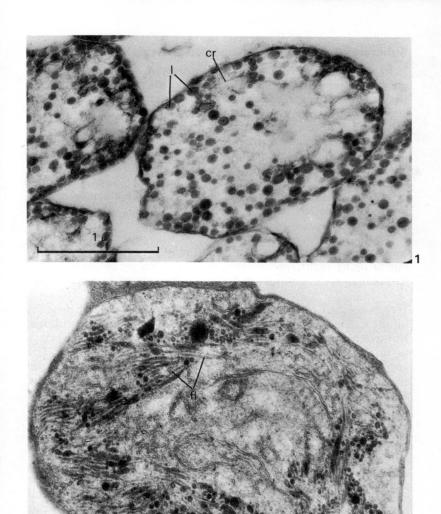

Substances synthesised inside the plastids

In most chromoplasts the process by which the carotenoid pigments grow, while simultaneously the parent substance of the plastid shrinks, can be regarded as a process of paraplasmic construction, coupled with an irreversible degeneration of the plastid. But plastids can also make temporary, and reversible, accumulations of paraplasmic substances as reserves. The reserve substances most often involved are starch, fats and proteins, and these are to be found in all three categories of plastids so far discussed: chloroplasts, leucoplasts and chromoplasts may become amyloplasts, oleoplasts or proteoplasts. Obviously these last three are mere names, and do not have the definitive quality of the terms chloroplast, leucoplast and chromoplast.

Amyloplasts In principle, any plastid may become an amyloplast, but in many plant species there are some tissues or plastids that habitually produce starch, and others where starch is never found.

1 *Occurrence in chloroplasts.* The ability to synthesise starch depends on the species, the organ concerned, and upon external conditions. For example, the leaves of the wheat plant, even during long days in bright sunshine, never form starch in their chloroplasts. The surplus sugars from photosynthesis accumulate in the vacuoles in the form of sucrose. On the other hand the ripening grain of the wheat makes a lot of starch, and so do certain tissues in the stems.

In contrast, chloroplasts in beetroot leaves build up grains of starch in the daylight, and these are hydrolysed during the night. The soluble sugars produced then flow into the tuberous root, or into the inflorescences.

2 *Occurrence in leucoplasts.* These so often produce starch that it is sometimes assumed – erroneously – that the terms leucoplast and amyloplast are synonymous. There are species of plant, however, where starch is not accumulated as a reserve: beetroot, again, receives its reserve material as sucrose, from the chloroplasts (see above) and stores it in vacuoles, and the leucoplasts do not produce starch. The same is true of the leucoplasts in the tuberous roots of various Compositae such as *Dahlia*, Chicory or *Scorzonera* in which the reserve sugar is inulin, and this, too, is stored in vacuoles, where it forms a colloidal solution.

3 *Occurrence in chromoplasts.* In chromoplasts many large starch grains appear during the process of differentiation, but these usually disappear when differentiation is complete (Guilliermond 1919, 1933). The chromoplasts of the carrot are exceptional in conserving their starch, but without the usual consequences of a progressive degeneration of the cell.

How starch is produced The classical studies of Guilliermond (1912–20) and of Emberger (1927) showed the various ways in which starch could be produced, especially in leucoplasts and chromoplasts. The first thing to appear, in the interior of the plastid, is a tiny clear vesicle, which soon gives the iodine reaction for starch. A minute particle can be detected which is the hilum of the future starch grain (figure 7·20). The starch is laid down round this hilum in successive layers, and this makes the vesicle progressively bigger, and locally distends the substance of the plastid.

In elongate leucoplasts the starch-forming vesicle can be either in the middle or towards one end. If a plastid has only one vesicle this produces a simple starch grain, but in many species of plant several vesicles appear within the same plastid, and these produce a compound starch grain, each component of which is separated from the others merely by a thin pellicle of the ground substance of

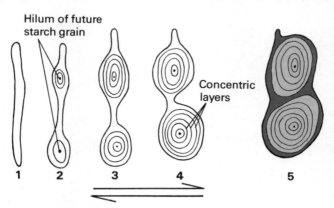

Hilum of future starch grain

Concentric layers

1   2   3   4   5

7·20 Starch formation in leucoplasts. **1** A young leucoplast in the form of a chondrioconte. **2** Beginning of the formation of two starch grains in small 'vacuoles', which arise within the plastid. **3–5** Successive stages of growth of the grains by accretion of more or less concentric layers. In certain circumstances leucoplasts may release their starch and revert to simple leucoplasts.

the plastid. In lily bulbs, or potato tubers, most of the leucoplasts contain simple starch grains, although these can grow very big. On the other hand, leucoplasts in the roots of peas, beans, the castor oil plant, and Cucurbitaceae, etc, normally contain compound grains. Finally, it is possible for a leucoplast to start with several vesicles, which then undergo a kind of fusion, resulting in a single grain with several hila. This grain is 'semi-compound'.

The build-up of starch grains may cause considerable stretching of the ground substance of the plastid, over all, or part of its surface. Sometimes it comes to resemble a hollow sphere thickened at one pole, and starch production goes on more actively on this side, resulting in grains with an eccentric hilum (as in potato). On the other hand, if the build-up of starch is uniform (as in wheat, maize, beans) the successive layers are laid down concentrically. As a general rule, the structure of the starch grains, in a particular tissue, is characteristic of the plant species (figure 7·21). This may exercise a control over the foodstuffs that the starch grain helps to produce.

Reversibility of synthetic processes within the plastid So long as organs or cells remain in active life, or when they return to active life

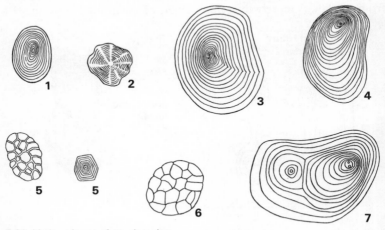

7·21 Various forms of starch grains.
1 Simple grain with concentric hilum (wheat). **2** A similar form from maize.
3 Simple grain from haricot bean. **4** A simple grain, but one with an eccentric hilum, from potato. **5** Composite grain from rice, with one of its components. **6** Composite grain from oats. **7** Semi-composite grain from potato.

after a period of quiescence, the plastids remain alive – even if considerably distorted – around the grains that they have built up. If the starch is utilised, then the plastid reverts to its original condition as a leucoplast or a chloroplast. Hydrolysis of starch into soluble sugars goes on continuously in the leucoplasts of various roots, sometimes even while others are elaborating. Hydrolysis takes place in chloroplasts at night, or after a revival of activity, as in many seeds, or in reserve tissues. Hence the amyloplasts of potato tubers are regenerated as leucoplasts, or sometimes as chloroplasts, after the tubers have sprouted.

So it seems that the constructional function of starch-forming plastids can definitely be reversed (Emberger 1927). When, however, a tissue normally degenerates after an organ has become mature, then its plastids wear out, and disappear, releasing their starch grains into the cytoplasm. This is particularly true of the albumens of seeds, which do not continue actively after the seed has germinated, but instead they are dissolved away.

According to Maige (1927), when the starch grains are hydrolysed inside the ground substance of the plastid, they retain their external shape as they dwindle, as if they were being dissolved. On the other hand, once the plastid substance has gone, the starch grains begin to be eroded away unevenly, with more or less convoluted tunnelling (bean seeds; the caryopsis of wheat).

In Euphorbiaceae the plastids in the latex-forming cells go on building up starch grains, sometimes over long periods, until they become so big that they split the plastid. When this happens the material of the plastid gathers into either one or several masses, and it is only here that starch production continues. In this way the starch forms grains that may be elongate, or swollen at their extremities, resembling long bones (including their apophyses), or the spicules of certain marine animals (Mangenot 1924, 1930). Eventually the plastid material and the starch grain are subsequently passed into the vacuole, where they are merged into the latex. This process is unique to Euphorbiaceae.

Physico-chemical constitution of starch Starch grains usually show growth lines round their central hilum. These lines represent variations in the state of hydration of the successive layers, since they are destroyed both by dehydrants such as alcohol, and by hydrating agents such as caustic potash. Other physico-chemical properties of starch grains are summarised below:

1 *Action of warm water.* When starch grains are immersed in water at about 70°C they swell, and produce a viscous liquid, starch-paste, which is a mixture of two phases. One phase is produced by the swelling of amylopectin, a colloid from the concentric layers of the grain, which forms a viscous medium; the other, more fluid phase, is produced from amylose, another colloid, but one that is more fully dispersed in water. Thus the action of warm water reveals that the macromolecules of the starch grain are heterogeneous.

2 *Biochemistry.* Acid hydrolysis of starch shows it to be composed of α glucose, together with phosphates of potassium and calcium. It has a high molecular weight, between 40,000 and 150,000 and so by inference must have from 200 to 900 molecules of glucose combined.

Enzymatic hydrolysis is carried out by a complex of enzymes, from which several specific hydrolases have been isolated. Thus there is an α-amylase which converts amylopectin into dextrins. Amylopectin is built up from branching chains of glucose, and α-amylase breaks off these branches, to produce smaller, non-branching fragments, which are the dextrins.

These fragments, as well as the non-branching molecules of amylose, are attacked by β-amylase, which converts them into maltose, which in turn is broken down to glucose by a maltase.

3 *Action of iodine in aqueous solution.* A solution of iodine in potassium iodide stains starch an intense blue, the colour disappearing when the solution is heated, and reappearing when it cools again. This is brought about by adsorption of the iodine molecules on to the molecules of the colloid, provided that thermal agitation is not too great. This aggregation does not take place in an alcoholic medium, where the starch is coloured yellow or brown.

4 *Ultrastructure.* Even in natural light it can often be seen that starch grains are anisotropic, and under polarised light this becomes clear. The starch grains then exhibit the 'black-cross phenomenon', which indicates a sphero-crystalline texture, but x-ray analysis proves that the molecular arrangement in the starch grain has not the regularity of a crystal. The black cross under polarised light is produced by the predominantly radial orientation of only a part of the molecules, in the interior of each growth-layer (figure 7·22).

The electron microscope confirms this irregularity. In ultra-thin sections the starch grains appear either transparent, or else amorphous. On the other hand, if a methacrylate impression is taken from a broken surface of the grain, and examined by oblique shadowing (see p. 68) this throws into relief a series of microfibrillae of about 200Å diameter, and of indefinite lengths, from 200 to 3,000Å, orientated more or less radially inside each layer. These fibrillae are often grouped together into bundles with a twisted appearance, and are immersed in a ground substance of amorphous starch. This explains why these fibrillae were not seen in the thin sections of *Zea mays* and *Triticum vulgare* (Sterling and Spit 1958).

Proteoplasts As long ago as 1880, W. Schimper described rhomboidal or needle-shaped inclusions both in chloroplasts and in leucoplasts (figure 7·23), which by their low refractive index, shapes and reaction to stains led him to consider them to be 'crystalloids' of a protein nature. They may sometimes be found in the same plant, in the leucoplasts of the roots and in the chloroplasts of tissues exposed to light, and they are particularly noticeable in chloroplasts, where they form a long colourless needle, penetrating right

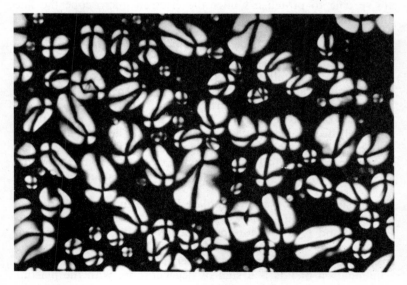

7·22 Black cross phenomenon, produced by starch grains from potato when they are viewed by polarised light with polariser and analyser 'crossed'.

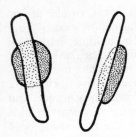

7·23 Left Proteochloroplasts in young leaves of *Phajus grandifolius* observed *in vivo*.

7·24 Right Proteoleucoplasts of *Phajus wallichii*. A thin section, fixed in OsO_4, is observed under the electron microscope, most of the section being taken up by a bundle of a microfibrillar protein. (× 90,000).

through the green plastid, and sticking out at both ends (figure 7·23). In the embryonic sac of *Lilium candidum* the leucoplasts also accumulate proteins (Guilliermond, cf. 1933, p. 84). A similar accumulation in the chloroplasts of the leaves can be stimulated by keeping the plant without food in nitrogen, and later giving it an excess of nitrates (Ulrich 1924).

When the plastid is fixed and stained, the inclusions often take up much the same tint as the ground substance of the plastid, and so are indistinct, but they can be detected by certain reactions that are specific to proteins. Under the electron microscope the fine fibrous texture of the inclusions makes them easily distinguishable from the plastid in general (Buvat 1959, figure 7·24). In the leucoplasts of the orchid *Phajus wallichii* they form bundles of granular fibrillae, with the grains disposed in transverse planes, which gives the bundle a crystalline structure. The leucoplasts also contain starch grains, and minute vesicles which constitute a primary granule, or centroplast (see p. 189).

Plastids of all types may accumulate proteins, and proteoplasts are widely distributed among the higher plants. They are particularly frequent in certain families: Orchidaceae, Borraginaceae, etc, where they may be found in the parenchyma of the roots, in the young leaves (*Phajus*), in embryonic sacs of *Lilium*, etc (Schimper 1885).

Oleoplasts Plastids may accumulate lipids, either temporarily (as in various cells from the flower buds of *Iris germanica*, according to Guilliermond 1913) or more permanently (as in chloroplasts from various cacti, according to J. Manuel 1936). In other cases (the epidermis of the anthers, and the sepal-hairs of *Iris* flowers) the accumulation of fats is a sign of degeneration, with the plastids evolving into chromoplasts. At least part of the fats concerned are either phospholipids (Guilliermond) or steroids (J. Manuel).

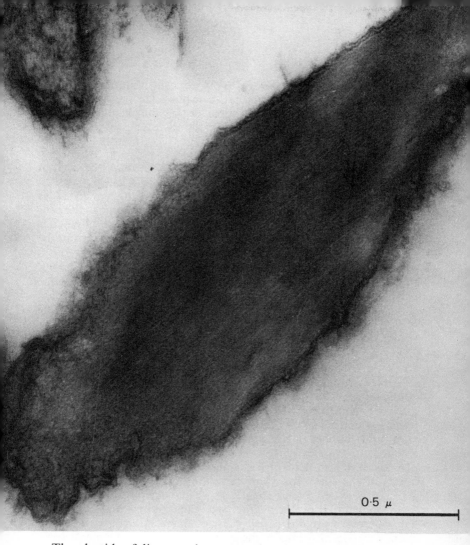

0·5 μ

The plastids of diatoms also accumulate fats, because the surplus products from photosynthesis in diatoms are lipids.

Finally it should be pointed out that a number of authors have erroneously given the name oleoplasts (or elaioplasts, or lipido-plasts) to inert fat-stores in the cytoplasm, which are merely ergastic accumulations, bearing no relation to the plastids.

Origin and differentiation of plastids

The descriptions given above apply to cells that have already reached their mature state, so that their plastids have finished their development. It remains now to consider how the plastids originate, and by what means they develop into different types.

Development in algae

(a) *Algae with neither meristematic nor differentiated tissues.* In *Chlamydomonas, Spirogyra*, and generally among algae in which all the cells are identical, the chloroplasts are quite distinct at all stages of the development cycle. They divide at the same time as the cells divide, and clearly demonstrate their genetic continuity. When a cell is fertilised, the plastids of the male gamete degenerate, and the continuity of the plastids is ensured by those of the female gamete.

(b) *Algae that have meristematic cells, and hence possess tissues.* In algae where genuine tissues are present (certain Rhodophyceae and Pheophyceae; Charophytes) the meristematic cells contain very small, lightly pigmented plastids, a little more bulky than the mitochondria, which they roughly resemble. In the course of differentiation of the cell, these plastids grow and develop more or less, according to the tissue concerned, but are always clearly distinguishable from the mitochondria (Mangenot 1922).

The daughter plastids in Pheophyceae are clearly distinguishable at all stages of the cycle, even in the oogonia, where they are very little different from the mitochondria. In the antherozoids the plastids change into chromoplasts (Mangenot, *ibid.*).

In those families of Rhodophyceae that are most strongly differentiated histologically (Nemalionaceae, Ceramiaceae, etc), the plastids may lose their pigment and regress completely at certain points of the cycle, for example in the oospheres and the trichogynes of *Lemanea* (Nemalionaceae), as well as in the gominoblastic filaments emitted by the zygote. It is thus very difficult under the light microscope to distinguish these de-differentiated plastids from chondriosomes. Eventually the terminal cells of the filaments form rhodoplasts anew, starting from filamentous organelles that look just the same as ordinary chondriocontes. During the development of the thallus, the cells of the filaments that have become rhizoids de-differentiate their plastids in the same way (Mangenot 1922).

Mangenot has shown that the same thing happens in *Charophytes*, where the chloroplasts regress completely after maturation of the

184

oogonia, until the time when amyloplasts appear (in the zygote) starting from filaments analogous to chondriocontes.

By extrapolating from the last two cases, and comparing this with what happens in Pheophyceae, it would seem that de-differentiated plastids are the only organelles that can recover their plastid characteristics after an interval. This means that the plastids have a genetic continuity of their own, independent of that of the mitochondria, in spite of their resemblance in the undifferentiated state.

Evolution in Bryophytes and Pteridophytes Cases similar to those in the algae can be found among Bryophytes and Pteridophytes, where those forms that are believed to be the most primitive demonstrate the genetic continuity and genetic independence of the plastids. Thus there are Bryophytes in which the chloroplasts regress completely after the formation of archegonia, and of the mother cells of the antherozoids, but not in the apical meristematic cells. On the other hand, in the primitive genus *Anthoceros*, where each cell has only one single chloroplast, this latter is distinguishable morphologically from the mitochondria at all stages of development of the cell.

Among Pteridophytes, the work of Emberger (1921) has shown that it is practically impossible to distinguish the plastids from the mitochondria in the definitive mother cells of the tetraspores, in the gametes, and in the zygotes of various Filicales. In these cells, which are derived from green cells of the epidermis of the sporophyte, or from the prothallial layer, the chloroplasts become divided, lose their pigments and their starch, until they take on the appearance of mitochondria. They resume their distinctive appearance in cells derived from the germination of the tetraspores (prothallial cells), or in cells which arise from segmentation of the zygote.

On the other hand, in other Pteridophytes such as *Selaginella*, which seem to come from a very ancient line, there may be one, two or a small number of plastids per cell, and in these cells the plastids are distinguishable from the mitochondria throughout the cycle.

These comparisons show that whenever the plastids of a cell can be distinguished morphologically from the mitochondria, the plastids are found to be genetically continuous, and independent of mitochondrial succession. This tempts one to assume that even when de-differentiation has made them temporarily indistinguishable (at least under the light microscope), the same will hold true.

Development in Phanerogams We should expect this to be even more true in plants where histological specialisation has gone further, and this is so in phanerogams. In the meristems of these plants, the cells that are destined to form the organs of the plant often have plastids that look just like mitochondria. Because of the shortening of the gametophyte it happens that the tetraspores, the sexual cells and the zygotes arise almost directly in contact with the meristems, and their plastids too, are no longer differentiated. At least, if they are, the power of the light microscope is inadequate to reveal this. So it would seem that the same rule of genetic continuity and genetic independence applies to the Phanerogams as to the Pteridophytes.

This view seems to be confirmed by recent electron microscope studies, which enable us to see the ultrastructure of 'proplastids' (the rudimentary plastids of the meristematic cells) and in almost every case they can be distinguished from mitochondria.

Ultrastructure of 'proplastids' The proplastid condition, that is, the most undifferentiated state that is possible in plastids, is to be found in primary meristems at the maximum of their active proliferation, either in the meristems of the roots or in the growing points of the stems. In very thin section the profile of the proplastids (figure 7·25) is very similar to the profile of a mitochondrion. Like mitochondria, plastids are bounded by a double plasma membrane, of which the inner member sends out folds or finger-like processes towards the interior of the organelle. The cristae and villi are, however, usually less abundant in plastids than they are in mitochondria, and this fact, coupled with the slightly larger size, makes the stroma of the plastid seem more homogeneous. The density of the stroma to an electron beam depends on how it has been fixed: after osmium fixation it seems about the same density as the mitochondria, but fixation in glutaraldehyde usually makes the stroma more dense, as it is also in differentiated plastids.

Mitochondria generally lack lipid granules, whereas proplastids acquire them at a very early stage. Apart from this one qualitative difference, nearly all the other differences between proplastids and mitochondria are quantitative: greater size; fewer cristae and villi. The same was true of the respective reactions of plastids and mito-chondria to fixatives and stains, as pointed out time and again by Guilliermond and his pupils, and which led them to suggest that plastids might be only a variety of mitochondrion. However, these differences, quantitative though they are, are traceable right

186

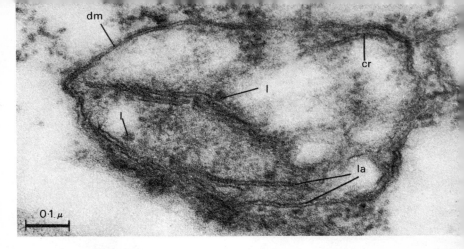

7·25 Proplastid of *Elodea canadensis* fixed in OsO$_4$ and still completely undifferentiated. l = lipid globules ; dm = double membrane forming an envelope ; cr=crista ; la=plastidial lamellae. (×115,000).

back to the most meristematic condition, and they substantiate the idea that plastids and mitochondria are genetically independent, developing on parallel lines.

The question arises, as it did for the mitochondria: does every proplastid arise inevitably from the division of a pre-existing proplastid? Up to now electron microscopy has not settled this problem. We can be certain that, once plastids have started to differentiate, they have proved to be genetically continuous, like the algae themselves in which we can trace the plastids through all stages of development. It is less sure, however, that in their most undifferentiated state plastids cannot be built up from components present in the protoplasm, under the direction of genetic information issuing either from the nucleus or from the DNA of the existing plastids. This problem still requires detailed study.

Differentiation of chloroplasts

1 *Information under the light microscope.* Most of the cells that are produced by the apical meristems of growing shoots become green with chlorophyll, and from 1922 onwards Guilliermond traced out this differentiation in the buds of *Elodea canadensis* (figure 7·26). This species generally has filamentous elements analogous to chondrio-contes, which develop into chloroplasts. As they develop chloro-phyll they thicken, swell in one or more places, and split up by

187

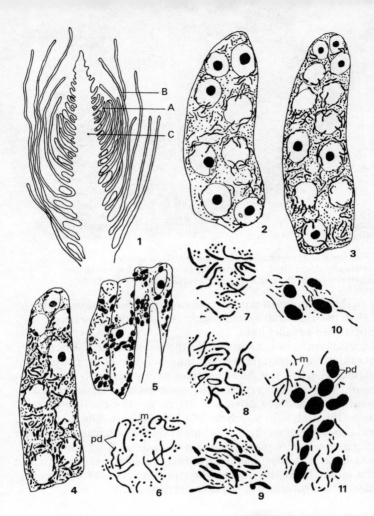

7·26 Differentiation of chloroplasts in a bud of *Elodea canadensis*.
1 A bud in longitudinal section at low magnification. A = outline of leaf just beginning to turn green ; B = outline containing differentiated chloroplasts ; C = part of stem where plastids are beginning to turn green.
2–4 Three stages in differentiation of chloroplasts from proplastids analogous to chondriocontes. **5** Cell of a differentiated leaf.
6–11 Successive views of mitochondria and plastids in the course of the differentiation of the leaf cells (**6–9**) and in well-formed leaves (**10–11**).
m = mitochondria ; pd = plastids.

188

pinching off in many places, at the same time as the cells are dividing. They may accumulate starch grains, either briefly or over a period. In young leaves these chloroplasts acquire the lenticular shape of differentiated chloroplasts, though they may go on dividing after cell division is over.

2 *The 'primary granum'*. The development has been followed through in a variety of species, and in *Elodea* under the electron microscope, and two conflicting situations have been discovered.

In certain cases (*Agapanthus, Chlorophytum, Helianthus,* and sometimes *Elodea*) the very young proplastids have an inclusion, visible in the living cell as a globule of low refractive index. This globule was described by Strugger (1953–4) under the name primary granum, and by Dangeard (1958) and Eymé (1958) as the centroplast. In fact, this corpuscle is not present in every proplastid and Heitz and Maly (1953) showed that when it exists it makes its appearance when the proplastid first begins to differentiate.

Under the electron microscope the primary granum may appear lamellate, built up from discs analogous to those which make up the grana (Strugger and Perner 1956; Strugger 1957). Alternately, the primary granum may arise from the aggregation of a large number of small, colourless vesicles, 100–200Å diameter, with outlines resembling those of plastidal lamellae (Hodge and colleagues 1956 on maize; Perner 1957 on *Chlorophytum comosum*, etc). Sometimes this assembly has a geometrical regularity, and so produces an apparently crystalline structure (Heitz 1954 on *Chlorophytum*; Leyon 1954 on *Aspidistra*, figure 7·27).

During development of the chloroplasts the primary granum participates in the formation of the thylakoids, the vesicles of which it is composed either growing, or fusing together.

Later on it was discovered that large primary grana could be produced by keeping young germinating tissues of maize (Hodge and colleagues 1956) or of barley (von Wettstein 1958) in the dark. The accumulated vesicles (the 'prolamellar body' of Hodge and colleagues) turn into lamellae when the plant is returned to the light (figure 7·27).

In *Elodea*, Mühlethaler and Frey Wyssling (1959) showed that the differentiation of the chloroplasts may go through the primary granum stage if the light is weak, or may omit this if the plant is adequately illuminated. Researches of this kind have led to an agreement between those who believe that a primary granum

189

is an essential component of the chloroplast, and those who do not.

3 *Direct differentiation.* If the illumination is sufficient, the proplastids of *Elodea* differentiate by the direct formation of long lamellae which, at least at first, come from the folds of the internal membrane of the plastid such as the mitochondrial cristae (figure 7·28). These lamellae press more or less against each other, and thus form the first granar surfaces. The multiplication of the lamellae takes place more and more at the expense of the stroma of the

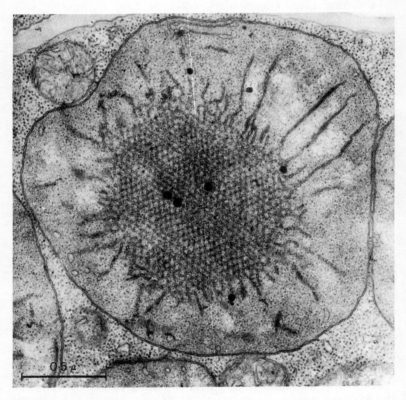

7·27 Prolamellar body (primary granum) in a plastid of *Phaseolus vulgaris,* blanched by a period of darkness and then placed in the light again. The vesicles have a pseudocrystalline arrangement. When light is restored the peripheral vesicles coalesce and form plastidial lamellae. (× 44,500).

plastid, which is reduced to a few ribs left in the spaces between the grana, and to a little on the periphery; and this despite the fact that the plastid as a whole is growing considerably. The lipid droplets in the stroma also become more numerous. When starch is formed it makes its appearance in a vacuole, a sort of decanter for the stroma.

It has still not been worked out exactly how the plastid lamellae grow. The coalescence of vesicles formed in the stroma does not seem to be enough, since vesicles are not normally abundant in

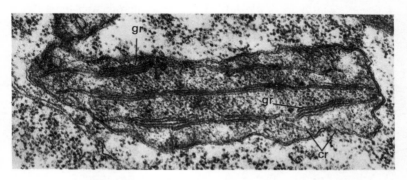

7·28 Young chloroplast of *Elodea* in the course of differentiation, fixed in OsO$_4$. cr=cristae forming lamellae; gr=beginning of grana formation. (×59,000).

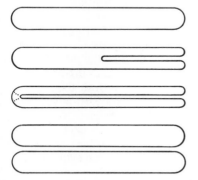

7·29 Diagram of one method of multiplication of the thylakoids by marginal folding of a saccule.

young plastids in the course of differentiation. Growth has been attributed to intussusception.

The multiplication of the thylakoids also raises similar questions. Menke (1960) has described how these may be duplicated by means of flattened cristae, which arise at the edges of the discs, and split them into thinner ones (figure 7·29). It is clear that there is still a great deal to be learned about growth processes in living membranes in general.

4 *Genetic continuity of plastids.* The foregoing indicates the genetic continuity of plastids, which arise by division of a predecessor. The presence of DNA in plastids also suggests genetic continuity and the relative autonomy of chloroplasts (flagellates by Scott *et al.* 1968; Green Algae by Ris and Plaut 1962; Brown and Red Algae by Bouck 1965; Bisalputra and Bisalputra 1967; higher plants by Kislev *et al.* 1964).

Chloroplast DNA looks the same as that of mitochondria, appearing as loosely tangled filaments of 15–25Å diameter, lying in one or several 'clear' spaces in the stroma which are not bounded by a membrane. This DNA can replicate inside the plastid, which has a DNA polymerase (Scott *et al.* 1968). The density of the molecules is slightly lower than that of nuclear DNA in the same cells (1,686 g.cm^{-3} for *Euglena*, 1,707 for the nucleus). The plastid DNA has a different base complement from nuclear DNA, the difference varying with the plant systematic group (Bisapultra and Bisapultra 1967).

As in mitochondria, it is not known exactly what this DNA does or how much autonomy it confers on the plastids. Chloroplast RNA is at least partially carried by particles analogous to ribosomes (Kislev *et al.* 1965) and it is probably synthesised by the plastid DNA. In anucleate fragments of Acetabularia, RNA synthesis in the chloroplasts can continue for weeks without assistance from the nucleus (Brachet 1961). But although an ability to replicate DNA gives plastids some autonomy, their differentiation is controlled by nuclear genes. This applies to chlorophyll *a* synthesis, which is essential in grana formation (von Wettstein 1958). Further, it has been suggested (Bell and Mühlthaler 1964) that protoplastids can arise from nuclear protrusions, thus conveying genetic matter from nucleus to plastid.

Just as the presence of mitochondrial DNA has given rise to speculation as to whether mitochondria might be compared with bacteria, so do the chloroplasts with their 'nucleoplasm' remind us of Blue-Green Algae. The latter also have a nucleoplasmic space in which filaments of DNA, like those in plastids, are immersed in a 'chromatoplasm', which contains chlorophyll pigments on lamellae. The idea that chloroplasts might be obligatory, symbiotic Blue-Green Algae living in the cell arises from the possible phylogenetic relationships between Protocaryotes and the earliest Green Algae (Ris and Plaut 1962).

Differentiation of leucoplasts The development of proplastids into leucoplasts, in underground tissues, as well as in various reserve tissues, is much simpler than that of chloroplasts. Under the light microscope there is little to be seen beyond a growth in volume, which is particularly noticeable if the plastid forms starch.

Under the electron microscope it can be seen that the increase of volume simultaneously involves the stroma and the starch-forming vesicles, if the latter exist. The cristae and villi of the proplastid develop at only a moderate rate. In certain leucoplasts, which make starch only slowly, either the cristae or the villi may swell, and break up into tiny vesicles, which disperse through the stroma.

All these membranous structures are pressed against the periphery of the starch grain as it grows, and so form a sort of collar, more or less regular in shape (Caporali 1958–9).

Leucoplasts, like other plastids, accumulate lipid globules, and sometimes other reserve products such as proteins, and iron compounds (ferritine).

So far the electron microscope has not shown how these leucoamyloplasts operate in the reverse sense.

Differentiation of chromoplasts Chromoplasts very rarely arise directly from the meristematic proplastids, but nearly always by secondary differentiation from either chloroplasts or leucoplasts. In flowers and fruit the chromoplasts regularly arise from leucoplasts in the epidermal cells, and from chloroplasts in the internal tissues, such as the mesophyll, and the mesocarp. Moreover, as is common knowledge, flower buds and young ('green') fruits already possess chlorophyll before they develop their mature colouring.

1 *Differentiation of chromoplasts from leucoplasts.* In the epidermal cells of buttercup petals (*Ranunculus repens*) Frey Wyssling and Kreutzer (1958) were able to trace the development of ordinary leucoplasts into chromoplasts in which the yellow pigment (xanthophyll) was dissolved in lipid droplets. This is a relatively simple

operation: the plastid enlarges, and progressively increases its stock of lipid droplets, which collect mainly in the peripheral zone. The cristae and villi diminish, and the material of the stroma is considerably reduced. The same sequence applied to cells from the petals of *Spartium junceum*, studied by A. Nougarède.

2 *Differentiation of chromoplasts from chloroplasts.* Frey Wyssling and Kreutzer (1958) made a similar study of the development of chromoplasts from the chloroplasts in the mesophyll of the petals of *Ranunculus,* in the course of which they noted how the lamellae disintegrated and disappeared. There was a simultaneous appearance of a great many lipid globules, which promptly filled with xanthophyll. The authors accounted for this by postulating a lipophanerose, which was produced by the breakdown of the lipidoproteins from the lamellae, and which in its turn gave rise to at least part of the contents of the lipid globules.

In fruits of *Capsicum annuum* the same authors traced the destruction of the lamellae of the chloroplasts, and then – after a period during which the plastid seemed to be in a very unstable state – the formation of filaments in which a denser cortex surrounded a clear axis. It seemed as if the substances produced by the disintegration of the lamellae were utilised to build up these fibrillae, and that the carotenoid pigment was attached to them in chemical combination. The resulting structure is in fact resistant to fat solvents and to lipase. The fibrillae are bound together in a few, loose bundles.

Steffen and Walter (1958) traced a morphologically similar process in *Solanum capsicastrum,* but they interpret it differently. They think that the destruction of the lamellae of the chloroplast produces lipid droplets, and that these form the pigmented fibrillae by becoming converted into lipoproteins, and elongating in the process. There are other examples in which the accumulation of carotenoid pigments dissolved in lipid droplets goes on while the chlorophyll-lamellae still remain in existence, resulting in a chromo-chloroplast. Gerola and his colleagues described such an occurrence in *Selaginella helvetica.*

De-differentiation of plastids We have already seen that in the Pteridophytes, as well as in the most advanced algae, those cells that give rise to the tetraspores or to the gametes contain chloroplasts that regress, and eventually revert to an undifferentiated state close to that of mitochondria. Although it is less easy to demonstrate,

194

this also happens in Phanerogams, for example when new meristems begin to form at the leaf axil, at such a slow rate that the early cells have already formed chloroplasts. A similar effect can easily be produced experimentally: thus, in many cases of propagation by stems or leaves from cuttings, it is cells with chloroplasts that give rise to the newly-formed meristematic rootlets, and in the process, go down the scale back to the undifferentiated state.

Generally speaking, chloroplasts regress in this way as an accompaniment to active proliferation of the cells. It can be observed that, during this proliferation, the chloroplasts also divide, and so become progressively smaller and smaller, ending up by losing their pigment and becoming proplastids again.

When these changes are studied under the light microscope we have to assume that there is a concurrent degeneration of the various lamellae and other structures that have been described above. Lance-Nougarède (1960) followed the progress of this disintegration under the electron microscope, during a normal and spontaneous example of de-differentiation of cells at the extreme tip of the growing point of *Chrysanthemum segetum*. During the period of vegetative growth of the plant, these cells, which constitute dormant meristems, differentiate tiny chloroplasts. When the plant begins to flower it starts a period of intense activity, and the dormant cells again become meristematic. Lance-Nougarède states that while the chloroplasts are dividing up by repeated constrictions they lose their lamellar organisation; the grana are dislodged and either disperse into the stroma, or gradually disappear. Soon the plastids have once again the appearance of meristematic proplastids, though their descendants may once again build up for themselves the structural complexes of fully differentiated chloroplasts. It is most remarkable that the structural complexity, which is, after all, no more than a poor reflection of the complexity of the molecular organisation beneath it, is sufficiently plastic to allow it to be dismantled and rebuilt while the life of the cell is still going on.

The leucoplasts without any chlorophyll, as they are present in many tissues, are equally capable of returning to the meristematic state along with the cells that contain them. At least as far as appearances go, their regression seems simpler than that of chloroplasts. Examples can be found from the time of bud-formation, starting from epidermal cells without chlorophyll (leaf buds of many Liliaceae, for example), or when parenchyma cells without chlorophyll produce roots or buds (such as the tubercles of chicory

195

or the rhizomes of Jerusalem artichoke cultured *in vitro*).

On the other hand, most chromoplasts, with the exception of those in carrot roots, rapidly enter into a state of senescence, which becomes irreversible.

Importance of plastids in the living world

The study of the physiological functions of plastids is one of the most important chapters of biology. Many works have been devoted to photosynthesis, too many to be adequately summarised in such an elementary book as this, and so we must be content with a few general considerations to show the importance of green plants and their chloroplasts.

We know that it is only thanks to their chloroplasts that green plants can trap solar energy, which falls on them in the form of light, and convert it into chemical energy which can be used in the synthesis of organic matter and protoplasm. Green plants are actually the only creatures capable of doing this, and all our human ingenuity has not yet succeeded in imitating them.

The study of the biophysical and biochemical mechanisms of photosynthesis is one of the most difficult subjects in all biology, but it has made spectacular advances during the last quarter of a century. The complex of photosynthetic reactions has now been elucidated, thanks to a combination of chromatographic techniques and the use of radioactive isotopes. On the other hand, we still know very little about how the chlorophyll functions during the light re-action of photosynthesis, and quantitative spectrography of chloro-

7·30 Diagram of the ultrastructure of the cytoplasm of plant cells as revealed by the electron microscope. s = starch in vacuolar space of a plastid ; d = dictyosome ; fib = fibrillae (probably holoproteins) of hyaloplasm to which are attached the 'free' ribosomes (rb) of the cytoplasm ; nf = nucleolar fibrillae ; I = invaginations of cell membrane, resembling pinocytosis, and sometimes producing small vacuoles (vi) ; l = fat-soluble granules ; m = mitochondria ; mea = meatus ; nm = nuclear membrane ; cw = cell wall ; n = nucleus (structure not shown) ; nu = nucleolus, with dense granules which resemble cytoplasmic ribosomes ; pd = a plastid, still undifferentiated, containing several cristae and tubules, some fatty granules (black) and a starch-bearing vacuole ; pl = plasmodesmata ; cm = cell membrane continuing along plasmodesmata from one cell to another ; p=pores of nuclear membrane ; pr.p=primary pit-field of membrane rich in plasmodesmata ; rug = 'rough' ER ; sm = 'smooth' ER without ribosomes and showing only a tendency to dilatation ; at=axial tract of

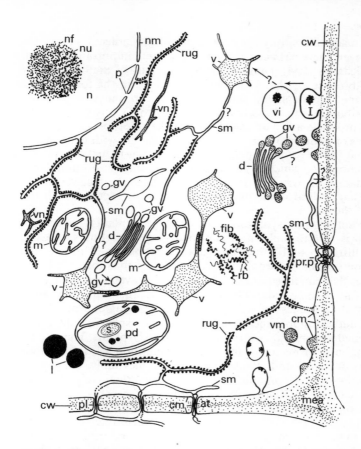

plasmodesmata in close contact (if not sometimes actually continuous) with diverticula of ER ; v = vacuoles enclosing a dense substance and provided with extensions which show a tendency to become applied to each other ; gv = Golgian vesicles emitted by the dictyosomes, and which disperse into the cytoplasm. Certain of these acquire dense contents which they are probably transporting towards the cell wall (arrow) ; vm = vesicles containing membranous material, which probably arises from dictyosomes ; vn = nascent vacuoles, scattered, or strung into filaments, with very dense contents. Question marks indicate points at which the relationships are still not fully understood, as, for example, between the ER and the vacuoles, or between the activity of the dictyosomes and of the ER in relation to the elaboration of the cell wall. Dotted lines indicate communications that are apparently occasional and only sporadically observed, between the ER and either the axial tracts of the plasmodesmata or cell wall.

197

phyll is made difficult by the complexity of the molecules involved.

However, there has been a discovery of great importance (Arnon and colleagues 1954), namely that at least part of the light energy that is absorbed by the chlorophyll is retained in the form of ATP (adenosine triphosphate). This ATP gives up the energy again by contributing it to those reactions by which CO_2 is reduced and organic products are synthesised. Hence the chloroplasts carry out processes of photophosphorylation which operate with light energy somewhat in the same manner as the oxidation-reduction systems of mitochondria, which utilise the chemical energy resulting from the oxidation of pyruvate. In both cases ATP is the receiver of the energy, and indeed is the universal purveyor of energy for all the needs of the cell.

The result of photosynthesis, as far as the green plant is concerned, is that it is able to build up organic substances starting with CO_2, water, nitrates, and other inorganic compounds. Through the operation of their chloroplasts, green cells are thus the only living creatures that can fix solar energy and make it available in the form of organic compounds. Photosynthesis is therefore the great compensating process of energy between the living and non-living worlds, and the global energy balance of the biosphere could not be maintained without the contribution of the green plants. The activity of living organisms calls for the consumption of tremendous amounts of energy and, by itself, would lead inevitably to a general degradation of all organic matter by oxidation, releasing the energy held in it. Photosynthesis is the only process that is big enough, on a world-scale, to act as counter-measure.

The plant world is thus seen to be indispensable to all living things, man included. An idea of its relative importance may be given by the fact that all the oxygen in the present atmosphere is the product of photosynthesis by green plants, and that the primaeval atmosphere on earth consisted of little more than nitrogen, water vapour and carbon dioxide.

Figure 7·30 assembles all the ultrastructures that we have described on the preceding pages.

8 Nucleus

Robert Brown was the first person who recognised the nucleus as a permanent organelle of the cell, when he was studying tissues from various orchids in 1831. Since that time the nucleus has undoubtedly been more studied than any other part of the cell, especially by the earlier cytologists. Its structure, chemical composition, metabolism, genetics, and the mechanism by which it divides, have all been the subject of innumerable studies, which still go on today.

It is necessary to give separate consideration to the nucleus when it is in its quiescent or resting state, and when it is actively dividing.

The resting nucleus

Morphology The nucleus assumes a variety of shapes, according to the type of cell, and to its state of differentiation. In primary (apical and intercalary) meristems the nucleus is globular, and occupies the centre of the cell. In most differentiated cells, where there is a single, large vacuole (figure 1·5), the nucleus lies against the cell wall and is more or less flattened. In cells that have become specially elongate in the course of their differentiation (translocating cells), the nucleus often shares in the elongation, and may even become cylindrical, but in secondary (lateral) meristematic cells, such as those of the cambium, the nucleus remains subspherical or lenticular, even if the cell is greatly elongated (fusiform initials). In cells which go to build up vascular tissues (pitted vessels, tracheids, sieve tubes) the nucleus first becomes enlarged, and then degenerates, assuming amoeboid shapes that are sometimes very contorted, and similar shapes can be seen in the nuclei of cells that have become polyploid by endomitosis: for example, collenchymatous cells of the tomato stem (Buvat 1944).

The nucleus may be deformed by the presence of paraplasmic products, which are more solid than the nuclear substance itself, and which accumulate either inside the nucleus or in the cytoplasm immediately surrounding it. For instance, epidermal cells of the fruits of *Campanula trachelium* may contain needle crystals of proteins which may distend the nucleus, or even pierce its membrane.

The dimensions of nuclei are as variable as their shapes. In meristematic cells the nucleus is generally between 7 and 10μ, whereas in differentiated cells it may reach 50μ. Except in the case of endopolyploids, the absolute size of the nucleus increases only moderately in the course of differentiation of the cell, in comparison with the other cell components such as vacuoles. As a result, the relative size of the nucleus falls rapidly during differentiation.

The sizes just mentioned are for average nuclei, but there also exist giant nuclei, like that of the zygote of *Cycas*, which may reach $500-1000\mu$, and which can bee seen with the naked eye. Most of the oospheres of Gymnosperms, too, have large nuclei, more than 100μ in diameter. At the opposite end of the scale are the very small nuclei found in many Thallophytes, with diameters between $1-10\mu$. The smallest of all are common in fungi.

Structure

1 *Appearance in living cells.* The living nucleus has a refractive index only slightly greater than that of the cytoplasm, but it becomes more clearly visible after death. In most plant species the contents of the living cell are heterogeneous, and among them can be distinguished one, two, or even several, more or less spherical bodies, the nucleoli. These have a greater refractive index than the ground substance of the nucleus, the nucleoplasm, which has a network of fine filaments. often granular, and also more highly refringent. This chromatic reticulum gets its name from the chromatin of which it is composed, which has an affinity for basic dyes (figure 8·1).

The nuclear contents are enclosed within an envelope or nuclear membrane, which is very thin, but which can be demonstrated by microdissection (Scarth 1927). In fact, using micro-needles one can detach the nuclear envelope and observe the nucleoplasm run out. Since 1927 Scarth showed that this membrane was a double one, by using punctures or narcotics to bring about changes in the cytoplasm, which caused the two layers of the envelope to separate. A quarter of a century later this duality was confirmed by the electron microscope.

Seifriz (1928) showed that the nuclear membrane becomes detached from the nucleoplasm when the cell is killed by coagulation, and it can then be completely separated and examined as a delicate, elastic veil. The nuclear contents are more unstable than the cytoplasm, and a touch of the needle of the micromanipulator causes rapid coagulation.

2 *Fixation and staining.* We have already seen that the nucleus contains chromatin, a substance that is easily stained with basic pigments, and which is generally present in the form of a filamentous network. This network was first observed after crude fixation in coagulants such as alcohol and acids, but has since been studied in more detail by using more nearly neutral fixatives, which give a finer preparation. However, fixation of the nucleus remains a difficult problem, particularly fixation for the electron microscope. Resting nuclei are best fixed with weakly acid fixatives, based on osmium tetroxide, or aldehydes such as formaldehyde, glutaraldehyde, acrolein, or again, by potassium dichromate.

Decisive progress was made in the staining of nuclei by the introduction of Feulgen's technique in 1926 (see Lison 1953). As far as the nucleus is concerned, this stain is strictly specific for DNA, and structures containing DNA are stained purple. Hence, in the nucleus, chromatin is specifically stained by Feulgen's reaction, while the chromatic reticulum can also be very delicately stained by using gentian violet.

The use of these methods on the resting nucleus, in interphase periods between two cell divisions, shows all the intermediate stages between two extreme cases. In wheat the nucleus has a chromatic reticulum with a very fine mesh, which is therefore very dense, and which fills the entire nucleus except for the space occupied by the nucleoli. One is forced to conclude that this network results from the tangling up of very fine filaments of chromatin, called chromonemas (figure $8 \cdot 1_1$). At the opposite extreme, nuclei

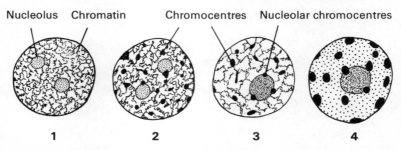

Nucleolus   Chromatin   Chromocentres   Nucleolar chromocentres

1   **2**   **3**   **4**

8·1 Several examples of chromatin structures found in the nucleus during interphase.
1 Eureticulate structure in *Triticum*. **2** Eureticulate with chromocentres in *Allium cepa*. **3** Semireticulate with chromocentres in *Solanum tuberosum*.
4 Areticulate with euchromocentres or prochromosomes in *Raphanus sativus*.

201

from the radish (*Raphanus sativus*) show no trace of a reticulum, but only masses of chromatin, called prochromosomes, or euchromocentres, most of which are attached to the nuclear membrane, and one, two or several masses to the nucleolus, of which there is generally only one. The nucleoplasm of these nuclei has a homogeneous appearance, and stains lightly in Feulgen, suggesting that the chromatin is 'diffused', that is, exists in a form that cannot be resolved in the light microscope (figure $8 \cdot 1_4$).

Between these two extremes there exist some nuclei in which the reticulum is less dense (*Pisum sativum*; *Hibiscus*), and others with a more or less dense reticulum in which the chromatin granules look like euchromocentres, but are generally smaller (*Allium cepa*, *Solanum tuberosum*) (see table and figure $8 \cdot 1_{2-3}$).

In nuclei where no reticulum is present (areticulate nuclei) the masses of chromatin may correspond in number to the chromosomes that will form during cell division. In that case they are genuine prochromosomes or euchromocentres (Cucumber), but in other nuclei the number of chromatin masses is less than the number of chromosomes. It could be that this results from the complete dechromatinisation of certain chromosomes, in which case the remaining masses are still properly regarded as euchromocentres (as in radish). Other areticulate nuclei contain masses of chromatin that are formed from the remains of several chromosomes, and these are composite chromocentres (*Bryonia dioica*). Table 3

Table 3 Classification of types of chromatin structures in resting nuclei

	Without chromocentres	With chromocentres
Eureticulate	*Triticum vulgare*	*Allium cepa*
Reticulate	*Pisum sativum*	*Zea mays*
Semi-reticulate	*Hibiscus syriacus*	*Solanum tuberosum*
	With euchromocentres	With composite chromocentres
Areticulate	*Cucumis sativus*	*Bryonia dioica*
Areticulate	*Raphanus sativus*	

summarises the main types of resting nucleus, according to the classification made by C. Delay in 1949.

Most stains also stain the nucleoli, though sometimes irregularly; the Feulgen technique, on the other hand, does not appreciably stain nucleoli.

Biochemistry

1 *Chromatin*. Analysis of tissues, the cells of which are almost entirely composed of nuclear matter (for example, spermatozoa or cells from the thymus gland), shows that animal cells contain nucleoproteins of a special category, the prosthetic groups being a 'thymonucleic acid'. Later, Feulgen's technique was used comparatively on animal and plant cells, and showed that analogous nucleic acids occurred in both. It is now known that these acids contain thymine and deoxyribose, and so are deoxyribonucleic acids, or DNA.

The DNA combines with heteroproteins to form deoxyribonucleoproteins, or DNP and this complex is found in the chromatin of the nucleus, where DNA is associated on the one hand with alkaline proteins of comparatively low molecular weight (histones, or, in spermatozoa, protamines), and on the other with proteins of high molecular weight, or 'non-histone' proteins. There are many of the latter group, which may constitute nearly 30 per cent of the dry matter of the nucleus, whereas the DNA accounts for only 20 per cent. The histones, and probably a part of the 'non-histone' protein, are bonded to the DNA by means of the acid bond that resides in each phosphoric residue. Nucleohistones, which can be extracted from the thymus and studied under the electron microscope, are long, filamentous molecules, twisted into loose spirals about 30–40Å diameter, whereas DNA molecules of the same shape measure only 20Å.

These results apply particularly to animal cells, but they are probably equally true for the cells of plants. Indeed, histones were detected in chromatin from wheat germ (Mirsky and Pollister 1946) and in embryonic tissues from cedar (Belozerskii and Uryson 1958), but it is hoped that these studies will soon be extended to other plants.

One fact that has so far been demonstrated only for animal cells is that diploid nuclei from the same species have a remarkably uniform DNA content, 20–25 per cent of the dry weight of the nuclear material.

2 *Ribonucleic acids.* The nucleus also has its content of RNA, but – in contrast to the DNA – RNA is found in extremely variable amounts, according to the age, state of differentiation, and physiological activity of the cells. The ribonucleic acids can be detected cytochemically by Brachet's test. The cells are fixed in a 'strong' fixative such as alcohol, acetic acid and formalin, and then stained on the slide with a mixture of Methyl Green and Pyronine, using a suitable concentration and pH. The Pyronine stains the RNA red, and the Methyl Green stains the DNA green. Since the differential staining is not absolutely specific, some of the slides are treated with ribonuclease before staining. Then, any structures that are stained in the one series of slides and not in the other definitely contain RNA.

This method shows that there is RNA in the nucleoli, but it also detects this same nucleic acid in the chromosomes, and in greater abundance in the chromocentres and prochromosomes of those species that possess these. These parts of the chromosomes are made up of heterochromatin, in contrast to other parts which have euchromatin. The latter is less rich in RNA, and seems to be the only one to have a genetic function.

Results from animal tissues (Frenster and colleagues 1960) indicate various types of nuclear RNA. Those found in the chromosomes, and which can be extracted with solutions of sodium chloride (either isotonic or molar solutions), differ from those found in nucleoli, which are insoluble in these reagents.

3 *Holoproteins.* We have seen that chromatin contains two kinds of protein which are connected with DNA, and in addition the nucleoli and the nucleoplasm contain holoproteins which are still poorly known. The nucleolus is remarkably dense, containing about 85 per cent of dry matter, which is essentially protein. There seem to be no histones among these, but from 20–25 per cent of basic proteins can be detected (Birnstiel and Hyde 1963) in nucleoli isolated from germinating peas. These authors give the following figures for the composition of their material, in percentage of the dry weight:

	RNA	DNA	Proteins
Nucleus	8	14	78
Nucleoli	11	5*	84
Chromatin	12	24	64

* This figure for the DNA is chromatin associated with the nucleoli, including any nucleolar chromocentres.

There are also proteins in the nucleoplasm, where they form a fluid system of low concentration. Unlike the cytoplasm, the nucleoplasm has no membranes between itself and the other components of the nucleus, and so its macromolecular network, fibrous in appearance, is continuous with the proteins of the nucleoli and the chromatin.

4 *Enzymes.* The nucleus contains a great many enzymes, which regulate its biochemical activity. Some of these are also to be found in the cytoplasm, the mitochondria and the plastids of most cells: such, for example, as phosphatases, esterases, phosphorylases. To these must be added cofactors such as NAD (nicotinamide-adenine-dinucleotide), which is one of the principal electron carriers in cells.

Other nuclear systems contain enzymes which participate in the catabolism of glucosides (dehydrogenase of phosphoglyceric acid, aldolase, kinases, etc). Enzymes of this group have been particularly associated with cells from wheat germ. We shall see how these enzymes make it possible for energy to be placed in reserve in the form of ATP, and later to be released to power biosyntheses in the nucleus.

Finally, work on animal cells has shown that the nucleus sometimes contains enzymes directly concerned with the specialisation of cells. For instance, the nucleus of pancreatic cells contains deoxyribonuclease and lipase. This fact indicates that the nucleus as well as the cytoplasm undergoes changes associated with the differentiation of cells, whereas it was previously thought that its function was confined to general metabolism and the passing on of genetic information.

5 *Affinity for* Ca^{++} *and* Mg^{++}. In pollinia in the course of development, and more precisely in reproductive nuclei in the process of division, Steffensen and Bergeron (1959) demonstrated that Ca^{45} was selectively incorporated, and seemed to attach itself preferentially to genetic material when growth was taking place. On the other hand chromatin contains magnesium, which seems especially to form magnesium bonds (–Mg–) between a proportion of the phosphate residues in nucleic acids, and the mononucleotides that are relatively abundant in the interior of the nucleus.

The magnesium in the chromatin is in competition with the histones for the possession of the acid bond of the phosphate residues. The work of Naora and his colleagues (1960) showed that the metabolic activity of nuclei isolated from the thymus gland – in particular the synthesis of ATP – is arrested if histones are added to the culture medium. These histones, which are strongly basic, drive out the magnesium, and take their place on the phosphate attachments. Putting it the other way round, one function of the magnesium is to safeguard the freedom of activity of some of the attachments on the nuclear molecules against the inhibitory action of the histones.

Judging from the other biochemical activities of the nucleus, it seems very likely that these results would apply to plants as well as to animals, but it is highly desirable that these enzymological and biochemical studies should be repeated on the nuclei of plant cells.

Ultrastructure The study of the nucleus with the aid of the electron microscope has proved more disappointing than the study of the cytoplasm, for a number of reasons. First of all, the ultrastructures of the nucleus are not surrounded by plasma membranes like those of the cytoplasm, which conveniently separate different colloidal phases from each other. On the contrary, the various macromolecular systems of the nucleus are closely interwoven. Another difficulty is that the nucleus is a particularly unstable system, very sensitive to the chemical and physical action of fixatives, so that fixation of the nucleus is very difficult, and generally very imperfect. Osmium tetroxide in slightly acid solution seems to give the best results. Finally, the lack of plasma membranes compels us to work on a molecular scale, and current techniques are only rarely adequate for this.

A further complication is the fact that the nucleus contains many long, twisted molecules that are difficult to see in ultra-thin sections, particularly since these molecules are very tightly packed together in such structures as chromosomes and nucleoli.

1 *Fine structure of chromatin.* In the ultra-thin sections that are possible with present-day techniques, the chromatin of the resting nucleus is filled with convoluted profiles, in some substance that has a density higher than that of the nucleoplasm, and without a limiting membrane. At first glance these chromatin structures look granular, though this fits in badly with the genetic evidence (figure 8·2). However, Ris (1954–6), using mainly resting nuclei, when the chromatin is as 'despiralled' as possible, showed that this granular appearance is an artefact, caused by a large number of cross-sections of what are really fibrillae cut at various angles. For

206

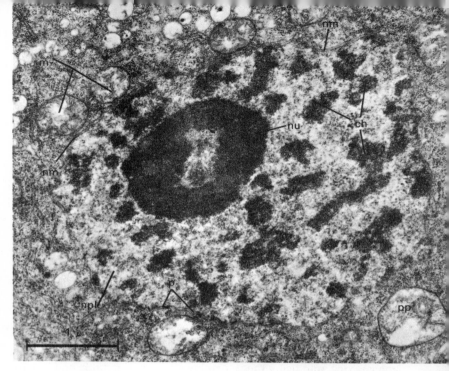

8·2 Electron micrograph of interphase nucleus of *Hordeum sativum* in thin section. nm=double membrane of nucleus with pores (p) ; ch=chromatin ; nu=nucleolus; npl=nucleoplasm ; m=mitochondrion ; pp=proplastid. Chromatin and nucleolus are not separated from the nucleoplasm by a membrane. (× 24,000).

example – in mother cells of the microspores of *Lilium* there are twisted fibrillae of about 500Å diameter, and similar fibrillae are also found in the oocytes of amphibia, and in the spermatocytes of insects as well as of rats. These fibrillae are double, each being composed of two microfibrillae of about 200Å in diameter.

In ordinary resting nuclei (*Lilium, Tradescantia, Allium,* as well as in animal cells from a newt and a rat), after eliminating any traces from the embedding medium, Ris showed that these fibrillae certainly exist, but that they are twisted into tight coils. After fixation in osmium, these fibrillae are heterogeneous: the axis is less dense than the outer sleeve; DNA-ase does not alter this appearance, which probably indicates that the DNA is in the axial zone, and that the outer sleeve is of protein. This structure is analogous to that of the tobacco mosaic virus where the axial zone is made of RNA.

Eventually Ris (1958) succeeded in stripping the protein sleeve from fibrillae of 200Å diameter, and in this way he discovered that each one is composed of two microfibrillae of 100Å, each of which in turn release two elementary microfibrillae of 40Å diameter, by autolysis of the 'non-histone' protein fraction that they contain. These last are molecules of nucleohistones.

Moreover, in the course of spermatogenesis in a variety of animals, at a certain stage the 'non-histone' proteins disappear spontaneously. Fixation at this point shows up the nuclei with a very peculiar structure: they contain long, contorted, fibrous structures, about 100Å in diameter, which are obviously double. These observations thus confirm the findings of Ris.

Tentative morphological analyses carried out on plant cells during meiosis (pachytene stage) led Bopp Hassenkamp (1958) to postulate four sets of helicoids in the chromonemas of the chromosomes, and only the fourth of these is visible under the light microscope.

Finally Camefort (1964) showed that oospheres of *Pinus* just before fertilisation contained fibrillar structures that were completely unrolled (figure 8·3).

2 *Fine structure of the nucleoli.* There are several techniques for the differential staining of nucleoli in a manner suitable for the light microscope, and using these, Estable (1930) and Estable and Sotelo (1954) described a wound filament, the nucleolonema, bathed in a ground substance which they called the 'pars amorpha'. Their description, however, did not lead to any very satisfactory interpretation of these structures, and it needed the electron microscope, with its associated cytochemical techniques, before the ultrastructure of nucleoli could be interpreted in more detail (Lafontaine 1958; Lafontaine and Chouinard 1963; Jezequel and Bernhard 1963; Marinozzi 1964; Thomas 1965).

When they have been suitably fixed, and cut into ultra-thin sections, the densest parts of the nucleoli are composed of two parts: one of these clearly consists of fibrillae of 40–100Å diameter; the other part consists mainly of granular particles of 150–200Å. These two components are immersed in an amorphous protein substance, which is very sensitive to pepsin (according to Marinozzi).

The distribution of fibrillar and granular constituents within the nucleolus varies according to the species of plant and the tissue concerned. They may be separated into zones, or into small blocks, or they may be thoroughly mixed together. In nucleoli from the

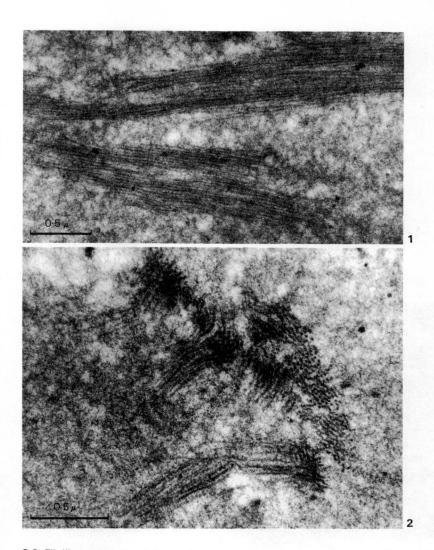

8·3 Fibrillar appearance of chromatin
in the resting nucleus of
the oosphere of *Pinus silvestris*
in (**1**) longitudinal section (×32,000)
and in (**2**) partly transverse section (×40,000).

roots of *Allium cepa, Vicia faba,* or *Raphanus sativus,* the fibrillar
constituent forms little islets surrounded by the granular constituent
(figure 8·4). In the central region there are often spaces of much
lower density, a kind of vacuole of a texture somewhat resembling
that of the nucleoplasm; other small cavities of low density may
also occur in the denser peripheral region of the nucleolus (Lafontaine and Chouinard). Furthermore, the two dense constituents,
as well as the clearer zones, are traversed by continuous threads,
like those which run between the nucleolus, the nucleoplasm, and
the chromatin (figure 8·4).

Marinozzi has shown that these fibrillar and granular structures
contain RNA, associated with proteins, as it is in the ribosomes
of the cytoplasm. It will be recalled that these nucleolar proteins,
otherwise poorly known, have no histones, but are partly alkaline.
In many animal cells there have been recognised at least two different fractions of the nucleolar RNA, one of which has the same
arrangement of bases as the DNA of the same nucleus, and perhaps
is a messenger-RNA (Vincent 1957; Sibatini and colleagues 1962).

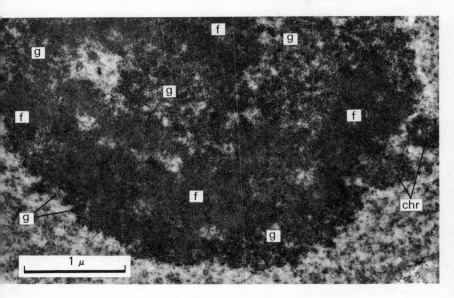

8·4 Part of a nucleolus of *Cucurbita pepo* fixed in glutaraldehyde,
showing fibrillar zones (f) and the granular zones (g).

Finally, one or more masses of chromatin usually penetrate into the nucleolus, often in the form of chromocentres, or nucleolar prochromosomes, and these make special contact with the fibrillar constituent of the nucleolus. On the other hand, the effect of actinomycin D – which inhibits DNA from synthesising RNA – is greatest on the fibrillae, which are thinned out (Schoell 1964). Similarly, if the RNA is radioactively marked with adenine or uridine containing tritium, H^3, the incorporation of the radio-active element begins at the point of contact of the nucleolar chromatin (P. and N. Gramboulan 1965).

Nuclear structures in Protocaryotes
1 *In bacteria.* The problem of whether bacteria have a nucleus has been hotly debated for more than half a century, and every possible hypothesis has been advanced to provide bacterial cells with some kind of nuclear mechanism. There are many reasons for these difficulties, but the small size of the structures is not one of them, because those in which we are interested are generally within the resolving power of good quality light microscopes.

Those basic stains which give good differential staining of the chromatin in Eurycaryotes, also stain the cytoplasm in bacteria, while the Feulgen technique, although more specific, gives shapes that are too varied to be interpreted clearly. This is because of the large number of ergastic substances (lipids, among others), which clutter up the cytoplasm of bacteria, and deform to a greater or lesser extent any nuclear structures that may be present (Delaporte 1950). However, by gentle hydrolysis with normal hydrochloric acid it is possible to suppress the basophily of the cytoplasm (Robinow 1942–4), and thus to obtain differential staining of an object which looks like a nucleus, at any rate in young cells that are in a stage of exponential growth (figure 8·5). A similar result is obtained by first treating bacteria with ribonuclease, which also suppresses the basophile properties of the cytoplasm (Boivin and colleagues 1947). This shows that the affinity of the cytoplasm for basic compounds is produced by its high content of RNA.

Using these techniques on bacterial cells in young cultures (up to 24 hours old), it is possible to show up one or more corpuscles, often globular, and with a diameter about half that of the bacterial cell. These 'nucleoids' divide by transverse constriction (figure 8·5), and this division sometimes occurs well in advance of the division of the cell itself.

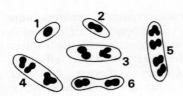

8·5 Division figures of the 'nucleoid' of *Escherichia coli*, as seen under the light microscope after gentle hydrolysis in hydrochloric acid and stained in giemsa.

The techniques used for fixing cells of Eurycaryotes for study under the electron microscope have proved defective for bacteria, and the first suitable technique is owed to Kellenberger, Ryter and Sechaud (1958). This consists of fixing with osmium tetroxide in a weak acid medium, and avoids causing the nucleoid to coagulate. The nucleoid now appears as a median zone with a lower density than the cytoplasm, and containing bundles of very fine fibrillae, in a ground substance that is finely granular. The diameter of these fibrillae is somewhere between 20 and 60Å, often in the region of 30Å, that is, about the same as the fibrous macromolecules of DNA. On the other hand, we know that osmium tetroxide does not react with DNA itself, but with the histones and protamines that are associated with DNA in the nuclei of Eurycaryotes. The low density to electrons of the nucleoids and especially of the fibrillae that they contain, makes it likely that the DNA in bacteria is not combined with similar proteins, but that it exists in a free state, and heavily hydrated (in a so-called expanded state).

The nucleoids of bacteria show no other structure. They are not bounded by a membrane, like true nuclei, but their substance is continuous with the cytoplasm. Nor do bacteria have nucleoli.

2 *The centroplasm of blue-green algae.* In 1853 the bacteriologist Cohn forecast that blue-green algae would prove to be more closely related to bacteria than to true algae. The classical work of Delaporte (1939–40), using particularly the Feulgen technique, showed that blue-green algae have a rudimentary nucleus, the 'central body', or centroplasm, which has a contorted and indefinite outline, suggesting that it has no membrane surrounding it. When this centroplasm divides, it does not form a spindle as in normal cell division.

The electron microscope confirms this absence of membrane, and it is claimed that the behaviour of the centroplasm under different conditions of fixation is exactly the same as that of the nucleoid of

212

bacteria. The techniques used by Kellenberger and his colleagues are suitable, and reveal structures in the centroplasm that are very similar to those structures that are Feulgen-positive in bacteria. In particular there are analogous fibrillae, which may be slightly thicker (50–70Å) (In *Anabaena cylindrica*, studied by Hopwood and Glauert 1960). The centroplasm has just about the same density to electrons as has the cytoplasm, (or chromatoplasm) which has less affinity for bases than the cytoplasm of bacteria.

Sometimes, there are dense granules inside the centroplasm (*Oscillaria, Phormidium,* according to Lefort 1960), but these may perhaps be fragments of cytoplasm that have penetrated into the sinuosities of the centroplasm. Some of them, at least, are metachromatic polyphosphates, analogous to the volutine of Thallophytes (Niklowitz and Drews 1956; Hopwood and Glauert 1960).

In conclusion, genetic research on bacteria has shown that they contain a single chromosome, which is closed up into a ring. At one point this chromosome adheres to the ectoplasmic pellicle ('cell membrane') (Jacob and Ryter 1961). It is probable that the bundles of microfibrillae that are to be seen in nucleoids are produced by foldings of this circular chromosome.

Functions

1 *Growth of the cell.* In many cases where a plant cell grows on one site only, the nucleus can be seen to migrate into that area. Thus, the vegetative nucleus of pollen grains is the first part of the cell to pass down the pollen-tube, and remains at its end as long as its growth continues, afterwards degenerating. In trichocysts (absorbent hairs) of roots, the nucleus again remains near the tip of the hair as long as this is elongating, after which the nucleus moves back towards the base of the hair-forming cell (Bouet 1954).

2 *Merotomy: experiments with cell fragments.* These experiments consist of obtaining fragments of cells – by sectioning or plasmolysis – in such a way that some fragments possess a nucleus and some do not. The oldest experiments were carried out by Balbiani (1889) (on *Stentor*) and by Hofer (1889) (on amoebae), and showed that fragments without nuclei were able to heal over their cut surface, and to survive for some time, but they did not grow, regenerate their missing parts, digest prey, or reproduce. They died after a few days.

In contrast, the fragments that did possess nuclei not only healed over, but they grew, regenerated the missing cytoplasmic structures,

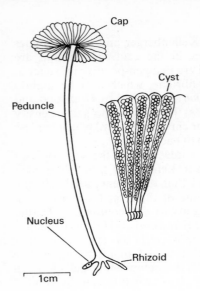

Cap

Cyst

Peduncle

Nucleus

Rhizoid

1cm

8·6 Left Diagram of *Acetabularia*.

8·7 Right Experiments on interspecific grafting of *Acetabularia* as carried out by Hämmerling. med = *A. mediterranea* with cap feebly lobate ; cren = *A. crenulata* with cap strongly lobate. **1** Intermediate form of cap produced when two nucleated fragments (med + cren) are grafted together. **2** First intermediate type of cap produced by grafting a nucleated fragment of med with a non-nucleated fragment of cren ; a second cap is produced when the first is sectioned, and is pure *mediterranea*. White circles = morphogenic substances producing *A. mediterranea* ; black circles = those producing *A. crenulata* (see text).

digested prey, and reproduced. These experiments proved that the nucleus is essential for growth and regeneration (that is, for morphogenesis), as well as for reproduction. Hence a nucleus is indispensable for the process of assimilation, by which materials taken in by the cell are converted into living substance of the same nature as that already present in the cell.

Nevertheless life does not become extinct at once in denucleated fragments: the cytoplasm can carry on for a time, exercising its functions such as respiration, movement and even some synthetic processes. Life for any length of time, however, requires a nucleus.

These facts received a remarkable counter-proof, when Comandon and de Fonbrune (1939) devised a technique that would allow them to re-introduce a nucleus into either a whole amoeba without a nucleus, or into an anucleate fragment. Within minutes, both types of cell resumed full activity, even, in some cases, to the point of being able to divide. Similar results have been obtained with plant cells. By plasmolysis various algal cells can be split into nucleate and anucleate fragments (Klebs 1879–87 on *Vaucheria, Zygnema*). Only those with nuclei were able to surround themselves with a new pectocellulose cell wall. Moreover, if an anucleate fragment was joined to a nucleate fragment by a cytoplasmic thread even as fine as those which run through the plasmodesmata (see p. 110) this

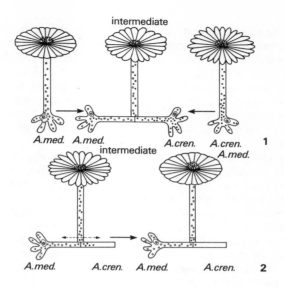

intermediate

A.med. A.med.   *A.cren. A.cren.*   **1**
intermediate   *A.med.*

A.med.   *A.cren.*   *A.med.*   *A.cren.*   **2**

was enough to make both fragments build their own cell walls (Townsend 1897).

3 *Exchange between nucleus and cytoplasm in Acetabularia.* The identical results for animal and plant cells leave little doubt that these facts apply universally throughout the living world, yet certain experiments in merotomy seem to contradict them. The experiments were carried out from 1934 onwards by Hämmerling, working with certain unicellular algae called *Acetabularia*. Anucleate fragments of these algae can, in fact, survive for several months, regenerating more or less perfectly the missing cytoplasmic structures, including the 'cap' or 'umbrella' structures that are so characteristic of this group. To do these things requires a power of cytoplasmic growth and morphogenetic organisation which normally depends on the nucleus.

To explain this discrepancy, Hämmerling postulates that certain morphogenic substances diffuse from the nucleus into the cytoplasm, where they are conserved over a period, and so may be available after the cell has been enucleated. This hypothesis is confirmed by experiments of grafting between different species (Hämmerling 1943, etc). Different species of *Acetabularia* have differently shaped caps. When a nucleate fragment of *Acetabularia mediterranea* was grafted on to an anucleate fragment of *A. crenulata* the cap that was regenerated was of an intermediate shape. If this cap was cut out, the alga regenerated a second, but this time the shape was pure *mediterranea* (figure 8·7). These results are consistent with the theory that the first new cap was made while the cytoplasm still contained morphogenetic materials derived from the lost *crenulata* nucleus, but that by the time of the second regeneration these substances were exhausted. Hence, the nucleate fragment of *mediterranea* was in sole control.

Later research has shown that the morphogenic substances are ribonucleic acids (RNA). The process of regeneration is hindered in either nucleate or anucleate fragments by any substance which interferes with the action of RNA, such as trypaflavine (Stich 1951; Brachet and colleagues 1955, etc), or by ultraviolet radiation, which is absorbed by RNA. Finally, ribonuclease permanently inhibits regeneration in anucleate fragments by destroying the cytoplasmic RNA, but its effect on nucleate fragments is only temporary. If the treated fragments are placed in normal saline solution, only the last ones recover their regenerative powers.

The conclusion to be drawn from these experiments is that the cytoplasmic RNA is essential for regeneration, but that it can be provided only by nuclear activity. Experiments on amoebae (Goldstein *et al* 1955, 63) showed that the nucleus is effective in synthesising RNA, which is later passed into the cytoplasm, while the cytoplasm uses this RNA to synthesise proteins, and then some of them pass back to the nucleus. Relations between nucleus and the cytoplasm are thus reciprocal, providing for exchanges in both directions. If the nucleus may be said to control the activity of the cytoplasm, through its genetic function, the cytoplasm may equally be said to control the nucleus, through its supply of metabolic substances. The influence of the cytoplasm upon the nucleus has been further demonstrated by the ingenious experiments of Hämmerling (1939, 53). *Acetabularia* has a single nucleus, which is situated at the base of the plant, in a rhizoid, as long as the cap is not fully developed. When this has taken place, the nucleus splits up, and daughter nuclei migrate into the sectors of the cap. Hämmerling cut out the cap just before the nucleus was due to divide, and found that the division was delayed until the cap had been completely regenerated. If the cap was cut out a second time, again just before nuclear division, the nucleus remained quiescent again, and this could go on indefinitely. Conversely, if a nucleate rhizoid from a young, immature cell is grafted on to an alga which has its cap fully developed, then the nucleus divides after about two weeks, instead of the two months that it would have taken normally.

4 *Biochemistry of the resting nucleus.* The expression 'resting nucleus' means no more than that the cell is not actively dividing; it does not mean that it is biochemically inactive. On the contrary, suspensions of nuclei in the test tube carry on a number of activities, some of which take place only when no cell division is going on. In particular the nucleus synthesises RNA, nuclear proteins, and ATP. These syntheses are abolished if the DNA is destroyed by DNA-ase, and resume when new DNA is introduced into the system. Hence DNA must be essential, not only to the genetic activities of the nucleus, but also to biochemical activities in which the specificity of the nucleus is not in question, such as making ATP.

Furthermore, after eliminating the DNA from a suspension of nuclei, the synthesis of ATP can be made to resume, not only by adding DNA from the same species of organism, but also DNA from a totally different organism (*Escherichia coli*, for example), or even polyacids of high molecular weight. So in this particular matter DNA is behaving simply as a polyacid. In contrast, the addition of polycations (histones, for example) inhibits the synthesis of ATP.

The synthesis of ATP involves an absorption of oxygen, and presupposes the existence of oxidative phosphorilations resembling those in mitochondria. There is a difference, however, since in this case the reactions are not sensitive to certain inhibitors of oxidative phosphorylations, such as 95 per cent CO, which acts on mitochondria.

The production of ATP provides the energy necessary for the various syntheses which take place in the nucleus.

As far as RNA is concerned, the use of radioactive markers in the precursory substances shows that synthesis of RNA takes place both earlier and more rapidly in the nucleus than in the cytoplasm. This synthesis is particularly active on the nucleoli, but it also involves the chromosomes. Precursors that have been marked with P^{32} are quickly incorporated by isolated nucleoli of *Acetabularia* in the form of RNA (Hämmerling and Stich 1956). P. and N. Gramboulan (1965) showed that the incorporation of RNA began in the nucleoli at the sites of contact of the nucleolar chromatin.

We do not know exactly what kinds of RNA are formed in the nucleus, and what happens to them all. One part at least, as we have just seen, is passed into the cytoplasm and takes part in extranuclear syntheses of proteins. But the nucleus itself also synthesises proteins, as can be shown by introducing radioactive amino acids into intact cells or into suspensions of nuclei. This protein-synthesis is notably more active in the nucleoli (Birnstiel and Hyde 1963, on isolated nucleoli of *Pisum*), but does also take place in the chromosomes. Ficq (1960) demonstrated this activity in the giant chromosomes from the salivary glands of the fly *Rhynchosciara*, along the bands that are most richly provided with RNA.

5 *Conclusions about the functions of the resting nucleus.* We have already said (p. 203) that the diploid nuclei of one species of animal or plant always contain the same amount of DNA. This constancy is part of the general stability of the DNA in the resting phase, which has been demonstrated by experiments of incorporating labelled precursors. Resting nuclei do not incorporate any radioactive materials, and if these have been introduced before the resting phase, they remain, at least for several months. The DNA is thus the most stable of the nuclear constituents, and all the biochemical activities of the nucleus depend on it.

These activities are of two kinds. One set is closely linked with the specificity of the molecules of DNA, or of structures that have been organised by these molecules; these are therefore the genetic activities of the nucleus, and lead to the synthesis of more DNA, and afterwards to that of specific proteins, among other substances. Other activities of the nucleus are non-specific, for example, the synthesis of nuclear ATP. In these activities the DNA is acting by virtue of its function as a polyacid, that is, by the negative charges of its molecules. Now we know that a high proportion of these negative charges are neutralised by basic proteins, the histones, while other negative bonds are in some way protected against the action of histones by magnesium atoms. It might be asked whether the sites that are active genetically are those which are bonded to magnesium, and the other, inactive sites are those that are 'blocked' by histones. Differences in distribution of histones and of Mg^{++} ions might then explain how different cells of the same organism which contain the same genes can carry out different functions, and how, in fact, they can be differentiated.

If this hypothesis could be confirmed, as present tendencies suggest that it may be, the problem of differentiation would resolve itself into a problem of distribution of histones and Mg^{++} along the molecule of nuclear DNA. It would then remain to look for factors which might determine this distribution, and many observations, some of them quite simple ones, suggest that these factors may come from the cytoplasm. In embryology, for instance, it is noteworthy that the nucleus divides into two precisely equal halves, but the cytoplasm does not. In merogone embryos, which have the nucleus of one species and the cytoplasm of another, segmentation starts normally, but then – no doubt at the point where exchanges begin between nucleus and cytoplasm – the incompatibility of the two species makes itself felt, and the embryo dies. No doubt the unequal division of the cytoplasm allowed some morphogenesis to go on normally in some areas for a while.

On the other hand we have already mentioned research work which proved that the cytoplasm passes proteins back to the nucleus, apparently with other substances that it has manufactured. Finally, it seems possible that the cytoplasm may intervene in some of the regulatory processes of the genes, but research into this question in Eucaryotes is a long way from reaching the level that it has already reached in bacteria (Jacob and Monod 1961).

Nucleus during somatic cell division

Although it is the changes in appearance of the nucleus that have attracted most attention from students of cell division, it has never been proved that the nucleus is predominant in determining when cell division starts, and by what mechanism it continues.

Mitosis and amitosis Among Eucaryotes it is very rarely that the nucleus divides by simple elongation and constriction across the middle. This type of cell division, called amitosis, most often occurs in pathological conditions: cancer-cells, plant-galls, or degenerating cells such as those in the tapetum of anthers. The macronucleus of ciliate Infusoria is a particular case, where the nucleus is composed of a large number of 'sub-nuclei', and these separate without any mechanism comparable to the usual process of mitosis. Mitosis is the usual method of nuclear division in Eucaryotes, when the chromatic reticulum resolves itself into a number of discrete chromosomes, which then go through a sequence of characteristic modifications and movements. Division of the nucleus (karyokinesis) precedes division of the cytoplasm (cytodiaëresis), thus marking two distinct stages of cell division.

Karyokinesis in higher plants The karyokinesis of cells from higher plants differs from that of animals in the absence of centrosomes or asters, and the morphological details of the successive figures vary according to the structure of the interphase resting nucleus. We shall start by looking at the special case of eureticulate nuclei such as those of *Allium cepa*, studied in particular by Mangenot (1942).

Karyokinesiṣ is classically divided into four phases: prophase, metaphase, anaphase and telophase, though strict logic would interpose a fifth phase – metakinesis or prometaphase – between the first and the second.

1 *Prophase.* Prophase is long and complex, involving nuclear phenomena at one moment and cytoplasmic phenomena at another.

(a) *Cytoplasmic preparations for karyokinesis.* Before cell division starts, the cytoplasm surrounding the nucleus frees itself from all the inclusions that it normally contains, and becomes a 'clear zone', observed in the living cell by Bajer (1957). At first this clear zone is isotropic, that is, has the same refractive index in all directions when seen under polarised light, but soon it begins to show the outline of a spindle, which extends along an axis between two regions of the perinuclear cytoplasm which are called the polar regions (figure 8·8).

(b) *Evolution of the chromatin.* During this period the chromatin has been undergoing 'condensation'. The chromatic reticulum behaves like a network of very long threads, tangled together in the nucleoplasm, and these are the chromonemas, which represent the chromosomes in their interphase state. Condensation means that these are rolled up more and more tightly into spirals (minor spiral, figure 8·8$_1$), resulting in a considerable shortening of the chromosomes. By this means the chromosomes are sorted out, and take on an individual character.

The next step is that these spirals appear to unroll, but the chromosomes thicken up at the same time, thus forming a loose spiral of larger diameter, the 'superspiral' (figure 8·8$_2$). From this moment on, each chromosome appears as two filaments, the chromatids, which join together only at one point where there is an uncoloured (and non-stainable) granule, the centromere (figure 8·8$_3$). At first the chromatids are twisted round each other, but towards the end of prophase they align themselves in parallel, all the while shortening and thickening. This process may continue right up to metaphase (Bajer 1959).

220

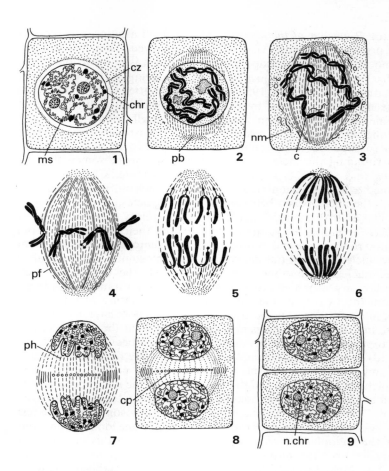

8·8 The main stages of mitosis in a plant cell with reticulated nucleus and chromocentres. **1–2** Prophase; ms = minor spiral; cz = clear zone; chr = chromocentres; pb = polar body. **3** Metakinesis; c = centromeres; nm = debris of nuclear membrane, the curved arrows representing the route followed by the centromeres (after A. Bajer).
4 Metaphase; pf = polar fibres (continuous lines) attached to centromeres.
5 Beginning of anaphase. **6** End of anaphase. **7–8** Telophase, where a new nuclear membrane forms around each chromosome bundle; ph = phragmaplast; cp = cell plate. **9** End of cell division; nch = nucleolar chromocentres.
One chromosome is shown with a satellite (SAT chromosome) and another with a secondary constriction that is not drawn out.

(c) *Behaviour of the nucleoli.* The nucleoli disappear at the end of prophase, as if they had suddenly dissolved. They first become amoeboid, changing shape constantly, but it is not possible to see what becomes of them just by watching a living cell. Some authors (Rattenbury and Serra, 1952, among others) tried to trace the fate of the nucleolar material by using special staining techniques, and came to the conclusion that it spread itself round the outside of the chromosomes as a sort of matrix. Unfortunately the electron microscope has not confirmed the existence of such a matrix surrounding the metaphase and anaphase chromosomes of *Vicia faba* and *Allium cepa*. In several Orchidaceae, Chardar (1962) noted a kind of crumbling away of the nucleoli, which dispersed into the nucleoplasm between the chromosomes.

Das and Alfert (1959) made use of the affinity of the nucleoli for silver (argentophilic property) to trace out their fate. In cells from onion roots, at the end of prophase, the argentophilic products from the nucleoli spread out between the chromosomes, and then, after the nuclear membrane had disintegrated, the cytoplasm itself became argentophilic while the argentophilic substance disappeared from the vicinity of the chromosomes. The nature of this argentophilic substance is not known, but, as we shall see later, it reappears around the chromosomes at telophase, while at the same time the cytoplasm ceases to have argentophilic properties.

(d) *Breakdown of the nuclear membrane.* The nuclear membrane disappears at the end of telophase. Moses (1958), Porter and Machado (1960) followed the breakdown of the nuclear membrane under the electron microscope. The first parts to come away are those areas that are not in contact with chromosomes, and the rest follows later. The fragments of nuclear membrane look like portions of the endoplasmic reticulum, and mingle with this, as they are repelled from the mitotic spindle that is being prepared (figure 8·9).

The breakdown of the nuclear membrane establishes contact between the nucleoplasm and the clear zone just outside, which was cleared, as we recall, at the start of prophase. This contact brings about a sudden gelation of the nucleoplasm clear zone, and this is the substance of the achromatic spindle, which is much more viscous that the cytoplasm.

(e) *The achromatic spindle.* According to Heilbrunn (1956), this gelation results from the polymerisation of protein molecules, which are built up into spindle fibres.

Mazia, Dan and their colleagues (1961–3) developed techniques

222

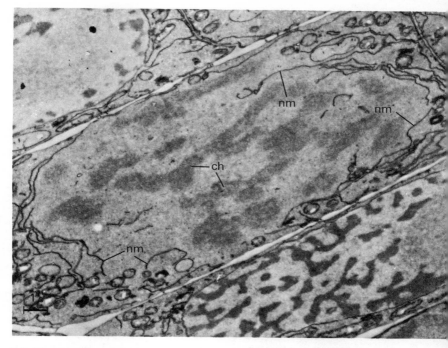

8·9 Electron micrograph showing nuclear membrane (nm) during prophase in a root cell of wheat fixed in permanganate. ch=chromosomes. (×6,250).

by which the mitotic apparatus can be isolated from the segmenting eggs of sea-urchins. Analysis of this material shows that more than 90 per cent of the dry weight is protein, and that most of this consists of either one single protein, or a very small number. This fraction is associated with RNA and lipids. The achromatic spindle also contains ATP-ase and other substances containing the -SH group, or sulphur bonds (-S-S-), which probably play a very important part in linking coils and causing the spindle fibres to contract.

From prophase on, therefore, the dividing cell contains a mitotic apparatus which is composed of an achromatic spindle which is anisotropic as a result of having protein fibres lying in roughly parallel lines. Inside this barrel-shaped structure lie the chromosomes, which are split longitudinally, sinuous, and scattered in a rather random fashion.

2 *Metakinesis or prometaphase.* It is convenient to recognise this phase, intermediate between prophase and metaphase, for descriptive and functional reasons. This is the moment when the chromosomes begin to move, and take up their positions around the equatorial plane of the spindle. In mechanical terms, therefore, metakinesis begins when the forces which move the chromosomes begin to act.

The nature of these forces has been the subject of many hypotheses, without any conclusive result, but it has been established – notably by the microcinematography of Bajer (1956 and later) – that these forces operate on the centromeres, while the arms of the chromosomes, as a rule, follow passively. The movement of the centromeres is hesitant and sinuous, at least at first, swinging to and fro across the equatorial plane of the spindle. These movements suggest that the centromeres are being pulled in opposite directions by two conflicting forces, and that they arrive at their position on the equator of the spindle as an equilibrium.

On the other hand it is known that at the end of metakinesis the centromeres are attached to the spindle fibres, and this suggests that the fibres may play some part in the forces acting on the centromeres. It is still not known at what moment this attachment between the fibre and the centromere comes into being, but once a fibre links a centromere to one of the two poles it no longer seems able to link itself to anything except a fibre running to the opposite pole. Thus the centromere seems to have become 'polarised' in some way. Furthermore, the work of Bajer (1966) has shown that each fibre is composed of ten to twenty microtubules, analogous to those which can be seen in the peripheral cytoplasm of the resting cell (figure 8·10).

It can therefore be postulated, hypothetically, that the spindle fibres exert upon the centromeres a force that is proportional to their length, that is to say, to the distance of the centromere from the poles. This would explain how the centromeres are maintained on the equator of the spindle. So long as this 'equilibrium' theory (of Oestergren) tells us nothing about the nature of the forces involved, it must remain a hypothesis, but experiments confirm that these forces do exist.

3 *Metaphase.* We have seen that the chromosomes remain for a time in the equatorial plane of the spindle, held there by the forces exerted upon the centromeres. In spite of the absence of any obvious movement, metaphase is a period of sustained dynamic activity.

224

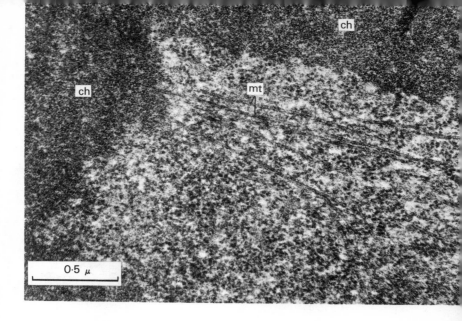

8·10 Ultrastructure of the spindle fibres, fixed in glutaraldehyde. Bundles of microtubules (mt) are attached to the metaphase chromosomes (ch) of a root cell of wheat. (×45,000).

This is confirmed when the chromosomes are filmed by microcinematography, and are seen to oscillate continuously throughout metaphase (Bajer and Mole-Bajer 1956).

Oestergren (1945) made observations of metaphase in cells which had trivalent chromosomes, each consisting of three chromatids. In this case there were two spindle fibres leading to one pole, and only one to the other, and under the unequal forces each trivalent chromosome took up position nearer to the pole with two fibres than to the pole with only one. A similar displacement towards one pole can be provoked by destroying one of the fibres with a microray of ultraviolet light (figure 8·11).

In order to exert a force on the chromosomes, the fibres must have some fixed point of application against which to pull. This is provided by fibres which run directly from one pole to the other, and form a firm axis to the spindle, maintaining the distance apart of the poles. The spindle axis repels any foreign body (which includes the chromosomes) outwards on to the spindle fibres; these bodies are generally driven out via the poles.

Sometimes the condensation of the chromosomes goes on during metaphase, and then each chromosome consists of two chromatids lying close together, and (typically) with one or two constrictions that are without chromatin (figure 8·8₄): the primary constriction, where the centromere is located, and – in some chromosomes – a secondary constriction that has no centromere but is sometimes drawn out, and which in that case isolates a terminal granule which is called the satellite (figure 8·12). We shall see the importance of this secondary constriction later, at telophase. It sometimes happens that the centromere itself becomes terminal especially if the chromosome is very short, or even punctiform.

Metaphase is the best time to study the chromosome number.

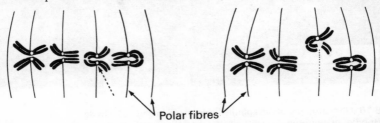

Polar fibres

8·11 Effects of the destruction of one of the fibres running between a centrosome and a pole of the spindle during the heterotypic metaphase of meiosis.
Left The arrow indicates the centrosome to which the fibre is attached.
Right Successive displacements of the two associated chromosomes after destruction of the centrosome.

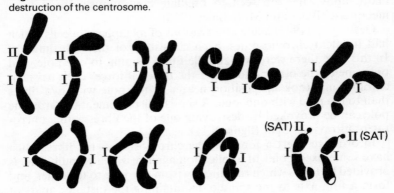

8·12 The chromosome complement of *Allium cepa* is eight pairs.
I = primary construction (where the centromeres are located);
II = secondary construction; SAT = satellites.

Every kind of living organism has a definite number of chromosomes in its diploid nucleus ($x = 2n$), in two identical sets of n chromosomes. These n chromosomes are characteristic, and morphologically recognisable. When the chromosomes are held on the equator of the spindle they are under forces of repulsion from each other, and from the axis of the spindle. Since the centromeres are attracted by the spindle fibres, the arms of all the chromosomes are generally repelled radially outwards, away from the axis of the spindle.

4 *Anaphase*. Metaphase comes to an end suddenly, when the centromere of each spindle divides and the two chromatids separate from each other. Important facts about the mechanism of anaphase, and the tensions involved in it, have been obtained by irradiating cells with β-rays, which causes the chromosomes to break up.

First of all, any fragments of chromosome that have no centromere (akinetic fragments) are shot out of the spindle altogether by way of the poles, yet in these fragments the two chromatids remain together, showing that their attachment to each other does not depend on the presence of a centromere.

The signal for anaphase to begin must be independent of the spindle, because when separation into the two chromatids takes place it happens simultaneously, in all the chromosomes, including those fragments that have been expelled from the spindle into the cytoplasm.

This same fact shows that the separation of the centromeres into two is not the signal for anaphase, because the akinetic fragments separate into chromatids at the same moment.

Hence it seems as if anaphase is started by some signal which involves the cell as a whole, and after this signal each chromatid moves to one pole, while its erstwhile partner moves to the other (figure 8·8$_5$). This movement is called the 'polar ascension', and is normally synchronised for all the chromosomes. This is the real kinetic moment of cell division, that in which the actual movement of chromosomes is greatest and most orderly, and implies that real forces act on the chromosomes and draw them towards the poles of the spindle. The nature of these forces is unknown, yet microcinematography gives plenty of evidence that these forces act on the centromeres, at least under normal conditions. It is certain that a fibre runs from each centromere to a pole, and that polar ascension is accompanied by shortening of the fibres; yet we cannot be sure that the contraction of the fibres draws the centromere polewards.

It might be that the movement causes the shortening.

In the rear of the chromosomes, as they move towards the poles, the middle of the spindle becomes a more or less homogeneous mass, which grows as the chromosomes retreat. It has been suggested that the growth of this substance – the phragmoplast – might exert pressure on the chromosomes and drive them polewards. This would explain the simultaneous movement of the chromosomes, but actually it often happens that one or two of them lag behind the others. Nevertheless the laggards eventually arrive at the poles, indicating that each chromosome has its own 'motor'.

However, the thickening up of the phragmoplast must contribute something to the pressure involved, because there is often a trace of elongation of the axis of the spindle, especially in some animal cells.

The speed with which the chromosomes move during polar ascension is much less than the speed of cyclosis at its best: only 0.2–5μ per minute, compared with the 250–300μ per minute of cyclosis in leaf cells of *Elodea*.

At the end of anaphase the centromeres come close to the poles and press against each other, and as a result of this 'polar bunching' the arms of all the chromosomes radiate into tufts at the two ends of the spindle (figure 8.8_6). In between the two bunches of chromosomes the remnants of the spindle constitute the phragmoplast, which is dense, homogeneous and weakly birefringent, with the consistency of a gel.

5 *Telophase*. This is the collective term for all the further steps necessary to complete the division of the cell, and is marked by a sequence of events that are often difficult to observe.

(a) *Re-construction of nuclear envelopes*. In most species of organism, the first event after polar bunching is the formation, round each group of chromosomes, of a new nuclear membrane, which is closely applied to them, and follows their contours. Later on the new nucleus swells, spaces appear between the chromosomes (constituting a new nucleoplasm), and the membrane no longer touches the chromatin, apart from the many tiny points of contact that subsist throughout interphase. Pores now appear in the nuclear membrane, in between these points.

(b) *Continued evolution of the chromosomes*. While the young nuclei of telophase are swelling, the chromosomes remain with their arms more or less straight, and become pitted with a multitude of small holes. This may indicate a process of hydration of the chromosomes; it certainly represents a despiralisation of the chromonemas (figure $8 \cdot 8_7$). The result is an elongation of the arms of the chromosomes, accompanied by the deformations that result from unwinding of the spiral structure. This tangles up the chromosomes, and produces the reticulate appearance that we noticed earlier, in the resting nucleus. It is thus impossible to say whether or not fusion (anastomosis) might not occur between one chromonema and another, but in any event this does not destroy the individuality of the chromosomes which must persist through interphase.

These despiralisation processes may save parts, especially in those many species which have nucleoli with chromocentres (see p. 202). These are compact masses of heterochromatin.

In areticulate nuclei, the masses of heterochromatin which constitute the euchromocentres, or prochromosomes, are very big, but nevertheless this is a part only of the chromosome material. The euchromatic portions also undergo despiralisation, but become so thin that they escape notice under the light microscope, and are consequently described as being 'dechromatinised'. Their evolution must be followed with the electron microscope. At the start of prophase certain structures which are delicately twisted fibres, Feulgen-positive, seem to attach themselves to the prochromosomes, as if the latter had provoked a regrouping of all the chromatin that was dispersed through the cytoplasm (Doulat 1943; Delay 1946–7).

(c) *Formation of nucleoli*. It is just as difficult to determine the reappearance of nucleoli at telophase as it was their disappearance at prophase. According to Das and Alfert (1959) the argentophilic substance that migrated into the cytoplasm at the time of prophase now reassembles around the chromosomes of the telophase nucleus, and then runs together into a nucleolus. Using an electron microscope, Lafontaine (1958) detected nucleolar material at the end of anaphase in *Allium cepa*, but not until telophase was under way in *Vicia faba*. In the *Allium* nucleus this substance forms tiny granular masses, which are scattered in between the arms of the chromosomes; whereas in *Vicia* it surrounds the chromosomes in a very thin layer.

The nucleolar substance concentrates bit by bit in those places where the new nucleoli are about to arise, and – in principle at least – there seems to be an allowance of one nucleolus for each set of n chromosomes. Thus, diploid cells normally form two nucleoli at the end of telophase, and then, generally, when the chromosomes are short, and the nuclear reticulum is loose, or non-existent, these two nucleoli eventually fuse into one.

The total volume of all the nucleoli in the two telophase nuclei is greater than that of the nucleoli in the mother cell; hence some new nucleolar material must be synthesised during nuclear division. In fact Wood and Taylor (1959) stated that they were able to detect the incorporation of cytidine labelled with tritium into the telophase nucleoli of *Vicia faba*. On the other hand Heitz (1932) and McClintock (1934) demonstrated that the nucleoli arose in contact with a secondary constriction of a particular chromosome; but, although we now concede that the secondary constriction is the assembly point of the nucleoli, it is not the place of synthesis; this appears to take place along the length of the chromosome (Lafontaine 1958).

This picture is confirmed by the behaviour of akinetic fragments in irradiated cells, which, at telophase, surround themselves with their own nuclear membrane and form micronuclei. Within these micronuclei there is generally argentophilic material to be found (that is, nucleolar material, according to Das and Alfert), but it does not form itself into a nucleolus unless the fragment of chromosome happens to include the secondary nucleolar constriction.

The phragmoplast and cytodiaeresis At the time that the daughter nuclei are forming, a dividing membrane appears equatorially in the phragmoplast. We have already noted that, at first, this phragmoplast is weakly birefringent. In fact it is composed only of fibres running from pole to pole of the spindle, immersed in a mass of isotropic protein gel. The fibres themselves are composed of bundles of microtubules of 150–250Å diameter. Here and there, too, can be found a few saccules of the ER, which appear to be derived from the polar regions of the spindle (Porter and Machado 1960). From the start of its existence the phragmoplast is being enriched by a significant influx of RNA, apparently derived from the chromosomes, which gradually become less basophile. Yet at first the phragmoplast contains no other structures, apart from tiny clear vesicles. Soon vesicles begin to appear that contain the material for the future membrane, and in the vicinity of these appear longitudinal striae, which have no connection with the fibres of the defunct chromatic spindle. The material in the vesicles is in the form of granules, which dispose themselves in the equatorial plane, and form the cell plate (figure 8·8$_8$).

The cell plate, dense, and with a high refractive index in the living cell, is formed from droplets that will stain with neutral red, and which can be stained after fixation (Becker 1938). Accumulating at first in the centre of the cell plate, these droplets spread towards the edge, and then over it, into the surrounding cytoplasm, till they reach the cell wall of the mother cell. The droplets later coalesce into a thin layer, which becomes the middle (pectic) layer of the cell wall that will separate the two daughter cells. The tiny globules are fluid at first, but chemical change makes them more viscous. According to Olszewska (1960) they present in succession the reactions typical of lipids, then of polysaccharides, then of proteins.

Under the electron microscope it can be seen that the droplets are each bounded by a membrane analogous to the cell membrane, and when they coalesce they leave between them channels of phragmoplast material which become the plasmodesmata of the cell wall (figures 8·13, 8·14). Some of these are later blocked, but others persist. The membrane that originally surrounded the droplets now becomes the two cell membranes of the two sides of the new dividing wall. Thus it is clear that continuity between the daughter cells, by way of the plasmodesmata, antedates by some time their separation by a new cell wall.

The electron microscope also makes it clear that the materials needed for the construction of the cell wall by the cell plate are provided, at least in part, by a multitude of Golgi vesicles. These vesicles arise from dictyosomes, which form in great number in the phragmoplast, after nuclear division is completed (Whaley and Mollenhauer 1963) (figure 8·13$_2$).

Finally, a little before the new cell wall joins on to that of the mother cell, there appear in the phragmoplast an important array of mitochondria, sometimes a few proplastids, as well as tiny vacuoles analogous to those which appear in the most active meristematic cells. Most of these structures make their appearance before the phragmoplast abandons its gel state, and merges with the cytoplasm. It is still not known where all these structures come from.

After the mother and daughter membranes have united, the viscosity of the gel of the phragmoplast diminishes gradually by a process of 'solation' that is barely perceptible by microcinematography (Bajer 1965). This transformation into a plasmasol starts against the daughter nuclei, and spreads towards the old equator, that is, towards the new dividing membrane.

231

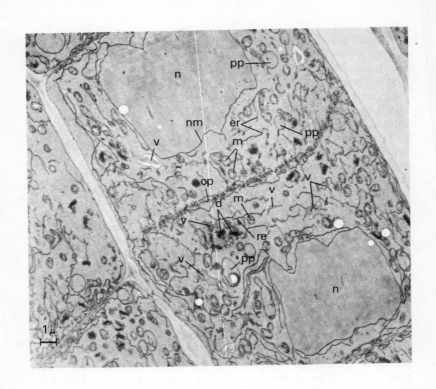

8·13 Above Telophase in a root cell of *Triticum*, shortly before the union of the cell plate with the wall of the mother cell. Note that the phragmoplast already contains the chief components of the cytoplasm.
d = dictyosomes ; er = endoplasmic reticulum ; m = mitochondrion ; n=nuclei ; cp=cell plate ; pp=proplastids ; v=nascent vacuoles. (×4,500).
Right One edge of the cell plate above, as seen under high magnification. It can be seen that the dictyosomes emit many vesicles (vg), which aggregate on the edge of the cell plate under construction, around future pectic vacuoles (pv). (×21,500). (Fixed in permanganate).

232

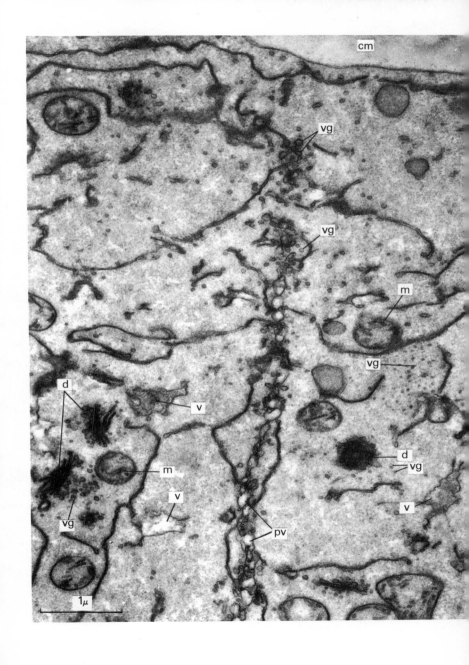

Exchanges between nucleus and cytoplasm during mitosis The phragmoplast evolves in such a manner that its substance is transformed into cytoplasmic material. Now we have seen that the phragmoplast represents the remains of the achromatic spindle, after the chromosomes have moved apart into polar bundles, at the close of anaphase. The spindle itself was the result of a fusion between the 'clear zone' and the nucleoplasm, and during nuclear division has received materials such as RNA from the chromosomes. It is thus very likely that the phragmoplast, when it is transformed, will contribute substances of nuclear origin into the cytoplasm of the daughter cells.

Conversely, although the nuclear membrane of the daughter cells is formed in more or less close contact with the chromosomes it will doubtless pick up with them substances derived from the former spindle, some of which are of cytoplasmic origin, and which will now find themselves included in the nucleoplasm.

It seems, therefore, pretty well certain that the time of mitosis is a time of important exchanges between nucleus and cytoplasm. Besides, we know that every cell division stirs up biochemical activity in the daughter cells. Respiration, which is at a minimum during nuclear division, abruptly intensifies after telophase, and a period of active growth testifies to an upsurge of biosynthesis. This activity declines when the daughter cells have grown to the size of their mother cell, and falls to a minimum when the next cell division is imminent. In short, every cell division produces a kind of rejuvenescence, involving interchanges between nucleus and cytoplasm that are different both quantitatively and qualitatively from what goes on during interphase, in resting cells.

Substances which inhibit mitosis A number of physical and chemical agents upset mitosis, and study of these has provided valuable information about the mechanisms of cell division. Some of these results are of great practical value, in such different fields as the treatment of cancer and the production of polyploid plants. Lack of space in a work such as the present obliges us to be brief about them.

Certain substances stop the cells from entering into cell division, or even reverse mitoses that have already started, turning them back to interphase. Antipyrine is an example of the latter category, whereas malic hydrazide cannot cope with a cell division that has already started.

Other substances are particularly interesting because they inhibit

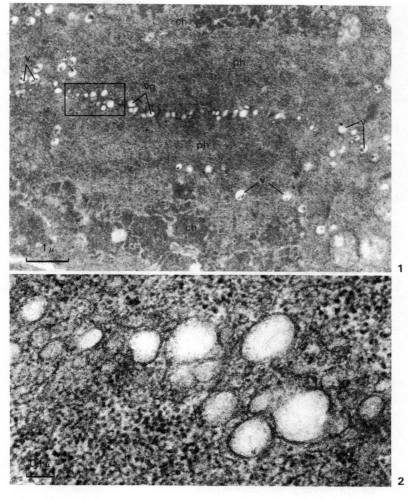

8·14 Root of *Hordeum vulgare* fixed in OsO₄.
1 Early telophase, showing the phragmoplast (ph) still homogeneous outside vesicles (vg) of the cell plate; ch = chromosomes in polar clumps; v=ordinary vacuoles. (×11,000).
2 A greatly enlarged view of the part of **1** enclosed within the square, showing the tripartite structure of the membrane of the future pectic vesicles, a structure analogous to that of the cell membrane. (×70,000).

235

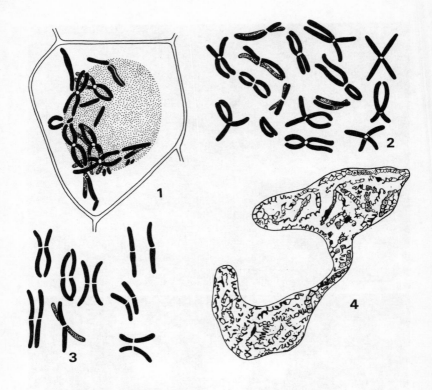

8·15 Certain aspects of mitosis of root cells of *Allium cepa* after treatment with colchicum. (After Mangenot 1942).
1 Prophase chromosome untwisted and dispersed round a 'pseudospindle' that is isotropic.
2 Pseudometaphase with bivalent chromosomes dispersed.
3 Pseudoanaphase, with no polar migration but with the chromatids separated.
4 Restitution nucleus.

the formation of the achromatic spindle. The best known of these is colchicin, in the presence of which (figure 8·15) prophase is normal, with condensation and the formation of chromosomes, but the movements of karyokinesis are suppressed, since a functional spindle is lacking. Metakinesis is thus non-existent, and there is a pseudometaphase in which the chromosomes are normal but they are not arranged in the equatorial plane (because there are no spindle fibres to pull them there). Chromatids and centromeres are formed, however, during a pseudoanaphase, but they do not separate (figure 8·15₃). The process of despiralisation in telophase is also normal, but as polar ascension does not take place, the final result is one single nucleus, called a 'restitution nucleus', in which the number of chromosomes is doubled.

Finally, mitoses can be seriously perturbed by the introduction of substances which hinder the synthesis of DNA (for example, triethylene melamine), or of associated proteins. On the other hand ionising radiations (ultraviolet, x-rays, or radiations from radioactive substances) produce aberrations in the chromosomes that are more or less serious, and which lead to either fragmentation of the chromosomes, or irregular associations among them. Then the separation of the chromosomes at anaphase is irregular, subject to chance, and cells which contain mutant chromosomes are most often inefficient, and do not live long. However, these ways of interfering with normal mitosis have considerable interest for the production of experimental mutations.

9 Conclusion: the importance of plants

Within the small compass of this book we have seen many examples of the important contribution that the methods of chemistry and physics have made to an understanding of the living cell. Biology is dependent on the continued progress of these sciences. From time to time in the history of chemistry and physics, discoveries have been made which have brought the two sciences nearer together, and now this is becoming a feature of the progress of cell biology, especially where it concerns the fine structures of the cell.

The electron microscope has reinforced the ideas, derived from the classical cytological researches at the beginning of the century, that living matter has one fundamental structure, common to both plants and animals. Those ultrastructures of the cell that are directly concerned with the most fundamental phenomena of the living state – reproduction, specificity, respiration, biosynthesis of proteins, among others – are the same in plant cells as they are in animals. The structures of nuclei and mitochondria, the endoplasmic reticulum, the Golgi apparatus, and the ectoplasmic pellicle, all these are similar in the two kingdoms, though they differ in detail as a result of cell differentiation, which diversifies the cells even within one and the same organism. This idea of the essential unity of all living matter, with its consequence that there can be a science of general cytology, or cellular biology which is not restricted to either plants or animals, is a triumph of modern biology.

All the same, plants and animals are different, both in their appearance and in their way of life, and this difference is reflected in the cells, and in the specialised functions of their tissues. However, only plant cells are discussed in this book, and they possess several structures that do not exist at all in animal cells. Among them are the plastids, the cell wall, and the vacuolar apparatus, and the last of these has no real equivalent in animals. The cell wall and the vacuoles are responsible for the characteristic habit of plants, whether they stand erect, or are pendant or creeping, while the plastids give them the power to synthesise organic matter from inorganic materials.

This special equipment peculiar to plants makes them into

veritable photosynthetic factories, the products of which are indispensable for the maintenance of the biosphere. Thanks to their chloroplasts, plants can make use of solar energy to convert mineral substances such as carbon dioxide, water, nitrates, sulphates, phosphates, etc, into organic compounds. Animals are unable to do anything like this, and must obtain the organic substances that they require either by eating plants, or by eating other animals. On balance, on a world-scale, animals are therefore completely dependent on plants for their food. Up to the present time all human ingenuity has not succeeded in imitating the photosynthesis of green plants, and therefore man, too, could not exist without plants, including those of the sea.

If living organisms are to continue to exist, it is essential that certain important elements such as carbon, nitrogen, phosphorus, etc should be recovered from their waste products, and fed back to them in a suitable form. Hence there are cycles of the elements concerned in biogenesis, and certain steps in these cycles can be carried out only by plants. For instance, the carbon dioxide that is a waste product of respiration in both animals and plants is useless to animals until plants have taken it up and incorporated it into the molecules of starch, sugars, proteins or fats. The quantities of material handled, and the amount of energy transformed, by all the plants of land and water, including the phytoplankton of the sea, are of an order of magnitude far greater than the total handled by all the animals plus man. We can get a faint idea of this by reflecting that all the oxygen of the atmosphere has been derived from photosynthesis by plants, and that it is the green plants that maintain the stability of the atmospheric composition. Plants compensate for the oxidative reactions of all living organisms, including all the micro-organisms.

So it seems that all the social and industrial progress made by man cannot release him from his dependence upon plants, and that man's very future depends on conserving plants. Not only does he derive all of his food from them (take cereals alone, for example), but over and above this, man is dependent on the natural vegetation to keep the atmosphere suitable for him. To this must be added the fact that plants provide much of the raw material for his industry, such as wood, vegetable fibres, and paper, and that paper is consumed in ever-increasing quantities by all the advanced countries of the world.

Bibliography

Altmann, R. 1890. *Die Elementarorganismen und ihre Beziehungen zu den Zellen,* Leipzig.

Arnon, D.I., Allen, M.B. and Whatley, F.R. 1954. Photosynthesis by isolated chloroplasts, *Nature London* **174**, 394.

Bailey, I.W. 1930. The cambium and its derivative tissues. A survey of the vacuole in living cells, *Zeitschr.f.Zellforsch.und Mikr.Anat.*, **10**, 651–82.

Bajer, A. 1957. Cine-micrographic studies on mitosis in endosperm. III. The origin of the mitotic spindle, *Exp.Cell Res.*, **13**, 493–502.

Bajer, A. 1958. Cine-micrographic studies on chromosome movements in β-irradiated cells, *Chromosoma*, **9**, 319–31.

Bajer, A. 1959. Change of length and volume of mitotic chromosomes in living cells, *Hereditas*, **45**, 579–96.

Bajer, A. 1965. Cine-micrographic analysis of cell-plate formation in endosperm, *Exptl.Cell Res.*, **37**, 376–98.

Bajer, A. 1966. Movements within the mitotic spindle in *Dynamics of fluids and plasmas*, (Ed. PAI) Academic Press, London, New York.

Bajer, A. and Molè-Bajer, J. 1956. Cine-micrographic studies on mitosis in endosperm. II. Chromosome, cytoplasmic and Brownian movements, *Chromosoma*, **7**, 558–607.

Becker, W.A. 1938. Recent investigations *in vivo* on the division of plant cells, *Bot. Rev.*, **4**, 446–72.

Becquerel, P. 1923. Observations sur la nécrobiose du protoplasme végétal à l'aide d'un nouveau réactif vital, *C.R.Acad.Sc.*

Bell, P. and Mühlethaler, K. 1964. The degeneration and reappearance of mitochondria in the egg cells of a plant, *J.Cell Biol.*, **20**, 235–48.

Belozerskii, A.N. and Uryson, S.O. 1958. On the composition of nuclear nucleoproteins of some plants, *Biokhimiya*, **23**, 568–73.

Benda, C. 1902. Die Mitochondria, *Ergebn.d.Anat.u.Entwick.*, **12**, 743–81.

Beneden, E.van, 1883. Recherches sur la maturation de l'oeuf et la fécondation (*Ascaris megalocephala*), *Arch.Biol.*, **4**, 265–640.

Berkaloff, C. 1961. Etude, au microscope électronique, des plastes de *Laminaria saccharina* L., *C.R.Acad.Sc.*, **252**, 2747–49.

Berkaloff, C. 1963. Les cellules méristématiques d'*Himanthalia lorea* (L.) SF.Gray. Etude au microscope électronique, *J.Microscopie*, **2**, 213–28.

Birnstiel, M.L. and Hyde, B.B. 1963. Protein synthesis by isolated Pea nucleoli, *J.Cell Biol.*, **18**, 41–50.

Bisalputra, T. and Bisalputra, A.A. 1967. The occurrence of DNA fibrils in chloroplasts of *Laurencia spectabilis*, *J.Ultrastruct.Res.*, **17**, 14–22.

240

Bisalputra, T. and Bisalputra, A.A. 1967. Chloroplast and mitochondrial DNA in a brown alga *Egregia menziesii*, *J. Cell Biol.*, **33**, 511–20

Bopp-Hassenkamp, G. 1958. Lichtmikroskopische und elektronenoptische Untersuchungen über den Aufbau pflanzlicher chromosomen im Pachytän der Meiosis, *Protoplasma*, **50**, 243–68.

Bouck, B.G. 1965. Fine structure and organelle associations in brown algae, *J. Cell Biol.*, **26**, 523–37.

Bouet, M. 1954. Etudes cytologiques sur le développement des poils absorbants, *Rev. Cytol. et Biol. Veget.*, **15**, 261–305.

Bowen, R.H. 1928. The osmiophilic platelets, *Zeitschr für Zellforsch. und Mikr. Anat.*, **6**, 689–725.

Brachet, J. 1942. La détection histochimique et le microdosage des acides pentose-nucléiques, *Enzymologia*, **10**, 87–93.

Brachet, J. 1956. The mode of action of ribonuclease on living root tips, *Biochimica and Bioph. Acta*, **19**, 583.

Brachet J., Chantrenne H. and Vanderhaege F. 1955. Recherches sur les interactions biochimiques entre le noyau et le cytoplasme chez les organismes unicellulaires. II. *Acetabularia mediterranea*, *Bioch. Bioph. Acta*, **18**, 544–63.

Brown, D.E.S. and Marsland, D.A. 1936. The viscosity of *Amoeba* at high hydrostatic pressure, *J. Cellular Comp. Phys.*, **8**, 159–65.

Brown, R. 1833. Observations on the organs and mode of fecundation in Orchidae and Asclepiadeae, *Trans. of the Linnean Soc.*, **16**, 685–745.

Buvat, R. 1944. Recherches sur la dédifférenciation des cellules végétales, *Ann. Sc. Nat. Bot.*, 11e serie, **5**, cf p. 81–82.

Buvat, R. 1948. Recherches sur les effets cytologiques de l'eau, *Rev. Cyt. et Cytophys. végét.*, **10**, 1–35.

Buvat, R. 1957. Formations de Golgi dans les cellules radiculaires d'*Allium cepa* L., *C. R. Acad. Sc.*, a, **244**, 1401–03.

Buvat, R. 1958. Recherches sur les infrastructures du cytoplasme, dans les cellules du méristème apical, des ébauches foliaires et des feuilles développées d'*Elodea canadensis*, *Ann. Sc. Nat. Bot.*, 11e serie, **19**, 121–61.

Buvat, R. 1959. Infrastructures des protéoplastes de la racine de *Phajus wallichii* (Orchidacées), *C. R. Acad. Sc.*, b, **249**, 289–91.

Buvat, R. 1962. Electron microscopy of plant protoplasm (bibliography), *Int. Rev. Cytol.*, **14**, 41–155.

Buvat, R. 1965. Le cytoplasme végétal in *Travaux dédiés à L. Plantefol*, ed. Masson and Cie, Paris.

Buvat, R. 1968. Diversité des vacuoles dans les cellules de la racine d'Orge (*Hordeum sativum*), *C. R. Ac. Sc.*, **267**, 296.

Buvat, R. and Poux, N. 1961. Observation de la trame fondamentale du hyaloplasme dans les cellules végétales différenciées, *C. R. Acad. Sc.*, **252**, 2915–17.

Byers, T.J., Platt, D.B. and Goldstein, L. 1963. The cytonucleoproteins of amoebae. I. Some chemical properties and intracellular distribution,

241

J. Cell. Biol., **19**, 453–66. II. Some aspects of cytonucleoprotein behaviour and synthesis, 467–75.

Calvin, M. and Lynch, V. 1952. Grana-like structures of *Synechococcus cedorum,. Nature, London*, **169**, 455.

Camefort, H. 1964. Observations sur la structure des chromosomes et des nucléoles de l'oosphère des Pins, *C. R. Acad. Sc.*, **259**, 4335–38.

Caporali, L. 1958. Infrastructure et évolution des plastes du méristème radiculaire de *Lens culinaris* L., *C. R. Acad. Sc.*, **246**, 1263–65.

Caporali, L. 1959. Recherches sur les infrastructures des cellules radiculaires de *Lens culinaris* et particulièrement sur l'évolution des leucoplastes, *Ann. Sc. Nat. Bot.*, IIe serie, **20**, 215–47.

Caro, L. G. and Palade, G. E. 1964. Protein synthesis, storage and discharge in the pancreatic exocrine cell. An autoradiographic study, *J. Cell Biol.*, 473–95.

Caspersson, T. 1941. Studien über den Eiweissumsatz der Zelle, *Naturwissenschaften*, **29**, 33–43.

Catesson, A. M. 1962. Modifications saisonnières des vacuoles et variations de la pression osmotique dans le cambium d'*Acer pseudoplatanus, C. R. Acad. Sc.*, **254**, 3887–9.

Catesson, A. M. 1964. Origine, fonctionnement et variations cytologiques saisonnières du cambium de l'*Acer pseudoplatanus* L. (Acéracées). *Ann. Sc. Nat., Bot.*, 12e serie **5**, 229–498.

Catesson, A. M. 1966. Présence de phytoferritine dans le cambium et les tissus conducteurs de la tige de Sycomore (*Acer pseudoplatanus*), *C. R. Acad. Sc.*, **262**, 1070–3.

Chardard, R. 1962. Recherches sur les cellules mères des microspores des Orchidées. Etude au microscope électronique, *Rev. Cytol. et Biol. végét.*, 2 **24**, 1–148.

Chardard, R. and Rouiller, C. 1957. L'ultrastructure de trois Algues desmidiées. Etude au microscope électronique, *Rev. Cytol. et Biol. végét.*, **18**, 153–78.

Christensen, A. K. and Fawcett, D. W. 1960. The fine structure of testicular interstitial cells in the Opossum, *Anat. Record*, **136**, 333.

Claude, A. 1941. Particulate components of cytoplasm, *Cold Spring Harbor Symposium* for *Quantitative Biol.*, **9**, 263–71.

Cohen Bazire, G. and Kunisawa R. 1963. The fine structure of *Rhodospirillum rubrum, J. Cell Biol.*, **16**, 401–19.

Comandon, J. and de Fonbrune, P. 1939. Greffe nucléaire totale, simple ou multiple, chez une Amibe, *C. R. Soc. Bio.*, **130**, 744–8.

Coulomb, C. 1968. Mise en évidence de structures analogues aux lysosomes dans le méristème radiculaire de la Courge (*Cucurbita pepo* L., Cucurbitacée), *J. Microscopie*.

Coulomb, C. and Buvat, R. 1968. Processus de dégénérescence cytoplasmique partielle dans les cellules de jeunes racines de *Cucurbita pepo, C. R. Ac. Sc.*

Dangeard, P. 1947. *Cytologie végétale et cytologie générale*, Lechevalier, Ed. Paris.

Dangeard, P. 1958. Observations sur un élément de la structure plastidaire: le centroplaste, *C.R.Acad.Sc.*, **246**, 2980–3.

Delaporte, B. 1939. Recherches cytologiques sur les Bactéries et les Cyanophycées, *Rev.Gen.Bot.*, **51**, 615–43, 689–708, 748–68; and 1940, **52**, 40–8, 75–96 and 112–60.

Delaporte, B. 1950. Observations on the cytology of Bacteria, *Advances in Genetics*, **3**, 1–32.

Delay, C. 1946–7. Recherches sur la structure des noyaux quiescents chez les Phanérogames, *Rev.Cytol. et Cytophysiol.végét.*, **9**, 169–223.

Doulat, E. 1943. *Le noyau et l'élément chromosomique chez les spermaphytes* (Thèse Doctorat), Grenoble.

Doutreligne, J. 1935. Note sur la structure des chloroplastes, *Koninkl.Akad. van Wetensch.Amsterdam, Proc.of the section of sc.*, **38**, 886–96.

Drawert, H. and Metzner, I. 1958. Fluorescenz-und elektronen mikroskopische untersuchungen an *Oscillatoria borneti* zukal. V.Mitteilung der Reihe; Zellmorphologische und Zellphysiologische Studien an Cyanophyceen, *Zeit.f.Bot.*, **46**, 16–25.

Duboscq, O. and Grassé, P.P. 1933. L'appareil parabasal des Flagellés, avec des remarques sur le trophosponge, l'appareil de Golgi, des mitochondries et le vacuome, *Arch.Zool.exp.et gén.*, **73**, 381–621.

Dujardin, F. 1835. Recherches sur les organismes inférieurs, *Ann. Sc. Nat. Zool.*, 2e serie, **4**, 343–77.

Dutrochet, H. 1824. *Recherches anatomiques et physiologiques sur la structure intime des Végétaux et des Animaux et sur leur motilité*, Ivol. in 8°, Baillere (ed.), Paris.

Duve, C.de, 1959. Lysosomes, a new group of cytoplasmic particles, in T.Hayashi: *Subcellular particles*, Ronald Press Co, New York, 128–59.

Duve, C.de, 1963. The lysosomes, *Scientific American*, **208**(5), 64–72.

Duve, C.de, Beaufay, H., Jacques, P., Rahman, Y., Sellinger, O.Z., Wattiaux, R. and de Coninck, S. 1960. Intracellular localization of catalase and of some oxidases in rat liver, *Biochim.Biophys.Acta*, **40**, 186–7.

Duve, C.de and Baudhuin, P. 1966. Peroxisomes (microbodies and related particles), *Physiol.Rev.*, **46**, 323–57.

Emberger, L. 1921. Recherches sur l'origine et l'évolution des plastides chez les Ptéridophytes. Contribution a l'étude de la cellule végétale, *Arch. Morph.gen.exp.*, **8**, 186.

Emberger, L. 1927. Nouvelles recherches sur le chondriome de la cellule végétale, *Rev.gle.Bot.*, **39**, 341–63 and 420–48.

Estable, C. and Sotelo, J.R., 1954. The behaviour of the nucleolonema during mitosis, *Symp. on fine struc. of cells*, Leiden, Noordoff. Ltd., Groningen (1950), 170–90.

Faure-Fremiet, E. 1910. Etudes sur les mitochondries des Protozoaires et des cellules sexuelles, *Arch.Anat.Micr.*, **II**, 458–648.

Fernández-Morán, H. 1962. Cell-membrane ultrastructure. Low temperature electron microscopy and X-ray diffraction studies of lipoprotein components in lamellar systems, *Circulation*, **26**, 1039–65.

Fernández-Morán, H., Oda, T., Blair, P.V. and Green, D.E. 1964. A macromolecular repeating unit of mitochondrial structure and function, *J. Cell Biol.*, **22**, 63–100.

Finean, J.B., Sjöstrand, F.S. and Steinmann, E. 1953. Submicroscopic organisation of some layered lipoprotein structures (nerve myelin, retinal rods, and chloroplasts), *Exp. Cell. Res.*, 5, 557–59.

Fontana, F. 1781. Traité sur le venin de la Vipère (On y a joint des observations sur la structure primitive du corps animal), 2 vol. in 4°, *Florence*.

Frederick, S.E., Newcomb, E.H., Vigil, E.L. and Wergin, W.P. 1968. Fine structural characterization of plant microbodies, *Planta (Berl.)*, **81**, 229–52.

Frenster, J.H., Allfrey, V.G. and Mirsky, A.E. 1960. Metabolism and morphology of ribonucleoprotein particles from the cell nucleus of lymphocytes, *Proc. Nat. Acad. Sc. US*, **46**, 432–44.

Frey-Wyssling, A. 1947. *Submicrosopic morphology of Protoplasm*, Elsevier (ed.), Amsterdam.

Frey-Wyssling, A. and Kreutzer, E. 1958. Die submikroskopische Entwicklung der chromoplasten in den Blüten von *Ranunculus repens* L., *Planta*, **51**, 104–14.

Frey-Wyssling, A. and Kreutzer, E. 1958. The submicroscopic development of chromoplasts in the fruit of *Capsicum annuum* L., *J. Ultras. Res.*, I, 397–411.

Frey-Wyssling, A. and Mülethaler, K. 1965. *Ultrastructural Plant Cytology*, Elsevier (ed.), Amsterdam, London.

Frey-Wyssling, A. and Steinmann, E. 1948. Die schichtendoppelbrechung grosser chloroplasten, *Bioch. and Biophys. Acta*, **2**, 254–9.

Fuhs, G.W. 1958. Untersuchungen an Ultradünnschnitten von *Oscillatoria amoena* (Kütz) Gomont, *Protoplasma*, **49**, 523–40.,

Garnier, C. 1897. Les 'filaments basaux' des cellules glandulaires. Note préliminaire, *Bibliographie anat.*, **5**, 278–89.

Genevès, L. 1955. Recherches sur les effets cytologiques du froid, *Rev. Cytol. et Biol. végét.*, **16**, 178.

Genevès, L., Lance, A. and Buvat, R. 1958. Sur la présence, dans le cytoplasme végétal, et sur la nature ergastoplasmique de constituants figurés analogues aux 'lysosomes' ou aux 'dense bodies' des cellules animales, *C.R. Ac. Sc.*, **247**, 2028–30.

Gibbs, S.P. 1960. The fine structure of *Euglena gracilis* with special reference to the chloroplasts and pyrenoids, *J. Ultrastructure Res.*, **4**, 127–48.

Giraud, G. 1963. La structure, les pigments et les caractéristiques fonctionnelles de l'appareil photosynthétique de diverses Algues, *Physiol. Végé.*, **1**, 203–55.

Giroud, A. 1921. Le chondriome. Recherches sur sa constitution chimique et physique, *Arch. Anat. Micr.*

Goldstein, L. 1963. RNA and protein in nucleocytoplasmic interactions, in Harris: *Cell growth and Cell division*, Academic Press, 129–49. (*Symposia of the intl.soc.for Cell Biol.*, **2**).

Goldstein, L. and Plaut, W. 1955. Direct evidence for nuclear synthesis of cytoplasmic ribose mucleic acid, *Proc.Natl.Acad.Sc.US*, **41**, 874–80.

Golgi, C. 1898. Sur la structure des cellules nerveuses, *Arch.ital.Biol.*, **30**, 60.

Gramboulan, N. and P. 1965. Cytochimie ultrastructurale du nucléole. II. Etude des sites de synthèse du RNA dans le nucléole et le noyau, *Exp.Cell Res.*, **38**, 604–19.

Grassé, P.P. 1957. Ultrastructure, polarité et reproduction de l'appareil de Golgi, *C.R.Acad.Sc.*, **245**, 1278–81

Grassé, P.P., Carasso, N. and Favard, P. 1955. Les dictyosomes (Appareil de Golgi) et leur ultrastructure, *C.R.Acad.Sc.*, **241**, 1430–2.

Green, D.E. 1959. Mitochondrial structure and function. In Teru Hayashi: *subcellular particles*, The Ronald Press Co., New York.

Green, D.E. 1964. The mitochondrion, *Scientific American*, **210**, 63–74.

Grew, N. 1682. *The Anatomy of Plants, with an idea of a philosophical history of Plants, and several other Lectures, read before the Royal Society.* I vol in 4°. W.Rawlins (ed.) London.

Guerineau, M., Grandchamp, C., Yotsuyanagi, Y. and Slonimski, P.P. 1968. Examen au microscope électronique, du DNA mitochondrial de la levure: Molécules circulaires, *C.R.Ac.Sc.*, **266**, série D, 2000–6 (voir aussi p. 1884–7).

Guignard, L. 1891. Nouvelles études sur la fécondation, *Ann. Sc. Nat. Bot.*, 7e série, **14**, 163–296.

Guilliermond, A. 1908. Recherches cytologiques sur la germination des graines de quelques graminées et contribution à l'étude des grains d'aleurone, *Arch.Anat.Micr.*, **10**, 142.

Guilliermond, A. 1911. Sur les mitochondries des cellules végétales, *C.R. Acad.Sc.*, **153**, 199–201.

Guilliermond, A. 1913. Sur la formation de l'anthocyane au sein des mitochondries, *C.R.Acad.Sc.*, **156**, 1924.

Guilliermond, A. 1919. Observations vitales sur le chondriome des Végétaux et recherches sur l'origine des chromoplastides etc., *Rev.Gén.Bot.*, **31**, 372.

Guilliermond, A. 1922. Remarques sur la formation des chloroplastes dans le bourgeon d'*Elodea canadensis*, *C.R.Acad.Sc.*, **175**, 286.

Guilliermond, A. 1926. Sur l'origine des vacuoles, *La Cellule*, **36**, 217.

Guilliermond, A. 1929. Sur le développement d'un *Saprolegnia* en milieu additionné de rouge neutre et coloration vitale de son vacuome pendant son développement, *C.R.Acad.Sc.*, **189**, 1261.

Guilliermond, A. 1930. Recherches ultramicroscopiques sur les cellules végétales et l'etat physique des constituants morphologiques de la cellule, *Rev.Gen.Bot.*, **42**, 129–43, 193–204, 272–82, 327–47, 391–408, and 473–90.

Guilliermond, A. (en collaboration avec Mangenot, G. et Plantefol, L.). 1933. *Traite de Cytologie végétale*, Le Francoid (ed.), Paris.

245

Guilliermond, A. 1935. Nouvelles recherches sur la nature et la signification des formations dites de Golgi, *Rev. Cytol. Cytophysiol. Végét.*, **I**, 197–259.

Hackett, D.P. 1959. Respiratory mechanisms in higher plants, *Ann. Rev. of Plant Physiol.*, **10**, 113–46.

Hämmerling, J. 1934. Regenerations versuche an Kernhabtigen und Kernlosen Zellteilen von *Acetabularia Wettsteinü*, *Biol. Zbl.*, **59**, 650–65.

Hämmerling, J. 1939. Ueber die Bedingungen der Kernteilung und der Zystenbildung bei *Acetabularia mediterranea*, *Biol. Zbl.*, **59**, 158–93.

Hämmerling, J. 1943. Ein- und zweikernige Transplantate zwischen *Acetabularia mediterranea* und *A. crenulata*, *Zeit. Abstamm. u. Vererbungslehre*, **81**, 84–113.

Hämmerling, J. 1953. Nucleocytoplasmic relationships in the development of *Acetabularia*, *Int. Rev. Cytol.*, **2**, 475–98.

Hämmerling, J. and Stich, H. 1956. Einbau und Ausbau von ³²P im Nukleolus etc. *Z. Naturforsch.*, **11**b, 158–61, 162–5.

Heilbrunn, L.V. 1956. *The Dynamics of living protoplasm*, Academic Press, New York.

Heim, P. 1947. Etudes sur la localisation des pigments carotiniens chez les Champignons, *Le Botaniste*, **34**, 231–41.

Heim, P. 1949. Nouvelles observations sur la localisation des caroténoïdes chez les Champignons, *Le Botaniste*, **34**, 231–41.

Heitz, E. 1932, Die Herkunft der Chromocentren, *Planta*, **18**, 571–636.

Heitz, E. 1936. Gerichtete Chlorophyllscheiben als Strukturelle Assimilationseinheiten der Chloroplasten, *Ber. deutsch. Bot. Ges.*, **54**, 362–8.

Heitz, E. 1937. Untersuchungen über den Bau der Plastiden. I. Die gerichteten Chlorophyllscheiben der Chloroplasten, *Planta*, **26**, 134–63.

Heitz, E. 1954. Kristallgitterstruktur des granum junger Chloroplasten von *Chlorophytum*, *Exp. Cell Res.*, **7**, 606–8.

Heitz, E. 1958. Plasmatische Lamellensysteme bei Pflanzen, *Proc. IVe intern. conf. on electron micros. Berlin*, **II**, 499–500, Springer (ed.) 1960.

Heitz, E. and Maly, R. 1953. Zur Frage der Herkunft der Grana, *Z. Naturforsch.*, **8**b, 243–9.

Heller, R. 1954. Les besoins minéraux des tissus en culture, *Année Biol.*, **30**, 261–81.

Hickman, D.D. and Frenkel, A. 1965. Observations on the structure of *Rhodospirillum molischianum*, *J. Cell Biol.*, **25**, 261–78.

Hickman, D.D. and Frenkel, A. 1965. Observations on the structure of *Rhodospirillum rubrum*, *J. Cell Biol.*, **25**, 279–91.

Hodge, A.J., McLean, J.D. and Mercer, F.V. 1956. A possible mechanism for the morphogenesis of lamellar systems in plant cells, *J. Biophys. Biochem. Cyt.*, **2**, 597–608.

Hofer, B. 1890. Experimentelle Untersuchungen über den Einfluss des kerns auf des Protoplasma, *Jenaische Zeitsch. f. Med. und Naturwiss.*, **24**, 105–76.

Hooke, R. 1667. Micrographia or some physiological description of minute bodies made by magnifying glasses with observations and enquiries thereupon. I. vol. in 4°, *John Martyn* (*ed.*), *London*.

Hopwood, D.A. and Glauert, A.M. 1960. The fine structure of the nuclear material of a Blue-green Alga, *Anabaena cylindrica* Lemm., *J. Biophys. Biochem. Cytol.*, **8**, 813–23.

Hovasse, R. 1937. Quelques données cytologiques nouvelles sur *Eudorina Illinoisensis* Kofoid.: Contribution à l'étude des Volvocales, *Bull. Biol. France et Belgique*, **71**, 220–37.

Ingram, V.M. 1966. *The Biosynthesis of Macromolecules*, *W.A.* Benjamin (ed.), New York and Amsterdam (Bibliography).

Iterson, W. van and Leene, W. 1964. A cytochemical localization of reductive sites in a gram-positive Bacterium Tellurite reduction in *Bacillus subtilis*, *J. Cell Biol.*, **20**, 361–75.

Iterson, W. van and Leene, W. 1964. A cytochemical localization of reductive sites in a gram-negative Bacterium Tellurite reduction in *Proteus vulgaris*, *J. Cell Biol.*, **20**, 377–87.

Jacob, F. and Monod, J. 1961. Genetic regulatory mechanisms in the synthesis of proteins, *J. Mol. Biol.*, **3**, 318–56.

Jarosch, R. 1957. Zur Mechanik der Protoplasmafibrillenbewegung, *Biochim. Biophys. Acta*, **25**, 204–5.

Jensen, W.A. and McLaren, A. 1960. Uptake of protein by plant cells. The possible occurrence of pinocytosis in plants, *Exp. Cell Res.*, **19**, 414–7.

Jezequel, A.M. and Bernhard, W. 1964. Modifications ultrastructurales du pancréas exocrine de Rat sous l'effet de l'actinomycine D, *J. Microscopie*, **3**, 279–96.

Kamiya, N. 1959. Protoplasmic streaming, *Protoplasmatologia*, 8, **3a**, Springer, Vienna.

Kamiya, N. 1960. Physics and chemistry of protoplasmic streaming, *Ann. Rev. Plant Physiol.*, **II**, 323.

Kausche, G.A. and Ruska, H. 1940. Zur Frage des Chloroplastenstruktur, *Naturwissensch.*, **28**, 303–4.

Kellenberger, E., Ryter, A. and Sechaud, J. 1958. Electron microscope study of DNA-containing plasms. II. Vegetative and mature phage DNA as compared with normal bacterial nucleoids in different physiological states, *J. Biophys. Biochem. Cyt.*, **4**, 671–8.

Kislev, N., Swift, H. and Bogorad, L. 1965. Nucleic acids of chloroplasts and mitochondria in Swiss Chard, *J. Cell Biol.*, **25**, 327–44.

Kuff, E.L. and Dalton, A.J. 1958. Biochemical studies of isolated Golgi membranes, in *Subcellular Particles*, *Vth Annual Symposium of the Soc. of Gene. Physiologists*.

Lafontaine, J.G. 1958. Structure and mode of formation of the nucleolus in meristematic cells of *Vicia faba* and *Allium cepa*, *J. Biophys. Biochem. Cyt.*, **4**, 777–84.

Lafontaine, J.G. and Chouinard, L.A. 1963. A correlated light and electron microscope study of the nucleolar material during mitosis in *Vicia faba*, *J. Cell Biol.*, **17**, 167–201.

Lance-Nougarede, A. 1960. Processus inframicroscopique de la régression plastidale et d'harmonisation de croissance de la pellicule ectoplasmique lors de l'initiation des méristèmes floraux chez *Chrysanthemum segetum* L., *C. R. Acad. Sc.*, **250**, 3371–3.

Lance-Nougarede, A. 1964. Evolution infrastructurale des chromoplastes au cours de l'ontogenèse des pétales chez le *Spartium junceum* L., (Papilionacées), *C. R. Acad. Sc.*, **258**, 683–5.

Lance-Nougarede, A. 1965. Sur l'existence de structures protéiques fibreuses dans les cavités du reticulum endoplasmique des cellules de jeunes ébauches foliares de Lentille (*Lens culinaris* L.)., *C. R. Acad. Sc.*, 261, 3451–4.

Ledbetter, M. C. and Porter, K. R. 1963. A 'microtubule' in plant cell fine structure, *J. Cell Biol.*, **19**, 239–50.

Ledbetter, M. C. and Porter, K. R. 1964. Morphology of microtubules of plant cells, *Science*, **144**, 872–4.

Lefort, M. 1960. Structure inframicroscopique du chromatoplasma de quelques Cyanophycées, *C. R. Acad. Sc.*, **250**, 1525–7.

Lehninger, A. L. 1965. *Bioenergetics*, W. A. Benjamin (ed.), New York and Amsterdam.

Lepeschkine, W. W. 1923. Ueber die Chemische Zusammensetzung der Protoplasma des Plasmodiums, *Ber. deut. Bot. Ges.*, **41**, 179–87.

Levitt, J. 1954. Investigations of the cytoplasmic particulates and proteins of Potato tubers. II. Nitrogen, Phosphorus and Carbohydrate contents, *Physiol. Plantarum*, **7**, 117–23.

Lewis, W. H. 1937. Pinocytosis by malignant cells, *Am. J. Cancer*, **29**, 666–79.

Leyon, H. 1953. The structure of chloroplasts. III. A study of pyrenoids, *Exp. Cell Res.*, **6**, 497–505.

Leyon, H. 1954. The structure of chloroplasts. IV. The development and structure of the *Aspidistra* chloroplast. *Exp. Cell Res.*, **7**, 265–73.

Link, H. F. 1812. Recherches sur l'anatomie des plantes, *Ann. Museum, Paris*, **19**, 307–44.

Lison, L. 1953. *Histochimie et cytolochimie animales. Principes et méthodes* (2nd ed.), Gauthier-Villars, Paris.

Luck, D. J. L. and Reich, E. 1964. DNA in mitochondria of *Neurospora crassa*, *Proc. Natl. Acad. Sci. (Wash.)*, **52**, 931–8.

Lucy, J. A. and Glauert, A. M. 1964. Structure and assembly of macromolecular lipid complexes composed of globular micelles, *J. Mol. Biol.*, **8**, 727–48.

Lund, H. A., Vatter, A. E. and Hanson, J. B. 1958. Biochemical and cytological changes accompanying growth and differentiation in the roots of *Zea mays*, *J. Biophys. Biochem. Cyt.*, **4**, 87–98.

McClintock, B. 1934. The relation of a particular chromosomal element to the development of the nucleoli of *Zea mays*, *Zeitschr. f. Zellforsch.*, **21**, 294–328.

Maige, A. 1928. Observations sur les divers modes de digestion des grains d'amidon dans les cellules végétales, *C. R. Acad. Sc.*

Malpighi, M. 1687. *Opera omnia*. I vol. in 4° Van den Aa, ed. Leyde.

Mangenot, G. 1922. Recherches sur les constituants morphologiques du cytoplasma des Algues, *Arch.morph.gén.exp.*, **9**, 330.

Mangenot, G. 1942. Action de la colchicine sur les racines d'*Allium cepa*, *Actualités scient.ind.*, no. 915, Hermann et Cie, Paris.

Manuel, J. 1936. Recherches sur la formation de stérides dans les chloroplastes de certaines Cactées, *Rev.gen.Bot.*, **48**, 49–80.

Marinozzi, V. 1964. Cytochimie ultrastructurale du nucléole. RNA et protéines intranucléolaires, *J.Ultrastructure Res.*, **10**, 433–56.

Marsland, D.A. 1939. The mechanism of protoplasmic streaming. The effects of high hydrostatic pressure upon cyclosis in *Elodea canadensis*, *J.Cellular comp. Physiol.*, **13**, 23–30.

Martin, E.M. and Morton, R.K. 1956. Enzymic Properties of microsomes and mitochondria from Silver Beet, *Biochem.J.*, **62**, 696–704.

Mayer, A. and Schaeffer, J. 1908. Sur la structure des gels. Application à l'étude de la constitution du protoplasme animal et des liquides de l'organisme, *C.R.Soc.Biol.*, **64**, 681–3.

Mazia, D. 1961–3. Mitosis and the Physiology of cell division. In Brachet and Mirsky: *The Cell*. III. Academic Press, New York.

Menke, W. 1940. Die lamellarstruktur der Chloroplasten im ultravioletten Licht, *Naturwissensch.*, **28**, 158–9.

Menke, W. 1940. Untersuchungen über den Feinbau des Protoplasmas mit dem Universal-Electronenmikroskope, *Protoplasma*, **35**, 115–30.

Menke, W. 1960. Weitere Untersuchungen zur Entwicklung der Plastiden von *Oenothera hookeri*, *Z.f.Naturforsch.*, **156**, 479–82.

Menke, W. 1960. Einige Beobachtungen zur Entwicklungsgeschichte der Plastiden von *Elodea canadensis*, *Z.f.Naturforsch.*, **15b**, 800–4.

Mensikai, S.W. 1939. Cytogenetic studies in the genus *Allium*, *J.Genetics*, **89**, 1–45.

Metzner, P. 1937. Uber den Bau der Chloroplasten, *Ber.d.Deutsch.Bot.Ges.*, **55**, Suppl. *Ber.über die* **51**: *Generalversammlung*, p. 16.

Meves, F. 1964. Ueber das Vorkommen von Mitochondrien, bezw. Chondriomiten in Pflanzenzellen, *Ber;d.Deutsch.Bot.Ges.*, **22**, 284–6.

Meyer, A. 1881. Ueber die Struktur des stärkekörner, *Bot.Zeit.*, 39ᵉ année, 841–64 and 857–64.

Meyer, A. 1883. Ueber Kristalloide der Trophoplasten und über die Chromoplasten der Angiosperm, *Bot.Zeit.*, 41ᵉ année, 489–98, 504–14 and 525–31.

Meyer, A. 1883. *Das Chlorophyllkorn in Chemicher, morphologischer und biologischer Beziehung*, Arthur Felix Verlay, Leipzig.

Millerd, A., Bonner, J., Axelrod, B. and Bandurski, R. 1951. Oxidative and phosphorylative activity of plant mitochondria, *Proc.Natl.Acad.Sc.*, USA, **37**, 855–62.

Milovidov, P.F. 1928. Sur la constitution chimique des chondriosomes et des plastes chez les Végétaux, *C.R.Acad.Sc.*

Mirande, M. 1923. Sur la nature protéolipoidïque des stérinoplastes du Lis blanc, *C.R. Acad.Sc.*, **176**, 596.

Mirsky, A.E. and Pollister, A.W. 1946. Chromosin, a desoxyribose nucleoprotein complex of the cell nucleus, *J. Gen. Physiol.*, **30**, 117–147.

Mohl, H.von. 1846. Ueber die saftbewegung im Inneren der Zellen, *Bot. Zeit.*, **4**, 73–8 and 89–94.

Moldenhawer, J.J.P. 1812. *Beiträge zur Anatomie der Pfanzen.* I vol. in 4°, Kiel.

Mollenhauer, H.H. 1965. An intercisternal structure in the Golgi apparatus, *J. Cell. Biol.*, **24**, 504–11.

Mollenhauer, H.H., Morré, D.J. and Kelley, A.G. 1966. The widespread occurrence of plant cytosomes resembling animal microbodies, *Protoplasma (Vienna)*, **62**, 44–52.

Mollenhauer, H.H., Whaley, W.G. and Leech, J.H. 1961. A function of the Golgi apparatus in outer rootcap cells, *J. Ultrast. Res.*, **5**, 193–200.

Mooré, D.J. and Mollenhauer, H.H. 1964. Isolation of the Golgi apparatus from plant cells, *J. Cell. Biol.*, **23**, 295–305.

Moore, R.T. and McAlear, J.H. 1962. Characterization of the Golgi dictyosoma of the Fungus *Neobulgaria pura*, *Elect. Micr.*, **2**, UU 7 (*5th intern. Cong. for Elect. Micr.* Philadelphia) *Academic Press*, New York.

Moses, M.J. 1958. Breakdown and reformation on the nuclear envelope at cell division. *IVth Int. Conf. on Elec. Micr.*, Berlin II, 230–3. (Springer, publ. 1960.

Mounolou, J.C., Jakob, H. and Slonimski, P.P. 1967. Molecular nature of hereditary cytoplasmic factors controlling gene expression in mitochondria, in *The Control of nuclear activity* (Soc. of General Physiologists), ed. L. Goldstein, 413–31, Prentice Hall Inc., Englewood Cliffs, New Jersey, USA.

Mühlethaler, K. 1958. Die entstehung des vacuolensystems in Pflanzenzellen. *IV Inter. Kong. f. Elektronemmikr.*, Berlin, **II**, 491–4. (Springer Verlag, Berlin 1960).

Mühlethaler, K. and Frey-Wyssling, A. 1959. Entwicklung und struktur der Protoplastiden, *J. Biophys. Biochem. Cyt.*, **6**, 507–12.

Mühlethaler, K., Moor, H. and Szarkowski, J.W. 1965. The ultrastructure of the chloroplast lamellae, *Planta*, **67**, 305–23.

Naegeli, C. 1884. Zellkern, Zellbildung und Zellenwachsthum bei den Pflanzen. *Zeitschr. f. Wiss. Bot.*, **1**, 34–133; **3–4**, 1846,

Naora, H., Mirsky, A.E. and Allfrey, V.G. 1960. Unpublished experiments. Cités par Mirsky and Osawa in Brachet: *The Cell, III*, 1961.

Nass, M.M.K., Nass, S. and Afzelius, B.A. 1965. The general occurrence of mitochondrial DNA, *Exp. Cell Res.*, **37**, 516–39.

Neurath, H. 1964. Protein digesting enzymes, *Scient. Am.* **211**, No. 6.

Niklowitz, W. and Drews, G. 1956. Beiträge zur Cytologie der Blaualgen. I. Mitteilung – Untersuchungen zur Substruktur von *Phormidium uncinatum* Gom., *Arch. f. Mikrobiol.*, **24**, 134–46.

Niklowitz, W. and Drews, G. 1957. Beiträge zur Cytologie der Blaualgen. IV.

Mitteilung. Vergleichende elektronenmikroskopische Untersuchungen zur substruktur einiger Hormogonales, *Arch.f.Mikrobiol.*, **27**, 150–65.

Novikoff, A.B., Beaufay, H. and de Duve, C. 1956. Electron microscopy of lysosome rich fractions from Rat liver, *J.Biophys. Biochem.Cytol.*, **2**, suppl., 179–84.

Novikoff, A.B. and Shin, W.Y. 1964. The endoplasmic reticulum in the Golgi zone and its relations to microbodies, Golgi Apparatus and autophagic vacuoles in Rat liver cells, *J.Microscopie*, **3**, 187–206.

O'Brien, T.P. and Thimann, K.V. 1967. Observations of the fine structure of the oat coleóptile. II. The parenchyma cells of the apex, *Protoplasma* (*Vienna*), **63**, 417–42.

Olszewska, M.J. 1960. Recherches sur le caractère chimique de la plaque cellulaire, *Acta Soc.Bot.Pol.*, **29**, 249–61.

Palade, G.E. 1956. The endoplasmic reticulum, *J.Biophys.Biochem.Cyt.*, **2**, suppl. 85–98.

Palade, G.E. and Siekevitz, P. 1956. Liver microsomes. An integrated morphological and biochemical study, *J.Biophys.Biochem.Cyt.*, **2**, 171–200.

Palay, S.L. and Karlin, L.J. 1959. An electron microscopic study of the intestinal villus. II. The pathway of fat absorption, *J.Biophys.Biochem. Cyt.*, **5**, 373–84.

Park, R.B. and Pon, N.G. 1961. Correlation of structure with function in *Spinacia oleracea* chloroplasts, *J.Mol.Biol.*, **3**, 1–10.

Perner, E.S. 1953. Die Sphärosomen (Mikrosomen) pflanzlicher zellen, *Protoplasma*, **42**, 457–81.

Perner, E.S. 1957. Zum elektronenmikroskopischen Nachveis des 'Golgi apparatus' in Zellen höherer Pflanzen, *Naturw.*, **44**, 336.

Phillips, D.C. 1966. The three dimensional structure of an enzyme molecule, *Scient.Am.*, **215**, No. 5, 78.

Pijper, A. 1940. Microcinematography of motile organs of thyphoid bacilli, *J.Biol.Photographic Assn.*, **8**, 158–64.

Porter, K.R. and Caulfield, J.B. 1958. The formation of the cell plate during cytokinesis in *Allium cepa*, *Proc.4th Int.Conf.Electron Microscopy*, Berlin, **2**, 503–7. (Springer, Berlin, 1960).

Porter, K.R. and Machado, R. 1960. The endoplasmic reticulum and the formation of plant cell walls, *European Reg.Conf.on Elect.Microsc.Delft*, **2**, 754–8.

Poux, N. 1963. Localisation des phosphates et de la phosphatase acide dans les cellules des embryons de Blé (*Triticum vulgare*, vill.) lors de la germination, *J.Microscopie*, **2**, 557–68.

Poux, N. 1963. Localisation de la phosphatase acide dans les cellules méristématiques de Blé (*Triticum vulgare* vill.), *J.Microscopie*, **2**, 485–90.

Poux, N. 1965. Localisation de l'activité phosphatasique acide et des phosphates dans les grains d'aleurone. I. Grains d'aleurone renfermans à la fois globoides et cristalloïdes, *J.Microscopie*, **4**, 771–82.

251

Puiseux-Dao, S. 1963. Les Acétabulaires, matériel de laboratoire. Les résultats obtenus avec ces Chlorophycées, *Année Biol.*, **2**, 99–154. (Bibliography).

Rabinowitz, M., Sinclair, J., De Salle, L., Haselkorn, R. and Swift, H.H. 1965. Isolation of deoxyribonucleic acid from mitochondria of chick embryo heart and liver, *Proc.Natl.Acad.Sci.(Wash.)*, **53**, 1126–33.

Raspail, F.V. 1833. *Nouveau système de chimie organique.* I vol. in 8°, Baillère, Paris.

Regaud, C. 1908. Sur les Mitochondries de l'épithélium séminal; IV. Faits et hypothèses relatifs à leur constitution, *C.R.Soc.Biol.*, 718.

Reilhes, R. 1936. Stérides et phospholipides dans le système vacuolaire de la cellule végétale, *Rev.Cytol.et Cytophysiol. végét.*, **2**, 97–212.

Rendi, R. and Hultin, T. 1960. Preparation and amino acid incorporating ability of ribonucleoprotein particles from different tissues of the Rat, *Exp.Cell Res.*, **19**, 253–66.

Rich, A. 1963. Polyribosomes. *Scientific American*, **209** (6) 44–53.

Ris, H. 1954. The submicroscopic structure of chromosomes. *Symposium on fine structure of Cells, Leiden*, 212–34. Noordhoff publ., Gröningen, The Netherlands.

Ris, H. 1956. A study of chromosomes with the electron microscope, *J.Biophys.Biochem.Cyt.*, **2**, suppl. 385–90.

Ris, H. 1958. Fine structure of the nucleus during spermiogenesis, *IVth Int. Conf.on Electron Microscopy, Berlin*, **II**, 211–2.

Ris, H. and Plaut, W. 1962. Ultrastructure of DNA-containing areas in the chloroplast of *Chlamydomonas*, *J.Cell.Biol.*, **13**, 383–91.

Robertson, J.D. 1959. The ultrastructure of cell membranes and their derivatives. In *The structure and function of subcellular components. Biochem.Soc.Symp.no.* 16, Ed. E.M. Crook, 3–43 University Press Cambridge.

Robinow, C.F. 1942. A study of the nuclear apparatus of bacteria, *Proc.Roy. Soc.London, B*, **130**, 299–324.

Robinow, C.F. 1944. Cytological observations on *Bac.Coli, Proteus vulgaris* and various aerobic spore forming bacteria with special reference to the nuclear structures, *J.Hyg.Camb.*, **43**, 413–23.

Rouiller, C. and Bernhard, W. 1956. 'Microbodies' and the problem of mitochondrial regeneration in liver cells, *J.Biophys.Biochem.Cytol.*, **2**, 355–60.

Sager, R. and Palade, G.E. 1957. Structure and development of the chloroplast in *Chlamydomonas*. I. The normal green cell, *J.Biophys.Biochem. Cytol.*, **3**, 463–88.

Scarth, G.W. 1927. The structural organization of plant protoplasm in the light of micrurgy, *Protoplasma*, **2**, 189–205.

Schimper, A.F.W. 1880. Untersuchungen über die Entstehung der Stärkekörner, *Bot.Zeit.*, **38**, 881–902.

Schimper, A.F.W. 1883. Ueber die Entwicklung der Chlorophyllkörner and

Farbkörper, *Bot.Zeit.*41ₑ *année*, 105–11, 121–31, 137–46, 153–62.

Schimper, A.F.W. 1885. Untersuchungen über die chlorophyllkörper und die ihnen homologen Gebilde, *Jahrb.f.wiss.Bot.*, **16**, 1–247.

Schleiden, M. 1838. Beiträge zur Phytogenesis, *Müller, Arch.f.Anat.Phys.u. Wiss.Med.*, 137.

Schneider, A. 1873. Untersuchungen über Plathelminthen, *Jahrb.d.Oberhessischen Gesellsch.f.Nat.und Heilkunde*, **14**, 5–77.

Schnepf, E. 1961. Licht und electronenmikroskopische Beobachtungen an insektivoren-Drüsen über die Sekretion des Fangschleimes, *Flora*, **151**, 73–87.

Schnepf, E. 1961. Struktur und Funktion der Golgi-Elemente in Insektivoren-Drüsen, *Ber.d.deutsch.Bot.Ges.*, **74**, 269.

Schnepf, E. 1964. Zur Cytologie un Physiologie Pflanzlicher Drüsen IV. Licht und electronenmikroskopische Untersuchungen an Septanektarien, *Protoplasma*, **58**, 137–71.

Schoefl, G.I. 1964. The effect of actinomycine D on the fine structure of the nucleolus, *J.Ultrastruc.Res.*, **10**, 224–43.

Schultze, M. 1861. Ueber Muskelkörperchen und das was man eine Zeller nennen habe, *Archiv.f.Anat.u.Physiol.*, I.

Schwann, T. 1839. *Mikroskopische Untersuchungen über die Ubereinstimmung in der Struktur und dem Wachstum der Tiere un der Pflanzen*, I vol. in 8°, Sandersche Buchhandlung (ed. Reimer), Berlin.

Scott, N.S., Shah, V.C. and Smillie, R.M. 1968. Synthesis of chloroplast DNA in isolated chloroplasts, *J.Cell Biol.*, **38**, 151–7.

Seifriz, W. 1928. New material for microdissection, *Protoplasma*, **3**, 191–6.

Shinke, N. and Ueda, K. 1956. A cytomorphological and cytochemical study of Cyanophyta. I. An electron microscope study of *Oscillatoria princeps*, *Mem.Coll.of Sc.University of Kyoto*, series B, **23**, 101–3.

Sibatani, A., Kloet, S.R.de, Allfrey, V.F. and Mirsky, A.E. 1962. Isolation of a nuclear RNA fraction resembling DNA in its base composition, *Proc. Nat.Acad.Sc.*, **48**, 471–7.

Sievers, A. 1963. Beteiligung des Golgi- Apparates beider Bildung der Zellwand von Wurzelhaaren, *Protoplasma*, **54**, 188–92.

Steffen, K. and Walter, F. 1957–8. Die Chromoplasten von *Solanum capsicastrum* L. und ihre genese. Elektronenmikroskopische untersuchungen zur Plastiden metamorphose, *Planta*, **50**, 640–70.

Steffensen, D. and Bergeron, J.A. 1959. Autoradiographs of pollen tube nuclei with Calcium-45, *J.Biophys.Bioch.Cytol.*, **6**, 339.

Sterling, C. and Spit, B.J. 1958. Submicroscopic structure of the cereal starch grain, *J.Exp.Bot.*, **9**, 75–81.

Stich, H. 1951. Trypaflavin und Ribonucleinsäure. Untersucht an Mäusegeweben, *Condylostoma* sp. und *Acetabularia mediterranea*, *Naturwissenschaften*, **38**, 435–6.

Stoeckenius, W. 1959. An electron microscope study of myelin figures, *J.Biophys.Biochem.Cytol.*, **5**, 491–500.

Strasburger, E. 1879. Neue Beobachtungen über Zellbildung und Zellteilung, *Bot. Zeit.*, **37**, 265–79 and 281–8.

Strugger, S. 1951. Die strukturordnung im Chloroplasten, *Ber. deut. Bot. Ges.*, **64**, 69–83.

Strugger, S. 1953. Uber die Struktur der Protoplastiden, *Ber. deut. Bot. Ges.*, **66**, 439–53.

Strugger, S. 1954. Die Proplastiden in den jungem Blättern von *Agapanthus umbellatus* l'Hérit, *Protoplasma*, **43**, 120–73.

Strugger, S. 1957. Elektronenmikroskopische Beobachtungen an den Proplastiden des Vegetationskegels von *Elodea densa*, *Protoplasma*, **48**, 360–4.

Strugger, S. and Perner, E. 1956. Beobachtungen zur Frage der ontogenetischen Entwicklung des somatischen Chloroplasten, *Protoplasma*, **46**, 711–42.

Takeda, S. and Izutsu, K. 1960. *Symp. Cell Chem. (Japan)*, **10**, 245.

Thomas, J. B., Post, L. C. and Vertregt, N. 1954. Localisation of Chlorophyll within the Chloroplast, *Biochim. Biophys. Acta*, **13**, 20–30.

Thomas, P. 1966. Etude, en microscopie électronique, de l'action de la pepsine et de la ribonucléase sur les cellules méristématiques de Radis et de Courge, *C. R. Acad. Sc.*, **262**, 745–8.

Thornton, R. M. 1967. The fine structure of Phycomyces. I. Autophagic vesicles. *J. Ultrastructure Res.*, **21**, 269–80.

Thornton, R. M. and Thimann, K. V. 1964. On a crystal-containing body in cells of the oat coleoptile, *J. Cell Biol.*, **20**, 345–50.

Thuret, G. 1850. Recherches sur les zoospores des Algues et les anthéridies des Cryptogames, *Ann. Sc. Nat. Bot.*, 3ᵉ série, **14**, 214–60.

Thuret, G. 1854–5. Recherches sur la fécondation des Fucacées, suivies des observations sur les Anthéridies des Algues, *Ann. Sc. Nat. Bot.*, série IV, **2** and **3**.

Tolbert, N. E., Oeser, A., Kisaki, T., Hageman, R. H. and Yamazaki, R. K. 1968. Peroxisomes from leaves with enzymes related to glycolate metabolism (Abstr.), *Fed. Proc.*, **27**, 344.

Ts'o, P. O. P., Bonner, J. and Vinograd, J. 1956. Microsomal nucleoprotein particles from Pea seedlings, *J. Biophys. Biochem. Cytol.*, **2**, 451–66.

Ts'o, P. P. and Sato, C. S. 1959. The incorporation of leucine C[14] into microsomal particles and other subcellular components of the Pea epicotyl, *J. Biophys. Biochem. Cytol.*, **5**, 59–68.

Turpin, P. J. P. 1826. Organographie microscopique élémentaire et comparée des Végétaux. Observations sur l'origine ou la forme du tissu cellulaire etc., *Mém. Mus. d'Hist. Nat.*, **18**, 161–212.

Virchow, R. 1855. Cellularpathologie, *Arch. f. Pathol. Anat.*, **8**, 1.

Vries, H. de. 1885. Plasmolytische Studien über die Wand der Vakuolen, *Jahrb. wiss. Bot.*, **16**, 465–598.

Walek-Czernecka, A. 1965. Histochemical demonstration of some hydrolytic enzymes in the spherosomes of plant cells, *Acta Soc. Bot. Pol.*, **34**, 573–88.

Watson, J.D. and Crick, F.H.C. 1953. Molecular structure of Nucleic acids. A structure for Deoxyribose Nucleic Acid, *Nature, London,* **171**, 737–8.

Watson, M.L. and Siekevitz 1956. Cytochemical studies of mitochondria. I. The separation and identification of a membrane fraction from isolated mitochondria, *J. Biophys. Biochem. Cytol.*, **2**, 639–52.

Webster, G.C. 1957. Amino acid incoporation by intact and disrupted ribonucleoprotein particles, *J. Biol. Chem.*, **229**, 535–46.

Wettstein, D. von. 1958. The formation of plastic structures. *Brookhaven Symposia in Biology.* II. *The photochemical apparatus.* 138–59. Brookhaven National laboratory (ed.), Upton New York.

Whaley, W.G. and Mollenhauer, H.H. 1963. The Golgi apparatus and cell plate formation. A postulate, *J. Cell Biol.*, **17**, 216–21.

Wolff, C.F. 1759. *Theoria generationis,* ed. Hendel, Halle-sur-la-Sale.

Wolken, J.J. and Palade, G.E. 1953. An electron microscope study of two Flagellates. Chloroplast structure and variation, *Ann. New York Acad. Sc.*, **56**, 873–89.

Wolken, J.J. and Schwertz, F.A. 1953. Chlorophyll monolayers in chloroplasts, *J. Gen. Physiol.*, **37**, 111–20.

Acknowledgments

Acknowledgment is due to the following for the illustrations (the number refers to the page on which the illustration appears).

12 Nachet; 28 Phillips; 37 (formula on left) Frey-Wyssling and Mühlethaler; 42, 50, 58, 71, 93, 105, 106, 107, 133, 140, 156, 215, 221 Biologie Cellulaire CPEM, published R.J.Gautheret (Armand Colin); 78 Kamiya; 80 Frey-Wyssling; 90, 174 Lance-Nougarede; 92 Ingram; 101, 160 (7·8) Berkaloff; 104 Mollenhauer, Whaley and Leech; 110, 111, 112 Lucy and Glauert; 123, 137, 151, 173, 188 Guilliermond; 125 Gautheret; 141 Fernández-Morán; 149 Ryter; 153 Steinmann; 155, 158, 159, 160 (7·9) Giraud; 162 Hickmann and Frankel; 166 Wolken and Schwertz; 167, 168 Mühlethaler, Moore and Szarkowski; 170 Emberger; 171 Caporali; 182 Schimper; 190 Lemoine; 191 Menke; 201 Delay; 209 Camefort; 212 Robinow; 225 Ahmadian; 226 (8·11) Takeda and Isutsu; 226 (8·12) Mensikai; 236 Mangenot.

Illustrations not acknowledged above were drawn or prepared by the author. The diagrams were drawn or adapted from the author's drawings by Design Practitioners Limited.

This book may be kept

FOURTEEN DAYS

A fine will be charged for each day the book is kept overtime.

APR 1 '75			
FEB 2 4 '76			
FEB 9 1993			
DEC 0 9 1997			
GAYLORD 142			PRINTED IN U.S.A.